Health and safety for managers, supervisors and safety representatives

Tim Deveaux

Chartered
Institute of
Environmental
Health

Contents

6. How can we control specific risks?

Introduction

It is health that is real wealth
and not pieces of gold and silver.
Mahatma (Mohandâs) Gandhi

He who has health has hope,
and he who has hope has everything.
Arab proverb

Prevention, rather than cure, is the bedrock of environmental health. This is true of all aspects of environmental health, including health and safety at work.

Health and safety for managers, supervisors and safety representatives is about managing and implementing the controls required to prevent accidents and ill health in the work environment. These measures are designed to protect employers and employees, the self-employed, visitors to a workplace and members of the general public who happen to be in the workplace or nearby.

The book covers the principles of what has been characterised as 'a good health and safety culture'. It describes the management systems that all organisations can use and the procedures that can be implemented to help to prevent accidents and ill health at work.

It is impossible to mention every type of workplace, but the principles, systems and procedures discussed will help all organisations (whether in the commercial or non-profit-making sectors) to achieve the highest possible standards. In turn, these standards will help to provide good evidence that an organisation is doing everything reasonably possible to maintain a good health and safety culture and comply with current legislation.

The book is aimed at managers, supervisors and safety representatives. It provides a solid foundation for the subject and a useful source of reference. It can also be used as an aid towards the Chartered Institute of Environmental Health's Level 3 and 4 qualifications in Health and Safety in the Workplace.

The chapters are divided into six parts, plus an extensive reference section. Each chapter starts with a list of key words and phrases. These are crucial for the understanding and implementation of health and safety at work. The key words and phrases are highlighted in the text and included in the Glossary, sometimes with an expanded definition.

Each part of the book asks and answers a simple question – what is health and safety at work; how can we control hazards and reduce risks; who is involved in health and safety at work; why should we create a health and safety culture; how can we implement health and safety standards; how can we control specific hazards and risks?

Part 1 defines health, safety, work and other key concepts, then considers the impact on health from workplace accidents and occupational ill health.

Part 2 explains the framework for improving health and safety at work. It outlines the key principles of establishing and implementing health and safety at work, including the necessary management systems and the main legal requirements.

Part 3 considers the people involved in health and safety. It outlines the roles of employers and boards of directors, employees, managers, supervisors and safety representatives and indicates how, by working together, they can create a health and safety culture that reduces accidents and ill health at work.

Part 4 describes how managers can manage health and safety by developing a sound health and safety culture and creating appropriate health and safety policies.

Part 5 discusses ways to implement health and safety through the principles and management systems outlined in Parts 2 and 4. It describes risk assessment; monitoring, recording and reporting health and safety; accidents and ill health; health surveillance systems; inspection and auditing; training and instruction; and the provision of information for employees.

Part 6 examines the typical hazards and risks at most workplaces and suggests some of the basic control measures that might be applicable. In the process, the chapter also considers the activities and systems that need to be managed and supervised.

The Reference section has sources of further help, including websites, sources of information used in the book and a Glossary of the key words and phrases in each chapter. The Reference section should help you to pin down information, advice and legal requirements relevant to your particular workplace and to use the key words and key expressions with confidence.

Getting the most from this book

It is important to note some conventions of the book.

For ease of reading we refer to people by their role within the health and safety system – employer, manager, supervisor, employee and safety representative. You may not have the word 'manager' or 'supervisor' in your job title, but if you act in these capacities, then you are the person we are addressing at this point.

Throughout the book you will find advice about things that *must* or *should* be done.

Where the text states that you *must* do something, it means that there is a legal requirement for a company to do so.

Where the text states that something *should* be done, it indicates advice or guidance from the government, a government body or a professional body that will enable a workplace to keep well within the law and achieve modern health and safety standards.

If the book says that *employers* must or should do something, this means that the employer has a legal obligation to ensure that the action is carried out, or that it is good practice to do so. Employers are legally accountable for the well-being of all their employees, but they may legitimately *delegate* tasks and responsibilities to managers or supervisors in order to carry out their legal duties. This means that managers and supervisors may have the operational responsibility for ensuring that the company carries out its legal obligations because their employer has delegated particular tasks to them through their job description and contract of employment.

The words *worker* and *employee* are used interchangeably in this book to indicate anyone who is engaged in work activities, irrespective of their seniority in the organisation. The words *staff* and *manager* are used to distinguish responsibility and accountability in an organisation.

The use of the word *company* includes any organisation, including not-for-profit organisations, to which health and safety at work legislation applies.

The checklists included in some chapters are suggestions only, and are not prescriptive: the lists may need to be adapted to suit the individual workplace.

Great care has been taken in compiling the book, but you should be aware that the guidance on legislation is not a complete or authoritative statement. The contributors and publishers cannot be held responsible for actions or omissions taken on the basis of this general guidance which is provided in good faith. You are advised to:

- always have to hand a copy of the current relevant legislation (including sector-specific or product-specific legislation, where relevant)

- keep yourself up to date

- continue your professional development (CPD) in health and safety topics including legislation

- take qualified specialist and/or legal advice on legal matters.

1. What is health and safety at work?

What does health and safety at work really mean?

Many people are killed or severely injured while carrying out their everyday work activities. Others have to endure long-term ill health which came about merely because they were working in a particular place.

There is well established legislation and many tried and tested procedures designed to protect the workforce from unnecessary risks to their personal safety, health and general well-being. Even so, many people around the world still have to carry out their work in the presence of avoidable hazards and face a high risk of injury and poor health.

Most workplace health and safety problems can, in fact, be avoided, or the risk from them can be minimised to levels that are acceptable for the well-being of the people carrying out the work and for others, such as customers, who may be affected by the work. To understand the whole subject better, let us consider some key words and phrases.

Key words and phrases

control measures – the arrangements made, or precautions taken, to reduce risk.

hazard – a source of danger: any thing, condition or circumstance that could cause harm to people or damage to property.

health – a state of complete physical, mental and social well-being, not merely the absence of disease or infirmity.

occupational health – a person's physical, mental and social well-being as a consequence of his or her work activities and environment.

risk – a measure or scale of the likelihood that harm will arise from a particular hazard, and the severity of the consequences of the hazards.

safety – freedom from danger.

welfare – in the context of health and safety, the promotion of employee well-being and comfort by the provision of facilities such as those for personal hygiene, eating and resting.

well-being – a person's general good health, safety, comfort and contentment.

work – activities that people carry out specifically in the course of their occupation.

workplace – any place, or places, where employees, or the self-employed, are likely to work or where they have to go in the course of their employment or incidentally to it.

Specific meanings of health and safety

Everyone has a general idea of what is involved in the phrase *health and safety at work*, but it is important to understand the specific ways in which the words are used.

What is health?

Health can be defined as the soundness of body. The World Health Organization defines it as 'the state of complete physical, mental and social well-being, and not merely the absence of disease or infirmity'.

When considering health and safety at work, the word *health* is associated with:

- the provision of such things as ventilation and lighting

- conditions such as cleanliness, overcrowding and temperature levels

- everyday practices in a particular workplace, such as handling chemicals

- procedures to deal with hazards, such as the exposure to dust, fumes and biological agents.

The lack of control of a workplace or a work procedure involving health risks can lead directly to ill health or can give rise to conditions that, in turn, lead to ill health.

What is safety?

Safety means freedom from danger or the risk of danger. The word is usually associated with injury and matters such as the:

- construction, design, guarding and use of machinery and work equipment

- handling of dangerous substances, such as hot metal

- construction, design and operation of lifting equipment

- condition of the structure of the workplace, such as floors, passages and stairs

- means of access to a workplace and places within the workplace

- employment of young people doing certain hazardous tasks

- training of employees

- provision of personal protective equipment.

The lack of control of a workplace or work procedure can result in injury.

What does work mean?

The word **work** covers the activities that people carry out specifically in the course of their occupation. The Health and Safety at Work etc. Act 1974 says that *work* 'means work as an employee or as a self-employed person'.

An employee can be described as an individual who works under a contract of employment. A contract of employment covers employment and apprenticeship, and the contract may be spoken or written, specific or implied. A self-employed person can be described as someone who works for gain or reward on his or her own behalf, rather than under a contract of employment. A self-employed person may employ others.

The Act makes it clear that an employee is at work throughout the time that he or she is 'in the course of employment, but not otherwise'. So, employees are *not* at work when they are not engaged in activities that are within the course of their specific employment.

For example, if a factory worker is driving to work from home, he is not at work until he arrives at the factory and clocks on. However, if a sales representative from the same factory has to visit clients away from the factory, she could be regarded as being at work as soon as she leaves home on the journey to the client's base. The precise definition of when an individual is 'at work' depends largely on his or her contract of employment.

Voluntary workers and those on work experience are also regarded as being employees as far as health and safety at work is concerned.

The Act explains that 'a self-employed person is at work throughout the time that he or she devotes to the work as a self-employed person'.

Other essential terms

You will come across several other terms and phrases when you consider any aspect of health and safety at work. These include *workplace, welfare, well-being, occupational health, hazard* and *risk*. The next few paragraphs look at all these words in turn.

What is a workplace?

A **workplace** is any place, or places, where employees, or the self-employed, are likely to work or have to go in the course of their employment or incidentally to it. (The definition is found in the Safety Representatives and Safety Committees Regulations 1977 and can be used to apply to other legislation.)

What do welfare and well-being mean?

Although the word **welfare** is not defined in legislation, it is generally understood to refer to a person's comfort and well-being at work in relation to such things as temperature, lighting, air quality and personal hygiene provision, all of which could become health issues. Welfare facilities covered by legislation include such things as the provision of drinking water, toilets, sanitary disposal and first aid equipment and facilities for washing, changing and storing clothing, eating and resting.

The phrase **well-being** (or *wellbeing*) is an everyday, rather wide-ranging, term indicating a person's general good health, safety, comfort and contentment.

What is occupational health?

Occupational health covers the overall state of people's physical, mental, and social well-being at work as a consequence of their work. A wide range of workplace conditions and practices are usually associated with occupational health. They include air quality, manual handling, the use of and exposure to chemicals and biological agents, exposure to noise and vibration and topics such as stress at work.

What are hazards and risk?

In general conversation we often use the words *hazard* and *risk* interchangeably, but it is important to understand the differences between them in the context of health and safety at work.

What is a hazard?

A **hazard** is a source of danger: it is any circumstance, condition or state with a potential to cause harm. That harm could be personal injury or illness, or damage to property, machines, products and the environment.

There are many examples of hazardous substances, objects, processes and procedures, some of which are covered in detail later in the book. Examples include work machinery and equipment, flammable substances, work at heights and lifting heavy objects.

Some hazards, such as the use of harmful chemicals, have the potential to cause long-term health consequences.

What is risk?

Risk is a measure or scale of the likelihood that harm will occur from a particular hazard and the severity of the bad consequences, which could be death, major injury, disease, minor injury, no injury or damage to property.

This means that risk cannot usually be measured in scientific terms. It is a matter of judgement in each circumstance whether something is a high risk or not.

As most circumstances are changeable, the skill is to take into account all the factors that can contribute to the degree of risk involved. This enables you to decide whether the risk is low, medium or high.

If the risk is low, then bad consequences are unlikely.

If something is a medium risk, then harm is more likely to arise – even so, it will probably not occur if reasonable precautions are taken.

If the risk is high, then the person making the assessment has to decide whether it is wise to carry out an activity in those circumstances, or to introduce more controls to reduce the risk to a level that is acceptable.

Severity

The **severity** of the harm that could result from a hazard should always be considered when assessing risk. The severity of injury can include death, major injury or disease, minor injury or disease, and no injury or illness at all.

Distinguishing hazards and risk

Hazards exist all around us, but many are extremely low risk so most of us get through most days without too much harm. Even so, there is no such thing as *no* risk and no such thing as *complete safety*. There is a risk in everything we do.

Take, for example, using a pair of scissors. The hazards are the sharp blades and pointed ends. Most of the time people use scissors without causing any sort of injury, and most people would regard a pair of scissors as presenting a low risk. If they are not used correctly, however, they could cause a death – for example, sharp scissors could cut an artery and the person could bleed to death.

Even so, particularly hazardous and risky activities can be done with an 'acceptable' risk. Take, for example, walking across Niagara Falls on a tightrope. Blondin did it in the nineteenth century. He would have assessed the risk by considering the weather conditions: wet or cold conditions would increase the risk of falling. He would have considered his skill as a tightrope walker, the pole he used for balance and the specially designed clothes. He did this risk assessment to such a degree that he was successful several times. In other words, he had minimised the risk as far as he could.

Who is at risk?

If you were to walk around any high street shop, office or residential care home, you could identify most of the people who could be at risk from activities in those workplaces. The following examples show that there is a wide variety of groups of people who are at risk from work activities.

In a shop, employees could be at risk when lifting boxes or working on ladders while cleaning light units. Customers could also be at some risk of being injured – by, for example, slipping on the liquid spilled from a bottle of soft drink. Children could be at risk from using play equipment or from climbing the steps to the toy department.

In an insurance office, employees operating the computers are at risk from eyestrain, backache and 'repetitive strain injury' unless control measures are in place. Delivery drivers who deliver the copier paper and other office materials may be unfamiliar with the layout of the delivery area, while employees could trip on the corner of the lowered tailgate of the delivery lorry. Just imagine that some rooms were being refurbished: the contractors could be at risk from cutting wall panels with power saws and they and the employees could be at risk if asbestos were stripped from the old heating pipes without the appropriate legal safety controls.

In a residential care home, the residents may be at risk because they are frail and cannot walk very well. They could trip on a rucked carpet or a vacuum cleaner cable. They may also be at risk of scalding if the temperature of bath water is not thermostatically controlled and checked before the resident gets into the bath.

Finally, there are occasional visitors to a workplace, such as an electricity meter reader, VAT officer, inland revenue officer, health and safety inspector or financial auditor. The degree of risk to which they are exposed clearly depends on where they go in the workplace. If they visit only the offices, the risk is lower than if they visit a warehouse where fork-lift trucks are operating. Similarly it is far riskier to read an electricity meter that involves going down steep steps to a basement than to read one in a well lit entrance hall.

Other groups of people may also be at risk. They include the self-employed, casual workers, agency workers, temporary staff, sales representatives, delivery personnel, passengers in trains, patients in hospitals, prisoners in secure accommodation, pupils in schools and students in universities.

What does health and safety at work involve?

Health and safety involves the prevention of injury and ill health resulting from work. It involves the assessment and control of risk. The standards we apply depend on the degree of risk that is currently considered acceptable.

Some hazards can be eliminated, but there are many hazards that cannot be eliminated, so we must introduce controls that *limit* that risk. In fact, the main emphasis of contemporary health and safety control is to limit risk. Control measures are the arrangements made, or precautions taken, to reduce risk.

So, if we evaluate risk, we are then in a position to reduce it to an acceptable level for human health, safety and well-being whenever someone has something hazardous to do at work.

Who is involved in health and safety at work?

Everyone at work has the right to work in a safe and healthy environment. This is paramount to health and safety legislation. Everyone has a part to play in making workplaces safe and healthy.

The government sets the framework for good health and safety in the workplace through legislation, guidance, enforcement, information and education.

Employers (and their boards of directors) and the self-employed have obligations to provide a safe and healthy workplace by complying with legislation, following guidance and providing information and training for employees about health and safety. Even if the company is a sole trader without any employees, there are still legal duties to ensure that the company does not create health and safety problems for customers and the general public. Manufacturers and suppliers have obligations to produce and sell goods that will not harm those who distribute and use them.

Employees have a duty to follow health and safety rules and regulations and to protect their own and other people's health and safety at work. Enforcing authorities and enforcement officers check that employers, employees, manufacturers and suppliers are abiding by the law.

So, health and safety is essentially a working partnership – everyone working together with one aim. That aim is fewer injuries and less ill health from work activities. In the end, safety in the workplace is also critical to the success of running a business, no matter what size it is. Knowing and understanding how to implement health and safety legislation will help you to avoid the unnecessary costs and damage to a company caused by work-related injury and illness.

How can work affect your health?

Occupational health is the term used to describe the way that work can affect your health. According to the World Health Organization and the International Labour Organization, occupational health is the promotion and maintenance of the highest degree of physical, mental and social well-being of workers in all occupations. It involves preventing ill health, controlling risks and the adaptation of work to people, and people to their jobs.

Key words and phrases

acute health effects – rapid onset of severe symptoms of ill health, usually after a single short-term exposure to a harmful substance.

aerosol – airborne droplet.

bacteria – a very large group of microscopic single-celled organisms (independent life forms) which may be essential, beneficial or harmful to human health. A small number of types of bacteria can cause diseases such as food poisoning and tetanus.

carcinogen – a substance that can cause cancer.

carcinogenic – a description of something that can cause cancer.

chronic health effects – symptoms of illness that may take a considerable time to develop, usually after prolonged or repeated low-level exposure over a long period.

ergonomics – the study of the interaction between people and their work.

fume – microscopic airborne particles produced when, for example, metals are heated during welding or as a result of certain chemical processes. A fume may smell foul and may be irritating or toxic.

gas – an air-like substance that expands freely to fill any space available, irrespective of its quantity.

musculoskeletal disorders (MSDs) – conditions affecting the muscles, nerves, tendons, ligaments, joints, cartilage or spinal discs.

occupational health – a person's physical, mental and social well-being as a consequence of his or her work activities and environment.

sensitisation – a process by which the body becomes sensitive to a substance after it has entered or touched the body.

vapour – a gaseous form of a substance that is normally a liquid at room temperature.

virus – an exceptionally small microscopic particle that can infect the cells of a host organism, such as humans, and cause diseases, such as 'flu or winter vomiting disease.

Identifying the problems

Occupational health is usually associated with illness and disease caused by work and workplaces. The causes of ill health and disease are sometimes difficult to understand and eliminate, and some illnesses associated with work take years to develop to a stage where they are recognised, even though there is much research being done to reduce occupational risks.

The management and supervision of occupational health involves:

- controlling hazards that affect the body over a long period – for example, breathing in asbestos fibres or sustaining a back injury from frequently lifting loads

- the surveillance of the factors in working practices that may affect employees' health – for example, exposure to noise or vibration.

Sources of illness and injury

Every day we handle articles and substances that can affect our health either in the short term or, in some cases, many years after being exposed to the substance.

Many people use chemicals in their workplaces. For example, in a school science laboratory teachers, technicians and children use chemicals that may affect their health either immediately or in the long term. In offices, employees can be exposed to chemicals in printers or to cleaning materials that may cause skin problems. In a hairdressing salon, stylists may experience skin rashes from working with hair dyes and other treatments.

It is important to identify and control anything that could cause harm at work. The controls could include designing safe systems of work, limiting the time that an employee is exposed to something harmful – such as welding fumes – and providing personal protective equipment, such as goggles.

There are many other examples of potentially harmful aspects of work that can cause respiratory illnesses. Engineering workers can be exposed to fumes produced during metal welding, dust from cutting insulation materials or gases from an industrial process. Mechanics in a garage can be exposed to harmful paint spray or damage to their hands as a result of regular contact with oil and other fluids used in vehicles. Maintenance staff can be exposed to asbestos when repairing a boiler in an old factory or in a house under renovation. Farmers can be exposed to dust and micro-organisms when handling hay and straw.

Other examples of a wide range of sources of ill health in the workplace are given in Part 6 where particular hazards are described.

It is important to understand how these substances can enter the body and cause health problems, so that the routes and causes of ill health can be identified and safe systems of work designed.

The effect on the body

Chemicals and other harmful substances can enter the body very easily. They can do so in various forms, including:

- aerosols
- fumes
- dust
- fibres
- liquids
- vapours
- gases.

The ease with which this can happen depends on the substance's physical and chemical properties. For instance, the size of a fibre is important: the smaller it is, the deeper it can be breathed into the lungs. If a chemical is soluble in water (in other words, if it can dissolve), then it can react with the body's fluids.

The effects on health can be acute or chronic. **Acute** effects on health usually involve sudden and severe exposure and rapid absorption of a substance. These effects are often reversible – for example, carbon monoxide poisoning can be treated if the dose is not lethal.

Chronic health effects usually involve prolonged or repeated exposure over a long period. Depending on the substance involved, this could be days, months or years. Symptoms may take a long time to appear and might not be reversible – for example, benzene can cause cancer.

How do harmful substances enter the body?

Harmful substances enter the body in four main ways, by:

- inhalation (breathing in)
- absorption (through the skin or eyes)
- ingestion (eating or drinking)
- injection (puncturing the skin).

Inhalation

Breathing is the most common way that chemicals and other harmful substances get into the body. The nasal hairs filter large fibres and particles of dust, but smaller ones can be breathed deep into the lungs and can even find their way into the blood via the lungs.

When **vapours, gases, fumes** and **aerosols** are inhaled, they can easily find their way into the lungs and into the blood. Some particles of dust and fibre that are breathed in can become trapped in the mouth and throat. They may be dislodged and removed as a result of coughing, but they can also be swallowed.

Absorption

Some solvents can be absorbed through the skin or through cuts and abrasions. Dust, fumes, aerosols, vapours and gases can affect the eyes. The fluids surrounding the eyes can react with the chemical, either causing an allergic reaction, or absorbing the chemical into the blood. Even simple skin contact by brushing against something can also result in a substance either being absorbed by the skin or affecting the surface layers of skin – touching some plants can cause rashes or blisters, for example.

Ingestion

Chemicals can get into the digestive tract via contaminated hands, food or drink. Particles of dust and fibre and traces of chemicals can be ingested by swallowing contaminated mucous that has come into the mouth from the lungs as a result of coughing.

Injection

Wood splinters and metal swarf are among the harmful materials that can puncture the skin and cause injury. Bacterial and viral illnesses can also result from needle stick injuries.

The reaction to harmful substances

As the body responds to harmful substances, people experience the symptoms of illness. The symptoms or effects can be described as:

■ irritation

■ toxic

■ sensitisation

■ carcinogenic (causing cancer).

Irritation

The respiratory system reacts in different ways. The nose reacts to some harmful substances by sneezing; the throat by coughing; and the lungs by becoming inflamed, possibly resulting in bronchitis.

The skin can develop a rash or, in severe circumstances, dermatitis (inflammation of the skin). If a strong acid gets onto the skin, this can result in chemical 'burns' where the acid reacts with the body fluids and the skin itself is badly damaged. Chemicals, dust and fibres that get into the eye can cause damage, ranging from severe irritation to blindness. People who work with plants – for example in horticulture, flower arranging, farming and forestry – may be affected by skin contact with plant sap which can cause a burning sensation and blistering after exposure to sunlight, and may lead to long-lasting skin discoloration.

There are tight legal controls on the use of harmful substances, such as pesticides.

Toxic

Some plants and fungi (mushrooms/toadstools) can cause food poisoning or death in extreme cases. Some chemicals, such as pesticides, are so toxic that they can poison the whole body if ingested in sufficient quantity.

Sensitisation

Exposure to some harmful chemicals, other substances and plants can cause sensitisation. Although there may be no immediate signs of a problem after the first exposure to the substance, the body is prompted into an adverse reaction after subsequent exposure. Skin rashes, asthma, 'farmer's lung', coughing and sneezing are among the typical symptoms.

Some plants and foods contain chemicals, known as *allergens*, that are harmless for most people who eat the food, but can prompt severe or even life-threatening reactions in a few individuals. (See the CIEH's book *Managing Food Safety* for more information on plants, foods and allergies.)

Carcinogenic

Some chemicals and other materials, described as carcinogens, can alter the way cells grow in the body and can lead to cancer. For example, exposure to ethylene oxide – a colourless and odourless gas used in the production of solvents, antifreeze, textiles, detergents, adhesives, polyurethane foam and pharmaceutical products – can cause leukaemia or other cancers.

The exposure to carcinogens is usually over a long period, and the symptoms of illness may not appear for a number of years.

Occupational health hazards

Occupational health problems can be categorised in various ways. They can, for example, be grouped as:

- chemical – such as dust and gas
- physical – such as noise and heat
- ergonomic – such as stress
- biological – such as tetanus and legionnaires' disease.

The main hazards in the workplace that can be regarded as occupational health problems, as opposed to those that can cause physical injury, are:

- noise and vibration
- ionising radiation
- hazardous substances
- biological hazards
- drugs and alcohol
- violence at work
- work-related upper limb disorders and back problems
- stress
- passive smoking.

Noise and vibration

Excessive noise – either as short bursts of loud noise or as longer-term exposure to lower levels of noise – can lead to permanent noise-induced hearing loss or even total deafness. As well as any safety problems the impairment may cause, the loss of hearing may be extremely distressing physically and

Noise and vibration can cause immediate or long-term health problems. Ship's riveters often damaged their hearing in the past.

socially. Shipbuilding, where riveting is an extremely noisy activity, is an industry where hearing impairment has been a particular problem.

Machines such as road drills cause severe vibration. The worker who has to operate one is exposed to that vibration, and this can cause back problems, damage to joints and circulation problems in the fingers known as 'white finger'.

There is more information about these topics on pages 248 to 265.

Ionising radiation

Ionising radiation is used in nuclear reactors for electricity generation and in hospitals for radiography. Particles and rays are emitted in the form of alpha particles, electrons and X-rays, for example. They produce electrically charged ions in the substances they hit – a process known as ionisation. If uncontrolled, the process can harm living tissue by causing cell changes that lead to ill health, such as cancer, and mutations in unborn children.

There is more information about radiation on pages 239 to 247.

Hazardous substances

Many substances commonly used in the workplace can be hazardous to human health. As we have seen above, they can enter the body and react with it, leading to rapid poisoning or to a gradual increase in the concentration in the body, causing illness or even death.

There is more information about hazardous substances on pages 222 to 238.

Biological hazards

Some employees are exposed to a range of biological hazards that could cause them harm. Viruses, bacteria and some plants and animals are included in this category. For example, sewer workers and watersports instructors are sometimes exposed to rats' urine, which may contain a bacterium that causes leptospirosis, a form of which is commonly known as Weil's disease. The hepatitis B virus, which can cause liver disease, is transmitted via human blood or other bodily fluids, so it is a danger to emergency workers and hospital staff including nurses, doctors, laboratory technicians, cleaners and porters.

Zoonoses are diseases that can be transmitted from animals to humans, such as bovine tuberculosis.

Drugs and alcohol

Drug, alcohol and other substance misuse at work can increase the risk of accidents, damage health, cause absenteeism and reduce productivity.

Drinking alcohol in moderation may have some positive benefits, but drinking excessively or in inappropriate circumstances can cause accidents and near-miss incidents. Drug and other substance misuse (such as solvent abuse) at work has severe social and economic consequences for crime and for absenteeism and sickness, costing in excess of £20 billion a year.

Violence at work

Verbal abuse and physical attacks on employees can be a significant problem. People who deal directly with the public could have to face aggressive or violent behaviour, particularly if they work alone. They might be sworn at, threatened or even attacked. This can result in damage to employees' health through distress, anxiety, stress, pain and even disability or death. Business operations can also suffer – through low staff morale and high staff turnover.

Musculoskeletal disorders and back injury

Many types of work involve physical activity. Some require lifting and carrying loads that can cause damage to the back, strained ligaments and tendons, hernias and trapped nerves – **musculoskeletal disorders**.

Staff in occupations requiring repetitive work, such as keyboard operators and supermarket checkout cashiers, can be subject to repetitive strain injury. This type of injury is caused by repeated movements of the upper limbs and torso that can result in continuous pain from the joints, muscles, ligaments or tendons.

Stress

Stress at work can have a damaging effect on the mental and physical health of staff. The work environment, job design, relationship with the employer and contractual conditions can all have an impact on an individual staff member. The symptoms of stress may range from loss of appetite, loss of weight, headache and backache, sleeping problems and indecision. These can lead, in turn, to ulcers and heart disease.

Passive smoking

In some countries employees are exposed to other people's cigarette smoke while they are at work. Bar, restaurant and office staff are just some of the people who breathe in the products of other people's cigarette-smoking. The effects of passive smoking are the same as those from actual smoking. Non-smokers who are exposed to smoke in the workplace can also suffer heart disease, lung disease and circulation problems even though they themselves do not smoke. The ban on smoking in the workplace in the UK, Ireland and other countries will prevent many workers becoming ill.

The risks from school visits to farms

A number of food poisoning outbreaks, mainly involving children, have been associated with educational and recreational visits to open farms. The problem is caused by contact with the *Escherichia coli (E. coli)* bacterium that normally lives harmlessly in the gut of humans and animals. When children stroke animals or touch the animal pens their hands easily become contaminated by the bacteria which can then make them ill. The children can also pass on the bacteria to other people who may then also become unwell. By stroking the animals or because of contact with animal faeces children have suffered illness ranging from severe diarrhoea to fatal kidney failure.

The risks are easily controlled by simple everyday measures. The most important control is good personal hygiene – washing hands thoroughly after handling animals and always before eating or drinking. It is very important to ensure that children do so too.

How can work affect your safety?

Every year hundreds of people in the UK lose their lives because of activities at work, and thousands more suffer injury of some kind. Yet accidents can be prevented: indeed, the aim of the law is to prevent them.

In general terms, the purpose of safety in the workplace is to reduce the number and outcomes of accidents.

To be successful in preventing accidents in your own workplace, you need to understand the most common causes of accidents, the apparent reasons why they happen and the underlying causes. First of all, however, it is worth taking a quick look at what exactly an accident is.

Key words and phrases

accident – any unplanned event that results, or could have resulted, in personal injury or ill health; damage to, or loss of, property, plant or materials; damage to the environment; or loss of business opportunity.

ergonomic principles – the degree to which a particular job is designed to fit the person, usually by a combination of the management of job design, workstation design, job rotation, training and so on.

health and safety culture – the integration of health and safety awareness and controls into day-to-day organisational management practices.

incident (near-miss or near-miss accident) – an unplanned event that does not result in personal injury, death or damage, but has the potential to do so.

intervention programme – a series of actions designed to improve workplace health and safety standards and to reduce the risks from health and safety hazards.

What is an accident?

Case law – the development and interpretation of law as a result of court decisions – has described an accident as 'an unlooked for mishap or untoward event which is not expected or designed' and as 'any unintended and unexpected loss or hurt'. What is clear is that an accident is an:

- unplanned and uncontrolled event
- event that causes injury, damage or loss
- event that could lead to a near-miss accident or could result in no loss or damage at all.

Accidents do not 'just happen'. They arise from uncontrolled events, usually from a *chain* of uncontrolled events.

For example, if a hairdresser is electrocuted by a hairdryer, a number of events and factors may have led to the electrocution. The hairdryer may have been poorly designed or poorly manufactured, for example. It may have been used regularly for the last four years without being maintained, serviced or inspected; or, because of its regular and intensive use, the securing screw to the live connection in the plug may have worked loose.

An important part of your job is to ensure that everything possible is done to prevent a loss of control that allows a chain of uncontrolled events to occur. This takes planning, implementation and monitoring – actions we discuss later in the book.

Outcome of an accident

The outcome of an accident could be one or several of the following:

- death
- personal injury
- long-term health problems
- damage to, or loss of, property and premises
- damage to the environment
- no injury or damage at all.

Studies of accidents show a pattern to the outcomes and most accidents do not result in injury or damage. These accidents are sometimes referred to as **incidents**, **near-misses** or **near-miss accidents**.

In this book we use the word accident for events that result in death, injury or damage, and we use the word incident or near-miss for events that result in no injury or damage.

Accident/incident triangle

The comparison of the outcomes of workplace accidents and incidents is often shown as a triangle – see page opposite.

The layers of the triangle show the relative number of outcomes of accidents, starting with the smallest number at the top and finishing with the largest number at the bottom.

The top of the triangle represents the number of fatalities at work: this is the smallest number of accidents.

The second layer down is the number of major injuries that result in more than three days' lost work, while the third layer down represents the number of minor injuries.

The bottom layer represents the near-miss accidents or incidents, and these are the greatest number.

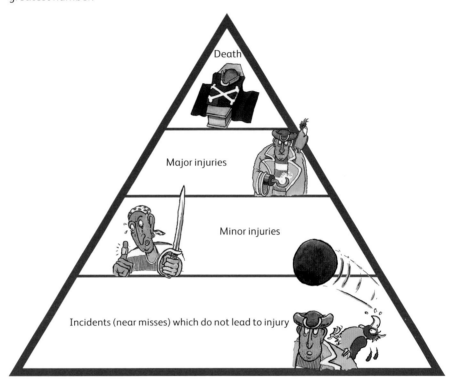

The following two examples indicate the variety of outcomes that are possible.

Example 1 – water on kitchen floor
If someone slipped on a kitchen floor because water had leaked from a freezer that was being defrosted, the outcome would range from wet clothing and injured pride, to a fatal injury. The leaking water in combination with electricity could cause the freezer to break down, electrocute someone or lead to an electrical fire. Employees could slip in the water and break a leg or burn themselves by catching an arm on hot equipment or food. As the outcome of an accident may be difficult to predict, it is essential to deal with the underlying causes. In this example, controlling the defrosting, so that water does not leak, would prevent a wide range of potential outcomes.

Example 2 – falling load from crane
A metal beam is being installed in a building using an overhead crane. The securing chains holding the beam break. There are several possible outcomes:

■ the beam hits the ground, which is dry, and absorbs the impact of the fall with no damage or injury occurring

- the beam lands on a parked lorry – the driver is in the construction site office dealing with paperwork and escapes injury, but there is considerable damage to the lorry and its load

- the beam lands on a pile of gravel, producing flying debris that causes cuts and bruises to people working nearby

- the beam falls on a construction worker, killing him outright.

The examples above show how difficult it is to predict the outcome of an accident. As you can see, you need to be concerned about *all* accidents and incidents, whether they result in injury or not. You will see later on, it is also important to write down all accidents, incidents and near-misses, so that you can use the information to identify the reasons why the accidents occurred and can then introduce control measures to prevent further similar accidents.

Why accidents occur

The two examples above indicate that most accidents and injury happen because of a failure to control an activity. The control of activities is usually affected by:

- occupational factors

- environmental factors

- human factors

- organisational factors.

Accidents and illness may result from any combination of factors, but the organisational factors give you the chance to influence the other three types of factor.

Ideally, tasks should be designed using ergonomic principles, so that employees can do their work without risk to their health and safety. For example, a computer workstation should be designed so that the operator is not subject to musculoskeletal disorders such as repetitive strain injury. The closer the task is designed to the individual, the lower the risk of an accident or injury.

Effective communication at all levels of the company hierarchy reduces the risk that an accident will occur. Effective control of working conditions also plays a significant part in reducing risk. There is more information about communication in Part 3 and more about effective controls in Part 6.

Occupational factors

These are the issues most closely related to the specific work that an individual carries out. A machine operator, for example, may risk damaged hearing, an abattoir worker may risk cuts and a computer operator may risk eye strain. The risk from specific tasks undertaken are likely to depend upon the:

- degree to which a particular job is designed to fit the person doing it – ergonomic principles

- specific safety standards applied to work equipment used.

Environmental factors

The conditions in which people work can affect the level of risk to which they are exposed. For example, poor lighting can make it difficult to carry out many types of work and to spot hazards, while the air quality, temperature and humidity may affect the level and duration of someone's concentration. The space available for carrying out particular tasks can also help staff to work easily and safely. Slips and trips are an example of the type of accident that could involve environmental factors.

The time available to do a job and the way in which it is done can also affect the degree of risk to a worker. For example, if there is severe pressure to meet deadlines and the design of the work procedure is unrealistic for meeting those deadlines, there will be a high risk that an accident will occur.

Human factors

Certain personal characteristics may have an influence on the level of risk a person is exposed to when at work. They include:

- general health and fitness, including physical capabilities such as strength, suppleness and co-ordination

- mental capabilities such as general intelligence and the ability to recognise hazards

- skill level

- general attitude towards safety and general awareness of safety

- inexperience of work or the workplace or both

- the influence of drugs or alcohol

- fatigue.

Daydreaming can be a factor leading to an accident. If your mind is wandering or you are thinking about things other than what you are doing, you may not notice things around you, and may bump into something and hurt yourself.

Organisational factors

Organisational factors which may influence the risk that an accident will occur include the:

- safety standards, precautions and procedures that are enforced and encouraged by an employer

- effectiveness of communication between the employer and employees

- effectiveness of communication between individual employees and groups of employees

- level of training, advice and supervision.

Safety standards are often set by managers on behalf of employers. Good communication systems need to be set up by managers for the use and benefit of all. Training and advice is determined by managers and supervisors with input from safety representatives. These matters are often implemented by supervisors.

The causes of accidents

The four types of factor mentioned above (occupational, environmental, human and organisational) help to explain what lies behind the failure to control an activity. The factors can be analysed so that changes can be made to reduce the likelihood of an accident. In practice, you need to identify the *actual* events and the *chain* of events that led to an accident, so that you can prevent such circumstances recurring.

Accidents happen in many ways, but their typical causes can be divided into three groups:

- unsafe acts
- unsafe conditions
- a combination of unsafe acts and unsafe conditions.

Unsafe acts

Examples of unsafe acts include:

- using work equipment incorrectly
- operating equipment or using hazardous chemicals without being trained and authorised to do so
- operating a dangerous machine without the guard in place
- using damaged or defective work equipment
- lifting loads in an unsafe manner
- failing to use personal protective equipment where it is provided and necessary
- using dangerous chemicals without taking proper precautions
- messing around or deliberately misusing safety equipment, such as fire extinguishers
- taking drugs or drinking alcohol.

Unsafe conditions

Examples of unsafe conditions include:

- inadequate maintenance of work equipment
- poor environmental conditions, such as high or low workplace temperatures, high humidity, dust or other reason for poor air quality, noise, low levels of lighting or glare from lighting, and poorly designed buildings for the type of work being carried out
- an untidy workplace
- broken or unsuitable machine guards
- poor construction and design of machinery

- systems of work that fail to take safety sufficiently into account
- loose or unsuitable clothing
- poor fire warning systems
- exposure to radiation.

Combination of unsafe acts and unsafe conditions

There is a much higher risk that accidents will happen if unsafe acts and unsafe conditions occur at the same time. For example:

- using a machine with a broken guard in a poorly lit work room
- using a damaged electric drill with a loose live connection in wet conditions
- using a pallet-truck to lift boxes in a crowded untidy store room where a carton of milk has been spilt.

Underlying reasons for accidents

The factors and events, or chain of events, mentioned above are the tangible signs of why accidents happen. There are, however, less visible, underlying causes of accidents that are mainly due to the failure of health and safety management systems.

Where there is a poor health and safety culture in the workplace, safety is regarded as a low priority – for example, where there is no health and safety policy, no organisation or arrangements for health and safety, no training policy, no health and safety procedures and no one given responsibility for health and safety matters. Poorly controlled work activities and bad attitudes towards health and safety among the workforce are likely to lead to more accidents than will occur in a workplace with a positive attitude towards health and safety.

There is a low risk of accidents in an organisation with a strong health and safety culture – for example, where there is a clear and genuine management commitment to good health and safety standards and there are records kept of training activities, eye testing, risk assessments, display screen equipment assessments, and accidents and near-misses. This can be described as a 'living' health and safety system.

In contrast, in a 'blame culture' an individual is made a scapegoat for an accident, but it is rare for someone to intend to cause an accident and the real 'blame' usually lies with underlying causes – mostly, the organisation's poor management of the workplace. There is more information about health and safety cultures in Part 4.

What is the cost of accidents and ill health at work?

Accidents and ill health at work can have a substantial effect on individuals and the organisations they work for – lives are lost, people are injured or become ill, money is wasted, machinery is damaged, products are rejected and reputations are lost.

About 2.3 million people a year suffer from ill health caused by work and more than 1 million people are injured at work. More than 7 million working days are lost every year when people take time off because of work-related illness and injury.

Key words and phrases

accident – any unplanned event that results, or could have resulted, in personal injury or ill health; damage to, or loss of, property, plant or materials; damage to the environment; or loss of business opportunity.

musculoskeletal disorders (MSDs) – conditions affecting the muscles, nerves, tendons, ligaments, joints, cartilage or spinal discs.

The cost of accidents and ill health

The cost of **accidents** and ill health may be counted in hard cash and in non-financial terms. Basil Butler, a former Managing Director, BP plc, summed it up when he said, 'Prevention is not only better, but also cheaper than cure… Profits and safety are not in competition'. The Health and Safety Executive was even more succinct when it coined the slogan, 'Good safety is good business'.

The next few paragraphs look at the cost of workplace accidents and ill health to employees, their families and close friends, members of the general public and employers.

Cost to employees of injury or illness

The cost of workplace injury or illness to employees includes:

- personal injury or death
- pain and suffering
- loss of earnings
- loss of quality of life.

Cost to employees' close friends and family

The people closest to employees who suffer a workplace injury or illness may experience:

- distress and grief
- anxiety
- loss of earnings while they look after the sick or injured person
- loss of quality of life.

Cost to the general public

The cost to members of the public involved in an accident connected to work activities includes:

- personal injury or death
- pain and suffering
- loss of earnings
- loss of quality of life
- medical costs.

There are also social costs to the public because of NHS costs, sickness, injury and unemployment benefits and increased costs of goods and services.

Cost to employers

The cost to employers can be considered as direct and indirect costs.

Direct costs

The direct costs of accidents and ill health to employers include:

- damage and repairs to buildings, vehicles, machinery or stock
- legal costs
- fines (criminal court case)
- compensation (civil court case or agreed compensation)
- loss of product
- sick pay
- overtime payments
- employee medical costs
- claims on employer's liability and public liability insurance
- increased insurance premiums.

Indirect costs

The indirect costs of accidents and ill health can spread far beyond the immediate obvious costs and may include:

- business interruption – for example, loss of output and contract penalties for delays
- product liability payments
- unbudgeted time and money spent because of the accident and occupational health investigations
- loss of goodwill between employees and management
- loss of consumer confidence
- damage to the corporate reputation
- the hiring and training of replacement staff
- loss of expertise
- clean-up costs.

Research indicates that back pain is a problem for nearly two thirds (63 per cent) of small businesses. One in five people working in small firms have back strain. The average small firm was said to be losing 22 days of work a year from employee back strain.

A woman tripped over a delivery ramp and injured her shoulder, so that she needed two weeks off work. Her employer calculated the cost of the accident to be about £15,000.

Working out losses due to accidents and ill health

You can work out the cost of accidents and ill health to your organisation by looking at the costs of each accident or incident in your workplace under some of the headings given below. They are not comprehensive and *you* may find there are other costs to be considered.

Budget headings

You may need to account for the pay of the ill or injured employee who is off work and for the cost of employing replacement workers. Overtime payments to recover lost production may need to be included, as well as any penalties for a failure to meet contracted deadlines.

The investigation of the accident will itself incur costs, such as the time of the people carrying out the investigation and meeting with enforcement officers.

There may be costs involved in restarting stopped work – for example, rescheduling work programmes, redesigning work procedures, cleaning up the site of the accident or incident, repair costs and the cost of hiring work equipment to replace any that was damaged.

There may also be the costs of dealing with a prosecution by the enforcing authorities. These may include legal fees, fines and the staff time to deal with the case. There may also be compensation costs in the case of a civil claim.

Types of injury or ill health

In addition, or as an alternative, you could look at the cost of a particular type of injury, such as the number of people who suffer back pain in your organisation or the number of people affected by wood dust in a wood working company. You could look at the cause of the back pain or the reason why a concentration of the dust in the air is excessive and the cost of it to your organisation. You could then look at how you could reduce the costs, injuries or ill health by introducing appropriate control measures.

The bigger picture

Good health and safety standards are a legal requirement, and most people would say that they are ethically desirable. In addition, high standards of health and safety can help to reduce the costs to an organisation, particularly if the health and safety system is part of a comprehensive management control system. In contrast, poor health and safety standards can lead to excessive costs and could even result in the failure of the business. Reducing these losses can be achieved by developing and promoting a health and safety culture – see pages 96 to 99 – and by tackling the underlying causes of accidents through intervention programmes that prevent accidents rather than reacting to them.

Simple controls

Effective controls need not be complicated or even costly. For example, a study of accidents in one factory recorded 6 major injuries, 31 requiring first aid and 888 non-injury accidents. These led to substantial financial losses, which were 1.4 per cent of operating costs.

The study found that a large number of the accidents occurred around the start of the shift at six o'clock in the morning when repair staff, such as electricians and mechanics, were not available. In fact, the repair staff did not have to report for work until eight o'clock. Operations continued despite repairs being necessary. The lack of repair made the operations more dangerous.

The simple control measure was to train a number of machine operators in preventive maintenance they could do themselves. This made the operation safer. The number of accidents dropped significantly because these staff were able to carry out small repairs which would previously have waited until the repair staff came in.

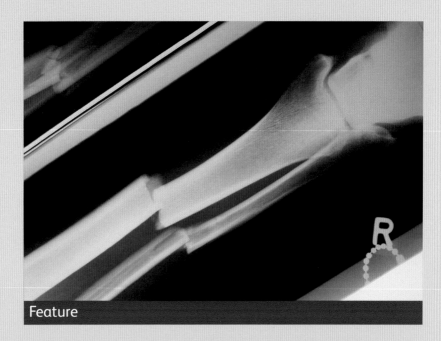

Feature

The impact of accidents

Accident statistics make grim reading. More than six hundred people lose their lives every year in the UK because of workplace activities. In 2008/09, 180 of these were employee deaths.

The longer-term trend in the fatal injury rate is downward but, even with a significant fall between 2007/08 and 2008/09, there has been little change in the numbers killed over the last six years.

Figures for reported accidents show that more than 28,000 employees suffered a major injury at work in 2008/09 and about 23,000 members of the public received non-fatal injuries because of workplace activities. The actual number of injuries may be at least double these figures because of under-reporting.

The impact on workplace because of absence from work is considerable – just over 104,000 workers were off work for more than three days ('three day injuries') due to a reported injury received at work.

Most fatal injures to workers are due to falls from a height (19 per cent), followed by being struck by a moving object (14 per cent) or being struck by a moving vehicle (15 per cent).

Most major injuries are due to slips and trips on the same level, although most 'three-day injuries' (minor injuries) occur as a consequence of handling , lifting or carrying something; slips, trips or falls on the same level or being struck by a moving or falling object.

Worker accidents resulting in death, major injury and minor injury

	2003/04	2004/05	2005/06	2006/07	2007/08	2008/09
Deaths	236	223	217	247	233	180
Major injuries	31,972	31,702	30,217	29,738	29,289	28,692
Minor injuries (3-day injuries)	132,131	122,922	120,268	115,799	111,175	105,222

Number of fatal injuries by occupation 2008/09

Skilled trades (37)

Elementary trades (35)

Process, plant and machine operatives (33)

Managers and senior officials (11)

Professional occupations (6)

Associate professionals and technical occupations (3)

Other (including not known) (4)

2. How can we eliminate hazards and reduce risk?

What are the principles involved?

The modern approach to health and safety at work is through risk management. By law all workplaces must take steps to prevent and control accidents, incidents, personal injury and ill health at work. This must be done firstly by assessing the hazards and risks involved in the work activity and then by introducing appropriate measures that eliminate the hazard altogether or reduce the risks from it to an acceptable level. This chapter introduces the principles involved. There is more detail in 'Risk assessment' on pages 110 to 120.

Key words and phrases

accident – any unplanned event that results, or could have resulted, in personal injury or ill health; damage to, or loss of, property, plant or materials; damage to the environment; or loss of business opportunity.

audit – a formal examination against a fixed standard by competent people who are independent of the area of work being audited.

competent person – a person with the appropriate qualifications, knowledge and experience to identify the risks arising from a situation and the measures needed to control them.

ergonomic design – the application of scientific data about human mental and physical capacities and performance to the design of work systems.

ergonomics – the study of the interaction between people and their work.

hazard – a source of danger: any thing, condition or circumstance that could cause harm to people or damage to property.

health and safety culture – the integration of health and safety awareness and controls into day-to-day management practices.

Health and Safety Executive (HSE) – the official British body responsible for enforcing health and safety law in many industries.

health and safety policy – a written statement of the organisation's arrangements for and implementation of its health and safety management system and activities.

hierarchy of control – a well tested system of graded health and safety controls.

incident (near-miss or near-miss accident) – an unplanned event that does not result in personal injury, death or damage, but has the potential to do so.

intervention programme – a series of actions designed to improve workplace health and safety standards and to reduce the risks from health and safety hazards.

management system – a framework of policies and procedures that helps an organisation to achieve its objectives.

monitoring – regular, often daily, checks on what is going on in the workplace to help to deal with problems as they arise.

performance indicators – measurements used to help an organisation to define and measure progress towards the organisation's health and safety goals.

permit to work – a formal document that specifies the work to be done and the precautions to be taken.

reasonably practicable – what is practicable based on whether the time, trouble and expense of the precautions suggested are proportionate to the risks involved.

risk – a measure or scale of the likelihood that harm will occur from a particular hazard, and the severity of the consequences, including death, major injury, disease, minor injury, no injury and damage to property.

risk assessment – a systematic process for identifying workplace hazards and assessing the risks involved from those hazards.

safe system of work – a set of procedures for carrying out a task safely.

Prevention and precaution

There are a number of typical stages involved in controlling hazards and reducing the risk from illness and accidents at work:

■ find out what causes harm

■ decide who in the workplace might be harmed

■ determine the preventive measures (controls) that can be introduced to reduce the risk of harm

■ plan the actions to introduce these measures

■ inform and train staff

■ implement the measures

■ record the outcomes of the work procedures and actions introduced to reduce risk

■ monitor and review success and make appropriate adjustments to procedures and controls.

How this is carried out varies from company to company but there are a number of recognised basic techniques for reducing accidents and ill health at work. They are based on general principles of prevention which are outlined opposite.

General principles of prevention

The general principles of prevention are:

- avoid hazards wherever possible

- evaluate the risks that cannot be avoided

- deal with the risks at source

- adapt the work to the individual – for example, the design of workstations, the choice of work equipment and the choice of working and production methods – including alleviating monotonous work where possible

- adapt work practices if there are suitable technical advances or improvements

- replace anything that is dangerous with something that is not dangerous or is less dangerous

- develop a coherent overall prevention policy that covers technology, organisation of work, working conditions, social relationships and the influence of factors relating to the working environment

- give *collective* protective measures priority over *individual* protective measures

- give appropriate instructions to employees

- monitor and review performance and make adjustments as necessary.

Controls

The main control techniques are outlined below and on pages 36 to 44:

- using management and monitoring systems

- eliminating hazards by using a hierarchy of control

- implementing intervention programmes

- introducing ergonomics into the workplace

- appointing competent persons

- training managers, supervisors, safety representatives and workers

- facilitating worker involvement and working together.

Management systems

The fundamental aim of good health and safety practices in the workplace is to reduce the number and severity of injuries, ill health and **incidents**. This requires a logical and systematic approach to identifying the hazards in the workplace and to controlling them so that the risk of being injured or becoming ill is the lowest it can possibly be. Health and safety management systems are designed to achieve this.

A good management system sets goals, describes the means to get there, supplies the necessary resources and checks to ensure that the system has indeed achieved the desired goals. A health and safety **management system** should have the following elements:

- policy – a written health and safety policy
- organising – an organisational structure for health and safety
- planning and implementing the health and safety policy
- measuring performance and monitoring procedures – making sure the required standards are being met
- auditing and reviewing – identifying problems and making sure that they are dealt with through continual improvement.

Management principles

There are several principles underlying the management of health and safety at work.

- Commitment – the employer and senior managers need to give, and demonstrate, their full support for a positive health and safety culture in the organisation, ensuring that a key corporate aim is the continual improvement of the organisation's health and safety standards following regular reviews.

- Partnership – there needs to be a genuine partnership between all the relevant parties in an organisation, such as the managers, supervisors, employees and safety representatives. They are the stakeholders in the health and safety of the organisation, so the chance to be involved in health and safety matters is likely to motivate them to make a useful contribution towards achieving a positive health and safety culture.

- Structure – the management structure for health and safety in the organisation should depend on the size of the organisation and the nature of the activities carried out. There should be good communications between all levels within the organisation.

- Integration – health and safety management systems should be integrated into the organisation's overall policy, management arrangements and operations.

Food company puts safety higher up the menu

By following the principles of commitment, partnership, structure and integration (see above), a major food company turned around a poor health and safety record. It had been prosecuted three times by the Health and Safety Executive in the late 1990s.

The company reorganised its health and safety management system. Employee representatives were appointed to help to improve the safety culture and to act as an intermediary between the management, safety team and the workforce. A health and safety team was set up to train company managers and safety representatives in risk assessment and accident investigation. Managers investigated accidents and used a list of suggested actions to decide what to do to prevent an accident from happening again. Reportable accidents have dropped from around 50 a year to 20 a year.

Health and safety policies

An organisation has a legal duty to implement a health and safety system that complies with health and safety legislation. Employers have a legal duty to make arrangements for the effective planning, organisation, control, monitoring and review of the preventive and protective measures, including any action needed for continual improvement.

The health and safety arrangements can be made by developing a **health and safety policy** for the organisation – a written statement of the organisation of, arrangements for, and implementation of a health and safety management system. This also helps employers to comply with their legal obligations and to show their commitment to health and safety.

The policy should be specific to the organisation and appropriate to the nature and scale of its activities. It should recognise the organisation's responsibilities and communicate them to its employees. Its principal aim should be to protect the health and safety of all members of the organisation by preventing work-related injuries, ill health, diseases and incidents (non-injury accidents). It should also include measures to prevent people who are not in their employment from being injured. It should direct the resources of the organisation in such a way to reduce risk or injury to anyone that may be affected by their operations.

A detailed description of health and safety policies is given on pages 100 to 104.

Organising

Responsibilities and relationships need to be defined and established to ensure the management structure and other arrangements are effective. Competent people must be identified to lead on health and safety issues and all staff need to be trained and instructed to the appropriate level. The systems introduced must ensure informed decision making, good communication and the allocation of resources.

Employees should be encouraged to take part in promoting health and safety, and there should be systems in place for consulting employees on health and safety issues.

Managers, supervisors and safety representatives should be *leaders*, demonstrating the importance of health and safety by example – such as by acting positively through regular meetings on health and safety, regular reports to the board of directors and the safety committee and including information about health and safety issues in the organisation's newsletter.

Everyone involved should regard health and safety as on ongoing issue that is part of their job.

Planning

The approach to health and safety issues should be planned and systematic. There should be a system for identifying hazards, assessing risks and deciding how they can be eliminated or controlled. This can be done through risk assessment methods and identifying priorities. The hierarchy of control should be used to deal with these hazards and risks.

A positive health and safety culture should be promoted through specific improvement actions. Standards of performance should be established and used to measure achievement and progress. These standards are the specific policies, safe work procedures and instructions for the organisation.

Measuring and monitoring performance

Health and safety management systems are effective only if they are integrated into the day-to-day working of an organisation. For continual improvement, performance should be monitored and reviewed at frequent intervals, and the system adjusted in light of the findings.

Monitoring consists of frequent (possibly daily) checks on what is going on in the workplace so that you can deal with problems as they arise. The monitoring of health and safety controls is just as important as measuring the bottom line of a company's accounts, and the performance of an effective health and safety management system should be capable of being measured accurately. This is active monitoring through looking at the premises, plant, substances, people, procedures and systems. This monitoring is done through records and documentation.

Health and safety performance standards should be set up so that you can measure your improvement, or failure, in implementing the health and safety policy. **Performance indicators** can help in measuring your health and safety performance – for example, you could monitor the accident and illness rates, the training of employees, the information distributed to employees or members of the public, the health and safety performance of contractors, or the performance of your health surveillance programme – this is reactive monitoring.

Findings from the analysis of such records should assist you in identifying any failures in the health and safety management system. This will help you to identify when and where action is needed to improve performance and the underlying health and safety management system.

Auditing and reviewing

Auditing

An **audit** is a formal examination by competent people who are independent of the area of work being audited or from outside the organisation. An audit normally considers what is happening in the workplace in comparison to a fixed standard, such as a quality health and safety management system. A regular audit of the management system makes it easier to decide whether the systems are effective. Such audits should include the health and safety policy, employee participation, the health and safety management system records, the prevention and control measures, and whether there is continual improvement. If possible, the results of an audit could be compared with other similar organisations.

Reviewing

By looking at the records of accidents, injury and absence from work you can identify trends and possible causes of absence, then recommend changes to the health and safety management system. This could result in people taking less time off because they have fewer injuries. It could also help people to get back to work more quickly if they do need to take time off – for example, a health and safety management system with a good first aid system is likely to provide rapid assistance to injured employees, helping to minimise their recovery time. If there is a problem of violence or stress in the workplace, the introduction of a counselling service may assist employees to recover more quickly.

Employers need to review the policy regularly to make sure that it is relevant to their current activities. A systematic review of the health and safety performance of the organisation is essential for the organisation to comply with the law and to achieve continual improvement. Information gathered from monitoring performance and from audits of the health and safety management system will help you to identify those areas that need to be improved. You can compare your performance with other similar businesses, or, if you work for a large organisation, with other outlets, branches or units.

Reporting

Larger organisations should consider reporting their health and safety performance in their annual reports. (See also pages 105 to 108.) This demonstrates the organisation's commitment to health and safety and may encourage stakeholders to comment on, or participate in, the health and safety management system.

The hierarchy of control

A hierarchy is a system of things arranged in grade order. A **hierarchy of control** is a simple-to-follow grading to help you make a choice of controls for health and safety matters. It helps you to decide which controls would be most effective for dealing with the hazards and risks you have identified,

The illustration on page 40 shows a *general* hierarchy of control. It is as follows.

1. Elimination or avoidance
   Eliminate the risk by removing the hazard from the workplace completely.

2. Substitution
   Substitute a less hazardous substance or piece of work equipment.

3. Controlling risks at source
   Contain the hazard by separating people from the hazard. For example, use guards to cover the dangerous parts of a machine, use local exhaust ventilation, enclose a machine to reduce noise, or use remote controls or automated processes so the employee does not need to go near the dangerous part of the machine or process.

4. Safe working procedures
   Design a **safe system of work** (see pages 121 to 126), or use a **permit to work** system to control the hazards and risks.

5. Training, instruction and/or supervision
   Provide training, information and instruction for employees, and supervise them.

6. Personal protective equipment (PPE)
   Use personal protective equipment to reduce the risk of harm.

The first control in the hierarchy is to remove a hazard completely. The levels farther down the hierarchy deal with ways to control the hazard if it cannot be eliminated.

The best method of preventing accidents and reducing risks to employees is to eliminate the hazard altogether. The next best thing is to reduce the risk from any hazard that cannot be removed. This might be achieved by, for example, replacing a dangerous substance (such as asbestos) with one with similar properties that is less hazardous (such as fibreboard), or designing and using better guarding systems on a machine, or redesigning a lifting operation so that the employees doing the lifting are unlikely to be hurt.

When considering control measures always start at the beginning of the list. If it is not possible to carry out the first course of action (elimination), consider the next measure down. Gradually work down the list if necessary.

Elimination is always the first choice and personal protective equipment is always the last choice. A combination of controls may be appropriate.

You might also come across a more detailed hierarchy for specific hazards such as hazardous substances – see page 230).

Any preventive measures taken need to be appropriate to the equipment, substance or system of operation. The prevention methods must be as simple as possible and the cost of introducing them needs to be reasonable. You need to balance this reasonable cost with what is practicable in the circumstances. This means what is practicable in the light of whether the time, trouble and expense of precautions suggested are proportionate (or not) to the risks involved. '**Reasonably practicable**' is a balance between the degree of risk and the cost of control.

Intervention programmes

Intervention programme is a term used to describe a number of actions which, in combination, aim to change the way health and safety is dealt with in an organisation. The actions *intervene* in the policies and procedures of an organisation and introduce new ways of working that aim to reduce the number of hazards and the number and severity of risks to health and safety. For example, an intervention programme could be designed and implemented to reduce the number of accidents in a workplace or to increase the health and safety awareness of employees.

When designing and implementing an intervention programme the following elements should be included:

- engage the commitment of the senior managers to high standards of health and safety
- carry out an audit of safety plans
- analyse the causes of accidents
- raise awareness of risk
- identify preventive measures
- set up work groups to identify the measures to be introduced
- redesign systems intended to protect employees by reviewing the method of work and ensuring that the environment is suitable for the work being carried out
- set up education, training and instruction programmes for employees
- analyse the health and safety behaviour of employees in a wide range of circumstances.

The results of intervention programmes can often lead to a reduction in the frequency and severity of accidents, and the cost of the safety measures introduced can be repaid in just a few months.

Ergonomics

Ergonomics is the study of the interaction between people and their work. **Ergonomic design** is normally defined as the application of scientific data about human mental and physical capacities and performance to the design of work systems. It aims to make the task, equipment, information and work environment suit each worker. In general, it involves designing tools, equipment, workstations and workplaces so that the job fits the person, rather than trying to make the person fit the job. An ergonomic approach takes into account the size and shape of the human body and even psychological aspects such as mental abilities, personality, knowledge and experience.

Ergonomics can be used for identifying and controlling hazards and solving physical problems – for example, in the use of display screen equipment, manual handling and work-related stress.

Competence and competent persons

Competence means being capable of doing a particular task or activity to a high recognised standard. In relation to health and safety at work, competence means being capable of carrying out work in a safe and healthy manner appropriate to the level of responsibility.

The factors that determine competence in health and safety are knowledge of, and skills and experience in a particular subject.

Knowledge is often, but not exclusively, obtained from structured learning on courses of study or training. The courses may be short – say, three days – focusing on a specific subject such as risk assessment, or longer at a higher level – for example, the CIEH level 4 Award in Health and Safety at Work or a degree.

Skills are normally physical skills but mental skills are also relevant to health and safety.

Experience is usually gained by performing a particular task or activity. Although the necessary skills and knowledge for a job can be gained from experience, that experience may be limited to only what is necessary for a *particular* task or activity, so may lack the breadth or depth of understanding really needed for the subject.

So, a competent person is someone with the appropriate qualifications, knowledge and experience to identify the risks arising from a situation and the measures needed to control them.

For example, a CORGI-registered gas engineer/technician is a person who is required by law to be approved by the Health and Safety Executive before being permitted to carry out work on gas supplies and installations. A tree surgeon or gardener requires a certificate of competence in the use of pesticides before being legally permitted to apply a herbicide to a tree stump to kill it.

However, certificates of competence are not always required to ensure and prove competence – for example, a well-trained employee would be competent to inspect a ladder before using it or to assess the suitability of a computer workstation for use by a particular employee. *Appropriate* training should be arranged to give employees an adequate knowledge of the hazards and failures of the equipment for which they are responsible. It should also provide the knowledge and understanding of the working practices used in the organisation for which employees work.

Competent persons

The Approved Code of Practice for The Management of Health and Safety at Work Regulations 1999 makes it clear that competence does not solely rest on skills or qualifications but also involves:

■ an understanding of relevant current best practice

■ awareness of the limitations of one's own experience and knowledge

■ the willingness and ability to supplement existing experience and knowledge.

Employers and managers must satisfy themselves that the people employed to control major hazards are competent to do so. They also need to be sure that the company has competent employees who have the skills, experience and knowledge to do their job properly and safely under all working conditions.

Some of the areas of work that need to be covered are to develop and review the organisation's health and safety strategy and policy; develop and implement effective communication systems for health and safety information; identify and evaluate health and safety hazards; assess health and safety risks; and determine and assist with the implementation of health and safety control measures and monitoring systems.

Throughout the book you will see that there are many examples of where employers need to make sure that the person carrying out a task is competent to do so.

Training and information

Employers and managers must satisfy themselves that they employ competent persons to carry out their activities safely and without risk to health. By providing training – helping people to learn how to do something – and information, employers and managers can encourage competence, create a positive **health and safety culture**, manage health and safety better and meet legal duties to protect the health and safety of their employees.

All people in an organisation need training that is appropriate to their work. For example, board members need training about their legal responsibilities and how they can fulfil them and about their responsibilities for setting the organisation's health and safety strategy.

Managers need training about their part in developing the strategy and the health and safety policy and the resources needed to implement them. Supervisors need training about how to implement the health and safety policy through risk assessment, monitoring systems and recording health and safety information.

Safety representatives need training about the health and safety system in the organisation and how they can influence the workplace health and safety issues. Employees need training to carry out their duties safety and without risks to health or safety and they also need information and training about their responsibilities to others who may be affected by their actions.

There is more information about training on pages 152 to 158.

Working together and worker involvement

The value of involving employees in redesigning systems of work to make them safer cannot be understated. After all, they know the job best, can advise on improvements and are the people who will probably benefit most from a system designed to protect them. There needs to be detailed discussion between the target group of employees, safety representatives, supervisors and managers.

Managers and supervisors should *listen* to what the safety representatives and employees have to say and *encourage* them to make suggestions on how the job can be done safely and more efficiently. This can be done through a safety committee, if one is set up in the organisation. It is important not to dismiss suggestions but to talk them through and get the *agreement* of the workforce to adopt safe methods of working.

There are bound to be disagreements during discussion, but supervisors and safety representatives are in a good position to deal with conflict. They can identify the cause of the disagreement and outline the possible solutions. They can then discuss the advantages and disadvantages of the proposals and help to negotiate an agreed solution.

Everyone with a stake in the safety of a particular operation or system should be involved in the redesign team. Team members might include representatives of senior management, supervisors and middle managers, workplace safety representatives and safety officers, other trade union officials, insurance loss adjusters, environmental health and health and safety specialists from your local enforcing authorities and the National Health Service staff.

Legal requirements

Under the Health and Safety at Work etc. Act 1974 employers with five or more employees must have a *written* statement of the company's health and safety policy and the organisation and arrangements for implementing it.

The Management of Health and Safety at Work Regulations 1999 require employers to carry out risk assessments, create safe systems of work and appoint one or more persons to assist them in complying with their legal duties.

Many other pieces of legislation also require risk assessments to be carried out. They include – The Health and Safety (Display Screen Equipment) Regulations 1992; The Manual Handling Operations Regulations 1992; The Provision and Use of Work Equipment Regulations 1998; The Control of Substances Hazardous to Health Regulations 2002 and The Control of Noise at Work Regulations 2005.

See pages 45 to 61 'What does legislation say we must do?' for general information about health and safety legislation and see Part 6 for information about specific risks, controls and their legal requirements.

What does legislation say we must do?

Most countries legislate for health and safety standards. Many of these standards are based on conventions and recommendations about working conditions drawn up by the European Union (EU) or the World Health Organization and the International Labour Organization – specialised agencies of the United Nations (UN). Conventions are international treaties, while recommendations can help to determine national policy and action even though they are not binding on member states of the UN or the EU.

The standards come about with the involvement of governments and representatives of employees and employers. Member states are obliged to put in place the standards as far as is possible. Standards are enforced by requiring member states to report regularly on implementation or when specific allegations are made against a member state.

Key words and phrases

approved code of practice – formal guidance, generally issued by the Health and Safety Executive (HSE) on behalf of the government, containing detailed information on how to comply with the law.

code of practice – practical guidance and advice on how to achieve the standards required by legislation.

(EU) Directive – European Union legislation that requires member states to achieve a particular result, but without dictating the means of achieving it.

environmental health officer (EHO) – an officer employed by local authorities to enforce health and safety law. Also known as environmental health practitioner (EHP) or regulatory officer.

(EU) Regulation – European Union legislation that immediately becomes enforceable as law in all member states at the same time.

European Commission – the executive branch of the European Union which proposes legislation and implements the decisions of the Union.

European Union – the economic and political partnership between 27 democratic European countries.

guidance – specific advice on how to achieve the standard required by legislation where there is no *approved* code of practice.

Health and Safety Executive (HSE) – the official British body responsible for enforcing health and safety law in many industries.

local authorities – local councils delegated by the Secretary of State to enforce health and safety law in the commercial and retail sectors.

plant – machinery or equipment used in an industrial or manufacturing process.

primary legislation – main laws passed by the legislative bodies in the UK.

reasonably practicable – what is practicable based on whether the time, trouble and expense of the precautions suggested are proportionate to the risks involved.

secondary legislation – the laws made under the authority of primary legislation.

The role and influence of European legislation

In the United Kingdom – England, Wales, Scotland and Northern Ireland – laws are made by elected Members of Parliament (MPs) and, under devolved powers, by the elected representatives of the Welsh Assembly, Scottish Parliament and Northern Ireland Assembly.

Acts of Parliament – such as the Health and Safety at Work etc. Act 1974 – usually deal with broad principles. Regulations and Orders are then made, where necessary, to deal with detailed requirements and powers.

British laws are aligned with and formed by European Community (EC) legislation created by the member countries of the European Union (EU). The UK is one of the member states and provides elected Members to the European Parliament (MEPs). The European Commission proposes the draft European laws, which are considered by the European Parliament and the Council of Ministers.

Two kinds of European legislation directly affect British laws. They are Regulations and Directives. (There are also EC Decisions, which are laws applying to particular member states, organisations or individuals.)

EU Regulations immediately become enforceable in all member states at the same time, and member states must carry them out word for word. They do not require additional national legislation to become law. In contrast, an **EU Directive** requires member states to achieve a particular result, but without dictating the precise way to achieve that result. This means that all member states must implement Directives through their own national legislation – they must *re-enact* (remake) the principles of the Directives in their own national laws.

Many of the health and safety regulations currently in force in the United Kingdom are a result of Directives, although similar legislation may have existed before EU membership. Seventeen health and safety Directives have been adopted since 1989 when Directives became possible under EU law. The principles of prevention and the responsibilities of employers and employees alike were set at the time. The Directives have established minimum requirements for health and safety for workplaces in general and for specific dangerous substances, materials, media and equipment. They also cover specific workplaces and specific categories of worker.

The EU approach to health and safety

Members of the European Union believe there is a need to improve working conditions throughout the member states for both humanitarian and economic reasons. One of the key objectives of the EU is to create more jobs of better quality. A safe and healthy working environment is an essential element of the quality of work.

The scope of the EU influence is not limited to legislation because it also provides information, guidance and the promotion of a healthy working environment, with a particular focus on medium and small businesses.

Several committees have been set up by the European Commission to advise on improving standards in health and safety. The Advisory Committee on Safety and Health at Work (ACSH) assists in 'the preparation, implementation and evaluation of activities in the fields of safety and health at work'. The Scientific Committee on Occupational Exposure Limits advises the European Commission on regulatory proposals for exposure limits for chemicals in the workplace.

Specific EU aims

The EU aims to cut work-related illness and accidents across the EU by a quarter by 2012 under a five-year strategy for health and safety at work. This strategy follows a 17 per cent reduction in fatal accidents from 2002-2004 and a 20 per cent fall in accidents leading to absence from work of three days or more. But progress is uneven across countries, sectors, companies and categories of worker. Changes in working life are leading to new risks at work, while certain workplace illnesses are on the rise.

The EU is using a number of methods to achieve its ambitious goal by:

■ guaranteeing the proper implementation of EU legislation

■ supporting small and medium businesses in the implementation of the legislation in force

■ adapting the legal framework to changes in the workplace and simplifying it

■ promoting the development and implementation of specific national strategies

■ encouraging changes in the behaviour of workers and encouraging their employers to adopt health-focused approaches

■ finalising the methods for identifying and evaluating new potential risks

■ improving the tracking of progress

■ promoting health and safety at an international level.

European Agency for Safety and Health at Work

The European Agency for Safety and Health at Work is the European agency with responsibility for health and safety. It aims to make Europe's workplaces safer, healthier and more productive.

The agency is a catalyst for developing, collecting, analysing and disseminating information that improves the state of occupational safety and health in Europe. It brings together representatives from three key decision-making groups in each of the EU's member states – governments, employers and workers' organisations.

The agency is based in Bilbao, Spain. 'Focal Points' – the agency's principal safety and health information network – have been set up in 17 countries in the EU to co-ordinate health and safety activity throughout Europe.

'Focal Points' are nominated by each government as the agency's official representative in that country and are normally the competent national authority for safety and health at work. In England, Scotland and Wales, the national authority is the Health and Safety Executive. In Northern Ireland it is the Health and Safety Executive for Northern Ireland.

These national organisations are responsible for the organisation and co-ordination of the national networks and are involved in the preparation and implementation of the agency's work programme.

Primary and secondary British legislation

European Directives and Regulations supersede UK law. As described above, Regulations must be implemented exactly as they are prescribed, while Directives require national legislation.

Primary (or *principal*) *legislation* is the name given to the main laws – for example, The Health and Safety at Work etc. Act 1974 – passed by the legislative bodies in the UK. They include Acts of Parliament, Acts of the Scottish Parliament and Acts of the Northern Ireland Assembly. *Secondary* (or *delegated* or *subordinate*) *legislation* is the description for laws made under the authority of the primary legislation – for example, The Management of Health and Safety at Work Regulations 1999. These laws are known as *Statutory Instruments* and have titles such as Regulations, Orders and Rules.

Most health and safety legislation in the UK follows an EU Directive and is implemented through one major piece of legislation – such as the Health and Safety at Work etc. Act 1974.

The legislation outlined in this chapter is *criminal* law which is dealt with by the criminal court system – for example, magistrates' and crown courts in England, Wales and Northern Ireland, and Sheriff courts in Scotland. Offences under this legislation are criminal matters and create a criminal record on conviction.

Under *civil* proceedings – for example, in county courts in England, Wales and Northern Ireland – a court may order a business to pay compensation to someone who suffered injury from an accident. For historical reasons the legal systems of Scotland and Northern Ireland vary slightly from that of England and Wales.

Health and Safety at Work Act and Northern Ireland Order

The main piece of primary legislation dealing with workplace health and safety in England, Wales and Scotland is the Health and Safety at Work etc. Act 1974. (This is sometimes abbreviated informally to HASAWA 74.) There are largely similar provisions in Northern Ireland under the Health and Safety at Work (Northern Ireland) Order 1978. (This is sometimes abbreviated informally to HSW Order.)

Background

Before these two major pieces of legislation came into force, legislation was largely based on nineteenth-century regulation and had not kept pace with the development of modern industrial and commercial practices. The Health and Safety at Work etc. Act 1974 and the Health and Safety at Work (Northern Ireland) Order 1978 rectified this situation.

The Act is largely based on the report of the Robens Committee on safety and health at work published in 1972. The legislation was reviewed between 1999 and 2000, but no major modifications were considered to be necessary, even though some of the Robens Committee recommendations have not been introduced. The Act has stood the test of time as a very useful piece of legislation that provides a robust framework for the health and safety provision and practices in the workplace.

Enabling legislation

The Health and Safety at Work etc. Act 1974 is an *enabling* Act. It makes it possible, for example, for the government to make regulations – more detailed legislation that prescribes the standards that organisations must comply with in their workplaces. The regulations are broadly grouped into those dealing with:

- health and safety management in general
- particular hazards
- particular industries.

To assist in the interpretation of these regulations, the Health and Safety Executive (HSE) issues **approved codes of practice** or **guidance** for employers and employees.

What is covered

The rest of this chapter looks at the structure of the legislation, codes of practice and guidance in more detail. For ease of reading, the chapter refers to the Health and Safety at Work etc. Act 1974 and the Health and Safety at Work (Northern Ireland) Order 1978 simply as 'the Act'.

Aims of 'the Act'

The aims of the Act are to:

- secure the health, safety and welfare of people at work
- protect people, other than those at work, against the risks to health and safety that arise out of, or in connection with, the activities of people at work
- control the keeping and use of explosive, highly flammable or otherwise dangerous substances at work.

The legislation describes the system of control, including the organisations that oversee health and safety legislation. It also provides for regulations and approved codes of practice which set the particular standards of health, safety and welfare at work.

The following paragraphs describe the main features of the Act.

Regulating workplace health and safety

There are two main organisations that regulate health and safety in workplaces throughout the UK:

- the Health and Safety Executive
- local authorities (local councils).

Health and Safety Executive

The Health and Safety Commission and the **Health and Safety Executive (HSE)** were originally established under the Act as two separate public bodies. From 1 April 2008 HSE became the single national regulatory body responsible for promoting the cause of better health and safety at work. The 'new' HSE retains its independence and works in the interests of employers, employees and local authorities.

It proposes health and safety law and standards and consults organisations and individuals with an interest in health and safety – such as professional bodies, businesses, trade unions and scientific experts. It regulates health and safety law in industries such as chemical plants, construction sites, factories, fairgrounds, farms, hospitals, mines, nuclear installations, off-shore gas and oil installations, quarries, railways and schools. It also provides information, advice and guidance about the workplace and work activities through publications and the work of field officers.

Local authorities

The HSE gives **local authorities** delegated power to regulate health and safety law in premises such as retail shops; offices; catering services, including restaurants, hotels and residential accommodation; caravan sites; warehouses and wholesalers; leisure and sports amenities; churches and church halls; child care facilities; and consumer services based in retail shops, such as launderettes and cosmetic services. Local authorities also provide information, advice and guidance – for example, through their **environmental health officers** (EHOs) and practitioners (EHPs).

Authorised officers

Health and safety law is enforced by:

- health and safety inspectors from the HSE

- environmental health officers (and EHPs) and technical officers from local authorities

- fire officers from the fire service (for workplace fire precautions).

If you work in a factory, farm or hospital, for example, your enforcement (or regulatory) officer is a health and safety inspector from the HSE. If you work in a shop, a restaurant, a pub, a warehouse or a private sports centre, for example, your enforcement officer is a local EHO. Fire officers can visit all of these premises for the purposes of enforcing the law on fire safety and fire precautions.

Authorised officers have considerable legal powers (see pages 56 to 57), such as the right to enter any workplace at any reasonable time and to serve legal notices.

Legal responsibilities

Everyone involved with a workplace has a responsibility for health and safety. A fundamental principle of health and safety legislation is to indicate what that is. The Act makes it clear that everyone at work – employers, managers, supervisors, safety representatives and workers – has some responsibility for health and safety in the workplace. Employers and managers, for example, have the obligation to identify hazards, assess the risks present in the workplace and to introduce precautions and preventive measures to reduce risks. The specific responsibilities imposed by the Health and Safety at Work etc. Act 1974 are outlined below. The provisions under the Health and Safety at Work (Northern Ireland) Order 1978 are virtually identical.

Employers' responsibilities to their employees

Every employer has a duty to ensure the health, safety and welfare at work of all employees, so far as is reasonably practicable. The responsibility includes:

■ providing and maintaining plant and systems of work that are safe and without risk to health

■ making arrangements for ensuring safety and the absence of risk to health in connection with the use, handling, storage and transport of articles and substances

■ providing information, instruction, training and supervision that is necessary to ensure the health and safety of employees at work

■ maintaining the place of work in a condition that is safe and without risk to health (this duty also applies to the owners of buildings and premises)

■ providing and maintaining entrances and exits to the workplace and access to work areas that are safe and without risk to health (this duty also applies to the owners of buildings and premises)

■ providing and maintaining a working environment that is safe for employees and without risk to their health, and providing and maintaining adequate facilities and arrangements for their welfare at work

■ providing, where necessary, health surveillance of the employees

■ providing measures to protect vulnerable groups such as children, young people, people with disabilities and pregnant women.

Employers must also prepare a written statement about:

■ their general policy towards employees' health and safety at work

■ the organisation and arrangements for carrying out that policy (see pages 100 to 104).

The policy must be brought to the attention of all employees. This can be done either by giving every employee a copy of the policy, or by posting the policy on a notice board or by informing the employees where they may obtain a copy of the policy. The content of the policy should be reinforced by instruction, information and training.

Employers have a general duty to consult their employees about health and safety issues that affect them. Where safety representatives have been appointed in the workplace, employers have a duty to consult them. This helps to make and maintain arrangements that enable employers and employees to co-operate effectively in promoting, developing and checking the effectiveness of measures designed to protect the health and safety of employees at work.

In certain circumstances (see page 85), the employer also has a duty to establish a safety committee which can keep under review the health and safety measures at work.

Employers also have a duty *not* to charge employees for anything done or provided in the interests of health and safety at work. Employers must not, for example, make a charge for personal protective equipment that is required for health and safety purposes.

An organisation with a board of directors or trustees needs to accept its collective role in providing health and safety leadership in the organisation in a formal and public manner. One of the board members should be appointed as a health and safety director, but each member of the board needs to accept his or her individual role in providing health and safety leadership for the organisation. The board also needs to:

- ensure that all board decisions reflect the company's health and safety intentions, as expressed in the health and safety policy

- recognise its role in engaging the active participation of workers in improving health and safety

- ensure that the board is kept informed of, and alerted to, relevant health and safety management issues.

Self-employed people are responsible for their own health and safety. They must look after their own health and safety as if they were their own employee.

Employers' duties to people other than employees

Most of this book concentrates on employers' responsibilities to their own employees, but employers and the self-employed also have responsibilities towards people who are not their own employees. They have a duty to carry out their work activities in such a way as to ensure, so far as is reasonably practicable, that people who are not their employees but who may be affected by the work activities, are not exposed to risks to their health and safety.

Employers and self-employed persons must provide information to people who are not in their employment about work activities that may affect the health and safety of non-employees. For example, a building contractor must provide information about the dangers on a construction site to any staff working on the site who are employed by sub-contractors.

All practicable steps

A local council was fined after three people were killed by a diseased tree that fell during high winds onto passing cars and a bus stop. The tree was the council's responsibility and the court decided that the council should have had a more effective inspection regime in place to check the condition of its trees. The council had breached its duty of care to people not in its employment.

Duties of persons in control of premises

People who have control of premises (or have control over the means of access to or from the premises, or control over any plant or substance in the premises) have health and safety responsibilities. They have a duty to take reasonable measures to make the premises, access and the plant or substances used on the premises safe and without risk to health. This responsibility also applies to people who repair and/or maintain premises, plant or substances, usually because of a clause in a tenancy or work contract.

Duties of designers, manufacturers, importers and suppliers

Designers, manufacturers, importers and suppliers also have health and safety responsibilities. They must:

- ensure, so far as is reasonably practicable, that an article is designed and constructed to be safe and without risk to health when it is used properly

- carry out research, testing and examination to ensure the article is safe and without risk to health

- provide adequate information about the use for which the article has been designed, and how it is to be used and operated.

This duty also applies to manufacturers, importers and suppliers of substances used at work.

Duty to members of the public

An elderly member of the public was killed by a reversing lorry while taking a short cut through the delivery yard of a DIY store. She did not hear the reversing alarm because she was deaf. The boundary fence between the delivery yard and a housing estate was regularly broken down by residents taking the short cut. The company was held liable for failure to ensure that the fence was properly secured to prevent members of the public gaining access to the yard.

Duties of employees

While at work every employee has a duty to take reasonable care of his or her own health and safety and that of other people who may be affected by what he or she does or does not do in the course of carrying out the work (his or her 'acts or omissions' at work).

Employees also have a duty to co-operate with their employer so that the employer can comply with the relevant employers' duties.

A general duty applies to everyone not to intentionally or recklessly interfere with, or misuse, anything provided in the interest of health, safety or welfare. Employees must use all work items provided by the employer in accordance with the training and instruction provided for them.

Staff should be encouraged to report any health and safety problems and any shortcomings in the arrangements in protecting the health and safety of the workforce and others who might be affected by the work activities.

Regulations

The detailed standards that apply in health and safety law are contained in UK regulations (secondary legislation) made under the Health and Safety at Work etc. Act 1974 and the Northern Ireland Order. The regulations set the standards for health and safety at work in the UK and control the organisation, arrangement, operations, processes and procedures in any workplace. Regulations can also delegate enforcement responsibility, create approved documents, specify the persons who are guilty of an offence, provide a specified defence in the event of proceedings, and apply to particular types of premises only.

Many health and safety regulations were made in 1992 to consolidate and replace a large number of regulations dealing with small details. Since then some of the regulations have been updated. Some regulations have been made under devolved powers in Wales, Scotland and Northern Ireland.

Examples of regulations

The Management of Health and Safety at Work Regulations 1999 require organisations to carry out risk assessments and managed the risks identified. (See pages 32 to 44 to and 110 to 120.)

Other important regulations include:

- The Health and Safety (First Aid) Regulations 1981

- The Electricity at Work Regulations 1989

- The Personal Protective Equipment Regulations 1992 (often referred to as 'the PPE regs')

- The Manual Handling Operations Regulations 1992

- The Workplace (Health, Safety and Welfare) Regulations 1992

- The Health and Safety (Display Screen Equipment) Regulations 1992 (often referred to as 'the DSE regs')

- The Reporting of Injuries, Diseases and Dangerous Occurrences Regulations 1995 (often abbreviated to RIDDOR)

- The Health and Safety (Safety Signs and Signals) Regulations 1996

- Health and Safety (Consultation with Employees) Regulations 1996

- The Safety Representatives and Safety Committees Regulations 1997

- The Confined Spaces Regulations 1997

- The Lifting Operations and Lifting Equipment Regulations 1998 (often abbreviated to LOLER)

- The Provision and Use of Work Equipment Regulations 1998 (often abbreviated to PUWER)

- The Gas Safety (Installation and Use) Regulations 1998

- The Ionising Radiations Regulations 1999

- The Pressure Systems Safety Regulations 2000

- The Control of Substances Hazardous to Health Regulations 2002, as amended (often abbreviated to COSHH)

- The Control of Lead at Work Regulations 2002

- The Control of Noise at Work Regulations 2005

- The Work at Height Regulations 2005, as amended 2007

- The Control of Vibration at Work Regulations 2005

- The Regulatory Reform (Fire Safety) Order 2005

- In Scotland, Part 3 of the Fire (Scotland) Act 2005, as amended, and the Fire Safety (Scotland) Regulations 2006

- The Control of Asbestos Regulations 2006.

Interpreting legal terms

When reading regulations you will come across the terms 'adequate', 'suitable and sufficient' and 'reasonably practicable' to describe a particular standard. Approved codes of practice and guidance give employers and enforcement officers advice on how to interpret these terms.

Codes of practice

The Health and Safety Executive can provide practical guidance for employers and employees to help them to comply with the regulations and duties that apply to them. The advice is issued as **codes of practice**.

Many professional and other bodies which set standards, such as trade unions, manufacturers and trade or professional associations, can also produce codes of practice.

Approved codes of practice

If the Health and Safety Executive approves the standards of a code of practice (after they have the consent of the Secretary of State), they can bear the title **approved code of practice**. They include a standard, a specification and any other form of practical advice.

Approved codes of practice have a special place in legislation. They are not law, but a failure to observe any part of an approved code of practice may be put forward as evidence in criminal court proceedings about a related alleged contravention of health and safety legislation. If the advice in the approved code of practice has not been followed, then it is up to the defendants to prove that they have satisfactorily complied with the requirement in some other equally effective way.

A similar example of this legal principle is the Highway Code. A failure to observe a provision of the Highway Code does not in itself make the perpetrator liable to criminal proceedings, but the failure to observe a provision may be used to establish liability.

Examples of approved codes of practice include:

- *Management of health and safety at work*
- *Workplace health, safety and welfare*
- *Control of substances hazardous to health*
- *Control of lead at work*
- *The management of asbestos in non-domestic premises*
- *Safe use of work equipment*
- *Safety of pressure systems*
- *Safe use of lifting equipment*
- *Rider-operated lift trucks – operator training*
- *Safety representatives and safety committees*
- *First aid at work.*

Guidance

The Health and Safety Executive also produces **guidance** on many other technical health and safety subjects. Guidance does not have the same standing in law as approved codes of practice but it can be used by employers, if followed, to show that they have complied with a recognised standard.

Examples of guidance include:

- *Manual handling*
- *Seating at work*
- *Workplace transport safety*
- *A step-by-step guide to COSHH assessment*
- *Reducing noise at work.*

Enforcement

Enforcement (or regulatory) officers are appointed by the enforcing authorities (the Health and Safety Executive or the local authority) by being issued with a *warrant*. The warrant specifies the officer's powers and must be produced if requested. Depending on the industrial sector in which you work and the work activities involved, your regulatory officer may be a Health and Safety Executive inspector, an environmental health officer, technical officer or fire officer, all of whom may also be known as *enforcement officers*. In certain circumstances, these officers can be issued with a 'flexible warrant' that allows them to operate in any premises, irrespective of the type of industry.

The powers of regulatory officers

Inspectors have wide-ranging powers including the right of entry to workplaces, the right to serve legal notices requiring improvement work to be done and the right to prohibit work procedures, processes or the use of work equipment. Inspectors may:

Health and safety inspectors have the legal right to examine any aspect of work that could affect safety or health. Here the pressure of a boiler is being checked.

- enter premises at any reasonable time

- take a police officer with them

- take any authorised person or any equipment or materials required to help in an inspection or investigation

- make necessary examinations and investigations

- direct that premises be left undisturbed

- take measurements, photographs or recordings

- take samples of any article or substance

- dismantle or test any article or substance

- take possession of and detain any article or substance for examination, or to ensure that no one tampers with it or that it is available as evidence

- require any person to give information to assist with any examination or investigation

- require books or documents to be produced, inspected and copied

- require that assistance and facilities be made available to allow the inspector's powers to be exercised

- seize and render harmless any article or substance that the inspector believes to be a cause of imminent danger of serious personal injury.

Risk-based inspections

Inspectors approach their work in several ways. They have a programme of regular (normally unannounced) inspections of premises at which they advise the owners or managers about any contraventions of the health and safety legislation. These inspection programmes are based on an assessment of the level of risk posed by the premises or its work activities. So, the higher risk premises are inspected more often that the lower-risk premises. The inspectors can give advice or they can take more formal action by serving an improvement or prohibition notice (see below). In the most extreme circumstances, they may prosecute without warning. However, enforcing authorities will only prosecute when formal proceedings are proportionate to the breach, and inspectors will invite discussions whenever possible before making a final decision on prosecution.

Improvement notices

If an inspector thinks there is a contravention of health and safety legislation, he or she can serve an improvement notice on the person responsible or in charge at the time. The notice states the details of the alleged contravention and the reasons why it is thought that there has been a breach of the law. The notice requires the person responsible to 'remedy the contravention' within a period specified in the notice. The person responsible is the employer, director, manager or supervisor in charge of the premises at the time of the inspection.

The notice must state:

■ that a contravention exists

■ the details of the law contravened

■ the inspector's reasons for his or her opinion

■ that the person responsible must remedy the contravention

■ the time given for the remedy to be carried out – this must be not less than 21 days.

If a person fails to comply with an improvement notice, he or she commits a criminal offence.

Prohibition notices

If an inspector believes that work activities will involve 'a risk of serious personal injury', he or she may serve a prohibition notice on the person in control of the work activity.

The notice must:

■ state that, in the inspector's opinion, there is a risk of serious personal injury

■ identify the matters which create the risk

■ give the reasons why the inspector believes there to have been any contravention of health and safety law

■ direct that the activities stated in the notice must not be carried on, by or under the control of the person served with the notice, unless the matters which create the risk have been remedied.

A prohibition notice can take immediate effect or can be deferred so that the situation can first be made safe.

Appeals

A person who is served with either an improvement or a prohibition notice can appeal against the notice to an employment tribunal.

An employment tribunal consists of a legally qualified chairperson and two other members, one representing employers, the other representing employees. The tribunal has the power to hold a pre-hearing review or a case management discussion. Other powers include ordering someone to answer questions in writing or to provide additional information; making orders for witnesses to attend a hearing or for witness statements to be prepared or exchanged; ordering documents to be disclosed; postponing or adjourning any hearing; making a decision on anything that has been agreed in writing by the parties before the hearing. The tribunal can make an order for costs up to £10,000 against either party.

The grounds for appeal might be that the inspector interpreted the law incorrectly or exceeded his or her powers. Alternatively, a contravention might be admitted, but the appeal would be that the remedy was not 'practicable' or not 'reasonably practicable'. In other circumstances, a contravention might be admitted, but the appeal would be that the incident was so insignificant that the notice should be cancelled.

If an appeal is made against an improvement notice, then the notice is suspended until the appeal is heard. If an appeal is made against a prohibition notice, the notice is suspended only if the employment tribunal suspends it.

If there is no compliance with the notice, the person served with the notice can be prosecuted.

Offences

A contravention of the Health and Safety at Work etc. Act 1974 (or the equivalent Order in Northern Ireland) or any of the regulations made under the Act is a criminal offence. Both an individual and a corporate body can commit an offence and be prosecuted in court. It is an offence to:

- fail to carry out a duty placed on employers, the self-employed, employees, owners of premises, designers, manufacturers, importers or suppliers

- intentionally or recklessly interfere with anything provided for safety

- ask an employee to pay for items, such as personal protective equipment, that an employer must legally provide in the interests of health and safety

- contravene any requirement of any health and safety regulations

- contravene any requirement imposed by an inspector

Legislation aims to protect employees (and others affected by work activities) from any situation, such as a badly wired fuse box or a blocked fire exit, that could lead to or cause injury or death.

- prevent or attempt to prevent a person from appearing before an inspector, or from answering his or her questions

- contravene an improvement or prohibition notice

- intentionally obstruct an inspector in the exercise of his or her powers or duties

- intentionally make a false entry in a register, book, notice or other document which is required to be kept

- intentionally or recklessly make false statements

- pretend to be a health and safety inspector

- fail to comply with a court order.

If an offence is specified as a *summary offence*, it is heard by magistrates in a Magistrates' Court in England, Wales or Northern Ireland. If the offence is an *indictable offence*, it is tried in a Crown Court (with a judge and jury) in England, Wales and Northern Ireland. Some offences can be tried 'either way' – in either a Magistrates' Court or the Crown Court.

In Scotland, the Procurator Fiscal decides which court shall hear health and safety cases. Minor summary offences can be dealt with by magistrates in the District Court. Most health and safety cases are heard in the Sheriff Court (a higher court than the District Court). Very serious cases may be referred to the High Court of Justiciary to be heard by a judge and jury.

Penalties

If found guilty of a health and safety offence on summary conviction, a maximum fine of £20,000 can be imposed by the court. On indictment, the level of fine for a health and safety offence is unlimited. On indictment, the level of fine for a health and safety offence is unlimited.

A maximum of twelve months' imprisonment can be imposed on summary conviction for contravening an enforcement notice (maximum two years' imprisonment when convicted on indictment). Fines (as specified above) may be imposed in addition to prison sentences in such cases.

Individual company directors and senior managers can be found guilty of an offence committed by their organisation (the 'body corporate') if it can be shown that the offence was committed with their consent or connivance, or was due to their neglect. In such cases, the director or manager would face the penalty specified for that offence.

For most health and safety offences, the courts also have the power to disqualify directors of companies – for up to five years in a Magistrates' Court and for up to fifteen years in the Crown Court.

The Act also states that where a person has committed an offence due to the act or default of someone else, then that other person may be found guilty of the offence, whether or not proceedings are taken against the first person.

Feature

Corporate responsibility for work-related deaths

The Corporate Manslaughter and Corporate Homicide Act 2007 creates an offence of 'corporate manslaughter' in England and Wales and 'corporate homicide' in Scotland. The difference in terminology reflects the different legal systems.

The legislation follows concern about the ultimate responsibility for deaths in a number of major accidents including the capsize of the *Herald of Free Enterprise* ferry and the Potters Bar and Hatfield railway crashes.

Organisations can now be prosecuted where there has been a gross failure in the management of health and safety that results in someone's death. An organisation commits an offence if the way in which its activities are managed or organised causes a death that amounts to a gross breach of a duty of care to the deceased.

A prosecution would be based upon a substantial failure within the organisation at a senior level – the people who make the significant decisions about the

organisation or substantial parts of it. Courts dealing with a prosecution under the Act would look at management systems and practices throughout the organisation.

The organisation itself would face prosecution under the legislation, *not* individuals. However, individuals could still be prosecuted for gross negligence, workplace deaths and for health and safety offences under separate legislation, such as the Health and Safety at Work etc. Act 1974. Prosecutions against individuals will continue to be taken where there is sufficient evidence and it is in the public interest to do so.

The introduction of the new corporate manslaughter and homicide offences should prompt organisations to review their health and safety management systems and, in particular, the way in which their activities are managed or organised by their senior management team. All employers should take a fresh look at their business activities and review their risk assessments.

3. Who should be involved in health and safety at work?

Employers

Employers have legal duties to manage health and safety risks arising from their work. They have the ultimate accountability for the impact their activities have upon the safety, health and well-being of employees and anyone else affected by their work.

What is an employer?

We all know that an employer is someone who gives work to others and pays them to do that work, but in the eyes of the law an employer is not a person but an organisation. An employer is a 'body corporate' – a legal status that is separate from the individuals who run the organisation.

In a sole tradership or partnership the person who runs all or most of the day-to-day business usually represents the body corporate. In large organisations there is often a board of directors that represents the employer. The board usually delegates health and safety responsibility to a particular director or to one or more managers.

In local authorities (councils), the responsibilities of the employer are represented by council officers who report to elected councillors. The employer's responsibilities in voluntary organisations are usually represented by trustees or directors who delegate the responsibility for health and safety to managers.

Board involvement improved safety record

Following the death of three workers, the board of a large company led a comprehensive review of health and safety. All directors were assigned health and safety responsibilities. The board received monthly reports on health and safety; created more effective working partnerships with employees, trade union representatives and safety representatives; established an audited programme of behavioural change; and published annual health and safety targets and initiatives to meet them. This resulted in a 43 per cent drop in time lost to injuries over two years and a 63 per cent reduction in major health and safety incidents in one year.

Responsibilities

The employer has a duty to ensure, so far as is reasonably practicable, the health, safety and welfare at work of all employees and others affected by the work of the organisation – see pages 45 to 61 for more information. Employers also have legal responsibilities for the health and safety of their customers if they design, manufacture or import products.

All employers and their directors have duties of care under the common law of negligence. If a breach of health and safety legislation occurs, the corporate body and/or individual managers or directors could be prosecuted. (See also 'Corporate responsibility for work-related deaths' on pages 62.)

Self-employed people have the same responsibilities as employers, as far as the general impact of their work is concerned.

Prison for director after paper shredder death

A company director received a twelve-month custodial sentence following the death of an employee at a paper recycling facility. The director pleaded guilty to manslaughter and health and safety charges. The company was also fined £30,000 with costs of £55,000.

The employee had climbed into an industrial paper-shredding machine to clear blockages when the machine restarted, fatally injuring him.

The machine contained a series of hammers projecting 15cm from a shaft, which revolved at high speed. There was no local electrical isolator provided for the machinery so it could not be securely isolated while the unblocking work was being carried out. This meant that it could be started up while someone was inside it. The company had not created a safe system of work for unblocking the machine and the electrical controls for the machine were contaminated with dust so that they were unreliable.

The court heard that the director chose not to follow the advice of his health and safety consultant and instead adopted a complacent attitude allowing the standards in his paper recycling business to fall. The death could have been prevented by having an isolator for the shredder, a safe system of work for clearing blockages, together with adequate instruction, training and supervision of the staff.

Managers

Managers are often the key to the health and safety culture of an organisation. Together with directors they set the policy. They organise financial resources, appoint people, design health and safety management systems, guide supervisors and work with safety representatives.

Key words and phrases

competent person – someone with the appropriate qualifications, knowledge and experience to identify the risks arising from a situation and the measures needed to control them.

health and safety culture – the integration of health and safety awareness and controls into day-to-day workplace practices. Also the attitudes, beliefs and behaviours towards health and safety within the organisation.

Managing health and safety

Individual directors and managers are delegated the legal duties of the employer, including health and safety responsibilities.

You do not have to have the words *health and safety* in your job title to be responsible for some aspect of the subject. Your exact role depends on your job description. Managing health and safety at work involves actions such as:

■ planning for health and safety

■ setting standards

■ implementing the health and safety policy

■ organising the employees in ways that they can implement the health and safety policy as part of their work activities

■ measuring health and safety performance

■ auditing of the whole health and safety system

■ reviewing health and safety performance

■ reporting performance to employers.

The following paragraphs outline aspects of health and safety management. An extended example of how this might work in practice is given in 'Working with contractors and consultants' on pages 70 to 72.

Planning and organising effective health and safety

Policies and implementation

Employers and managers establish the health and safety policies in the organisation and managers lead the implementation of those policies.

Managers design the health and safety management system and policy for the organisation based on the organisation's aims, objectives, ethos and values. They should do this with the aid of information from the board of directors (if there is one), supervisors, safety representatives and employees.

Managers set up the structure of the health and safety management system and appoint the key people for health and safety in the organisation – for example, they decide on the job descriptions for supervisors and specify their health and safety responsibilities, and they appoint safety representatives on the recommendation of the recognised trade union(s) at the workplace. Where appropriate (see page 85), they may also set up health and safety committees in consultation with trade unions.

Resources

Adequate resources are essential and it is up to managers to ensure that there are appropriate financial and personnel resources.

Communication and involvement

Managers need to establish ways to involve employees, or their representatives, in health and safety matters. Staff involvement improves awareness of and commitment to safe and healthy work practices, and employees can provide essential information that can improve overall health and safety standards.

Managers need to create and maintain good relationships with supervisors, safety representatives and employees.

With employers they should set up procedures for dealing with disputes, discipline and grievances. In some cases they will be involved in resolving conflicts on health and safety issues and will generally make the final decision.

The tasks involved in managing can seem lonely and complicated at times, but regular and effective communication with other managers, supervisors and others, not only helps the manager's own work, but also benefits the organisation and individual employees, and makes for effective teamwork.

There is a legal requirement to obtain competent advice from competent people who can advise on health and safety issues (see page 42 to 43), and **competent persons** are usually appointed by managers.

Risk assessment

The management of health and safety at work is based on risk management. Managers must ensure that systems are in place to assess risks and implement appropriate controls.

Recording, monitoring and reporting health and safety performance

Managers should receive monitoring reports from supervisors and make decisions about any recommended changes – for example, changes in work procedures. They need to ensure that adequate records are kept, although it may be a supervisor who makes the records. Managers also gather other information from supervisors and safety representatives to help to improve the health and safety policy or work procedures.

Routine reports on health and safety performance can help to improve the management of health and safety, show commitment and provide evidence of a good health and safety culture. Managers should monitor the impact of new systems, procedures and legislation and report the main issues to the board.

Managers should ensure that health and safety performance is monitored and that periodic audits are carried out to demonstrate that management systems and structures and risk controls are working. There should be procedures for adjusting systems and practices where monitoring and audits show that performance is not up to scratch.

Monitoring and periodically analysing sickness absence and other records, such as accidents, helps to alert managers to possible underlying problems that could put individuals at risk and damage the performance of the whole organisation.

Reviewing health and safety performance

Formal reviews of performance give managers confidence that there is a strong health and safety culture in the organisation. The information in these reports must be both incident data and cultural issues such as prevention measures, training and maintenance programmes. Reviews should be held once a year. The review should examine whether the health and safety policy reflects the organisation's priorities, plans and targets; check whether risk management and other health and safety management systems have been reported effectively to the board; tease out shortcomings and address weaknesses.

Leading health and safety

Good health and safety managers are strong and active leaders. They are active on health and safety issues and show active commitment to a positive health and safety culture by, for example, attending safety committees.

Working with contractors and consultants

Many organisations engage contractors and consultants to help them to carry out their work. When this work takes place at an employer's premises, both the employer and the contractor (or consultant) have legal duties to one another to safeguard health and safety, and they have *joint* legal responsibilities to work together on health and safety matters.

Who is a contractor or consultant?

Contractors and consultants are people who carry out work on a client organisation's behalf who are not pay-as-you-earn employees of the client. Examples include a development company engaging specialists to demolish a building before new construction starts; a manufacturer engaging an approved asbestos contractor to remove asbestos from a building; a bank contracting out their office cleaning to a specialist cleaning firm; a concert hall engaging a health and safety expert to measure noise; a publishing company engaging a specialist editor for a book; a tree surgery company calling in a specialist twice a year to check the safety of their climbing equipment.

Joint and mutual responsibility

Employers and contractors (consultants and subcontractors) have joint responsibilities to work together in the interests of health and safety under The Management of Health and Safety at Work Regulations 1999 and under regulations (and their amendments) dealing with specific hazards, such as The Control of Substances Hazardous to Health Regulations 2002, The Control of Lead at Work Regulations 2002, The Control of Asbestos Regulations 2006 and The Construction (Design and Management) Regulations 2007. Managers and supervisors from the client organisation and the contracted company must work together to ensure that the workforce and others affected by work activities are protected from harm. The managers (and supervisors) have the delegated responsibility of the employer.

Management role

Through their managers (and supervisors), client employers need to clearly identify all aspects of the work they want the contractor to do. Both the employer and the contractor (and any subcontractors) must carry out a risk assessment of the task to be done, including the risks from each other's work, and set up appropriate controls for the work. Documents should make clear issues such as:

- safe systems of work
- emergency procedures
- what equipment should or should not be used (and permits to work)
- personal protective equipment to be used
- who is responsible for contracting the right number of people to do the job safely.

Managers of the client employer need to select a contractor who is suitable to do the job. They should decide what information, instruction and training is required for the client company's employees, how co-operation and co-ordination between all parties can be achieved, how the workforce is to be consulted and the level of management and supervision required.

The four key issues are:

- communication
- co-operation
- control
- competence.

Communication

All parties must provide their employees with information, instruction and training on the issues involved in the contracted task. Just as importantly, they need to consider what information should be passed between them and agree appropriate ways to make sure this is done. They need to exchange clear information about the risks arising from their operations, including preventive measures, relevant safety rules and procedures, and procedures for dealing with emergencies. Each of the parties needs also to consult its workforce on the contract and the issues that arise from the risk assessment. In other words, everyone must talk to one another.

Managers or supervisors with delegated responsibility must ensure that contractors know and understand what standard of performance is expected. (See also 'Working together' on pages 87 to 92.)

Co-operation

In any client/contractor relationship, there must be co-operation and co-ordination between all the parties involved to maintain a good health and safety culture. The manager of the client organisation should set up liaison arrangements with all parties.

This could take the form of regular meetings or briefings. This is particularly important where variations of the work are proposed or where more than one contractor or sub-contractor is engaged. (See also 'Construction management' on pages 93 to 94.)

Control

The managers of the client organisation should decide what needs to be done to manage and supervise the work of contractors effectively. The more impact the contractor's work could have on the health and safety of anyone likely to be affected, the greater the management and supervisory responsibilities of the employer.

Client organisations, contractors and subcontractors should all monitor their health and safety performance. This means checking whether the risk assessment is up to date and that control measures are working.

Through their managers and supervisors, client employers should make periodic checks on the contractor's performance to see whether the work is being done as agreed. Where health and safety requirements are not being met, the first step is for the employer and the contractor to find out why and to put matters right. If health and safety performance is not brought up to requirements, the client employer may need to stop the contractor working on the job until those requirements can be met.

Competence

The managers of client organisations need to select a suitable contractor who is competent to do the job in question. They need to satisfy themselves that the contractors have sufficient skills, knowledge, qualifications and experience to do the job safely.

The degree of competence required will depend on the work to be done. Some of the things that could be taken into account when employing a contractor are:

- their experience in the type of work you want done
- their health and safety policies and practices
- their recent health and safety performance (number of accidents and so on)
- what qualifications and skills their staff have
- their selection procedure for their subcontractors
- their safety method statement for the job
- what health and safety training and supervision they provide
- their arrangements for consulting their workforce
- whether they have any independent assessment of their competence
- whether they are members of a relevant professional or trade body
- what their arrangements are for refresher training and continuing professional development
- levels of insurance, such as public liability and professional indemnity.

Supervisors

Supervisors have a unique and pivotal role in the workplace because they can influence both employees and managers. In supervising the day-to-day work of employees, supervisors can monitor employees' activities, train them to understand best practice, and ensure that they achieve the highest possible standards. In providing crucial information to the senior management team, supervisors can persuade, encourage or even pressurise managers into improving the health and safety system at work and into fulfilling the organisation's legal obligations.

Key words and phrases

audit – a formal examination against a fixed standard by competent people who are independent of the area of work being audited.

competent person – someone with the appropriate qualifications, knowledge and experience to identify the risks arising from a situation and the measures needed to control them.

hazard – a source of danger: any thing, condition or circumstance that could cause harm to people or damage to property.

health and safety culture – the integration of health and safety awareness and controls into day-to-day workplace practices.

monitor – regular, often daily, checks on what is going on in the workplace, which help to deal with problems as they arise.

risk – a measure or scale of the likelihood that harm will occur from a particular hazard, and the severity of the consequences.

risk assessment – a systematic process for identifying workplace hazards and assessing the risks involved from those hazards.

supervisory management (of health and safety) – the implementation and development of an organisation's health and safety policy.

training needs – what sort of, and how much, training the workforce and/or individual employees require.

The role of supervisors

Supervisors help managers to manage health and safety at work. Their main role is to implement the organisation's health and safety policy.

The exact part they play in the management process depends upon the particular job specification but probably falls into the range of activities described as **supervisory management**. Whatever the job title, the supervisor's responsibilities include putting into practice the health and safety systems and controls designed by the management team, after having consulted supervisors, employees and safety representatives.

The most likely activities of a supervisor with responsibility for some aspect of health and safety include:

- planning, monitoring, measuring performance and auditing
- keeping effective records
- organising the employees in ways that they can implement the health and safety policy as part of their work activities
- developing good working relationships – with employees, safety representatives and managers
- providing motivation
- handling conflict and dealing with disciplinary procedures
- organising training and development.

Planning, monitoring, measuring performance and auditing health and safety

Supervisors need to be involved in the planning of health and safety activities, the training of employees and the monitoring of health and safety performance standards.

Their knowledge and understanding of the hazards at work should enable them to carry out, or to organise, a **risk assessment** and make suggestions about suitable controls to reduce risks.

They should **monitor** work activities to make sure that health and safety procedures are being followed. If, however, things do go wrong and an accident happens, they may be asked to investigate and make recommendations to managers about improvements to prevent further accidents.

They need to air any concerns about health and safety, by dealing with them directly, by working with safety representatives and safety committees or by telling managers about them.

They should also help to identify the training needs of the organisation – what sort of, and how much, training the workforce requires – by looking at employees' tasks and skills and deciding whether individuals are **competent** to do their jobs in safety.

Keeping records

Supervisors need access to a wide variety of company documents and are likely to be involved in creating and maintaining some types of record, and in influencing others. The documents that a supervisor may need to handle include:

- the organisation's health and safety policy
- generic and specific risk assessments and their findings, including **COSHH** and other legally-required risk assessments
- company rules and procedures
- written **safe systems of work**
- monitoring records
- accident records, including F2508 forms
- health and safety training records
- a register of **competent persons**
- health surveillance records
- first aid records, including first aiders and appointed persons
- a fire plan and/or fire risk assessment
- written fire and emergency procedures
- fire inspection records, including fire drill records and alarm test records
- examination and test certificates for work equipment, lifting equipment and fork-lift trucks
- maintenance and repair records for work equipment
- written schemes of examination for pressure systems
- a health and safety law poster
- safety committee minutes
- employee consultation records
- details of visits by enforcement officers
- health and safety legislation, for example, Health and Safety at Work etc. Act 1974
- approved codes of practice
- Health and Safety Executive publications
- industry standards and publications.

The use of such records is good evidence of a robust health and safety culture and helps managers and supervisors to improve communication throughout the company and to avoid any biased judgements that can occur if employees and employers try to remember details that have not been written down.

Supervisors should ensure that sufficient information is recorded, particularly the key facts, and that the record keeping is accurate and consistent. (A consistent format makes comparisons easier between different records.)

Organising and supervising tasks

Supervisors implement the health and safety policy of the organisation by overseeing tasks on behalf of management. Tasks should be carried out in accordance with the organisation's health and safety policy and safe working procedures. The general aim is to carry out tasks safely and consistently to a high standard.

The role involves ensuring that the employees under the particular supervisor's control fully understand the procedures, the standards expected of them and their responsibilities towards others and for themselves. This usually means that supervisors need to direct day-to-day operations, give guidance, help to demonstrate good practice and ensure that work activities are carried out in a disciplined and appropriate manner.

Level of supervision

The level of supervision required is a matter of discussion between the supervisor and the senior managers: it depends on his or her own competence, the competence of employees working in the team and the degree of risk involved.

New employees and people who have changed jobs within an organisation may need more supervision than others. Competent people also need a certain amount of supervision to make sure that they maintain standards and do not fall into bad habits. In some cases the level of supervision is prescribed by law – for example, a young person working with a dangerous machine should be supervised all the time until he or she demonstrates complete competence.

Supervisors should be involved in the induction of new staff and in their training, development and motivation.

Supervision should be proactive and should give particular attention to those at a higher risk of injury or ill health than others – for example, people working alone or part-time workers.

Developing good relationships

Relationship with managers

It is important for supervisors to develop and maintain an effective working relationship with their more senior managers and fellow supervisors. It may be helpful to consider their role as that of *supporting* the more senior managers in dealing with health and safety management issues.

Members of the senior management team expect supervisors to implement and monitor health and safety matters including the health and safety policy and report to middle or senior managers any major issues that may require a change in procedures or the introduction of new equipment or safety measures. However, they also expect supervisors to deal with relatively minor issues themselves. For example, if safety procedures are not being followed, the supervisor will need to remind employees of what is correct.

Communication – the strong link

Communication is a two-way process. Supervisors are an essential channel between employees and managers. They can help to ensure that communication is effective between the two groups and that problems are dealt with swiftly. When the employer wants to consult with the employees, the supervisor can help to make the consultation effective and, possibly, trouble free. They also work with safety representatives to facilitate their role in the organisation.

Employee relations

Supervisors also need to be team builders, encouraging employees to work together to achieve the aims of the health and safety policy of the organisation. This involves supporting team members so that they can appreciate the risks involved in tasks and therefore help to eliminate or control risks themselves. Supervisors can also be trainers and may act as mentors, working alongside colleagues.

Providing motivation

Providing motivation and encouragement is an important part of achieving a health and safety culture in the workplace – the integration of health and safety awareness and controls into day-to-day workplace practices.

Supervisors can help to motivate employees to follow good health and safety practices by seeking their views. It is important for staff to know that their contribution really counts. Supervisors should encourage staff to report problems by welcoming any comments they make. It is essential to treat the employees who make the reports fairly and openly, giving them confidence and trust in the individual supervisor and a sense of security in making comments about health, safety and welfare issues.

Supervisors can exchange information, pass information, requests and worries 'up the line' and ensure that staff see the outcome of their comments, complaints and suggestions. This may involve supervisors in giving support and advice and leading project teams. They should always record comments and respond quickly by investigating them and providing feedback on progress.

Handling conflict and dealing with disciplinary procedures

Health and safety supervisors may also be expected to deal with conflicts between employees – on personal, professional and health and safety matters, for example – and between employees and managers. They need to smooth the working relationships and suggest solutions that can, eventually, be agreed and accepted by all the parties involved. (See also pages 91 to 92.)

At some point, supervisors may be involved in disciplining an employee for a breach of health and safety rules. It is important that they can follow clear guidelines laid down by their manager.

Constraints

Health and safety is just one of many demands on an organisation and its management, so supervisors may also need to juggle the demands and available resources of the organisation with health and safety requirements. Risks cannot be eliminated totally, and the controls implemented to reduce the risk of injury and ill health need to be reasonably practicable in the interests of health and safety. The supervisor has a very important role in finding reasonable solutions in consultation with managers, safety representatives and employees.

Organising the training and development activities

Supervisors are likely to be involved in the identification of **training needs**, the induction of new employees, on-the-job instruction and training, formal training, and organising emergency procedures. (See also pages 152 to 158.)

Personal characteristics

Good supervisors are open, fair, well informed and well organised. They keep employees informed and treat them with respect and as individuals. They also ensure that managers have all the information and support they need to establish policies and procedures.

Supervisors are normally given some discretionary powers by their employer or manager for dealing with health and safety issues. Even so, they must always act within the procedures laid down in the health and safety policies. Whatever responsibilities they are given, they must be competent to do the task which has been set.

Supervisors must have had the appropriate training and experience relevant to undertake their role. Their employer should ensure that they are given suitable training, instruction and guidance to do the job they are employed to do. It is also in their own interest to keep abreast of the training and development opportunities available from professional bodies and training providers that could enhance their own work performance and, in turn, the health and safety record of the organisation. (See pages 381 to 385 for details of professional organisations and sources of further information.)

Employees and other stakeholders

Several groups of people are affected by the health and safety conditions in a workplace, including employees, the self-employed, contractors, members of the public, visitors, voluntary workers and work experience students.

Employees and other workers

The majority of people at work are employees. They may also be referred to as workers. An employee/worker works under a contract of employment, which sets out what the job is and often includes terms and conditions.

Employees have certain rights, including a right to work in a safe and healthy environment. They also have certain responsibilities, such as taking reasonable care of their own health and safety and that of their colleagues – see page 53).

Some people working for an employer may not have a contract of employment with that employer, or have different contractual agreements. They include agency workers, short-term casual workers and freelances. These workers have the same rights as employees as far as health and safety is concerned.

The self-employed

Self-employed people do not have a contract of employment with an employer. They are normally contracted to provide services over a certain period for an agreed fee.

The self-employed have similar rights to an employee for health and safety purposes when working in someone else's workplace. They also have similar responsibilities for their own health and safety and for the health and safety of others who may be affected by their actions.

Voluntary workers, trainees and work experience students

Voluntary workers, trainees and people on work experience are regarded as employees as far as health and safety at work is concerned.

Employers must assess the risks to them, and particularly to people under the age of 18, *before* they start work and must tell them what the risks are. Supervisors may be involved in assessing the risks involved and ensuring that there is an appropriate induction, health and safety training, advice and supervision. Any necessary personal protective equipment required for the work must be supplied by the employer.

Young or inexperienced employees may need extra supervision and support until they fully appreciate any risks to their health and safety.

When engaging voluntary workers, trainees and work experience candidates:

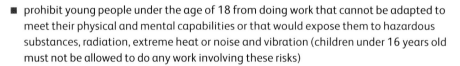

- take into account the inexperience of young people and their physical and mental immaturity

- adopt measures to reduce the risk of injury to the lowest possible level

- tell the parents or guardians of young people what the outcome of the relevant risk assessments are before work starts

- prohibit voluntary workers, trainees and work experience students from doing any work where a significant risk remains after reasonable precautions have been taken

- prohibit young people under the age of 18 from doing work that cannot be adapted to meet their physical and mental capabilities or that would expose them to hazardous substances, radiation, extreme heat or noise and vibration (children under 16 years old must not be allowed to do any work involving these risks)

- train the workers to do the work in ways that do not put them or others at risk

- ensure that the training covers hazards, risks and control measures in the workplace and basic health and safety practices

- provide closer supervision of young people than for adults.

Contractors

Contractors are engaged to do work for a client organisation but are not employees of that company. (See pages 70 to 72 for more information about contracting.)

Members of the public and visitors

All employers owe a duty of care to members of the public who may be affected by their operations. These include shoppers, people walking by a construction site or residents who live nearby.

Employers also have a responsibility to visitors to the workplace such as customers, suppliers and members of the public.

In general, employers should warn visitors about any hazards that they may be exposed to and they should be made aware of any emergency procedures.

Safety representatives

Trade unions have the legal right to appoint official safety representatives in workplaces where any union is officially recognised by the employer. With the agreement of the employer, employees can also elect non-union representatives of employee safety.

The representatives put the employees' views on health, safety and welfare matters to the employer, Health and Safety Executive (HSE) and other enforcing authorities, such as local councils. For their part, employers must consult the representatives in good time about developing health and safety measures in the workplace.

The number of representatives is normally negotiated between the employer and the union, or between the employer and the employees where there is no union recognition. The number usually depends on the number of employees and size of the workplace, the variety of occupations, the type of work activity and the hazards and risks involved.

Key words and phrases

competent person – someone with the appropriate qualifications, knowledge and experience to identify the risks arising from a situation and the measures needed to control them.

inspection – the assessment of the health and safety performance of a workplace, which enables any necessary remedial measures to be taken.

reportable accident – an accident that must, by law, be reported to the enforcing authorities.

representative of employee safety – an employee elected by non-union employees to represent them in health and safety matters.

safety committee – a committee set up to deal with health and safety matters in the workplace.

safety representative – an employee appointed by a trade union to represent them on health and safety issues.

Roles

The functions of safety representatives and the requirements for safety committees (see pages 81 to 86) are described in The Safety Representatives and Safety Committees Regulations 1977. Under The Health and Safety (Consultation with Employees) Regulations 1996 representatives of employee safety have similar functions to trade union safety representatives.

Safety representatives need to be trained to carry out their responsibilities. The training may be informal or formal, or a mixture of the two.

Union-appointed **safety representatives** have the legal function of carrying out the following duties:

- identify hazards in the workplace

- investigate accidents

- investigate complaints by employees about health and safety issues

- carry out safety inspections

- be consulted by employers about health, safety and welfare issues

- take part in formulating risk assessment procedures

- represent employees in discussions with the employer and enforcement officers

- receive information from the employer and enforcing officers

- attend meetings of the organisation's safety committee

- investigate notifiable accidents, cases of diseases or ill health, and dangerous occurrences.

Representatives of employee safety have similar roles.

Employers have a legal duty to allow union-appointed safety representatives to take paid time off during working hours to carry out their role and to undertake training.

Training

Representatives need to know how best to carry out their responsibilities. Training courses are often provided free of charge by individual trade unions, the Trades Union Congress and the Scottish Trades Union Congress. Training topics include health and safety legislation; the role of safety representatives; identifying hazards and minimising risk; workplace inspections and accident investigations. Non-union courses are offered by other training providers.

Access to information

As well as knowing the workplace and its procedures thoroughly, representatives also need to have access to:

- relevant health and safety information
- suitable facilities and assistance to enable them to carry out their functions.

Relevant health and safety information includes accident and health surveillance records – see also below.

Suitable facilities depend on the circumstances. They might include the use of:

- a telephone
- an office where they can meet with employees in private
- a lockable filing cabinet
- a camera
- a notice board for employee information.

Assistance includes help from a supervisor or manager who might prepare a report (to the safety committee, for instance) at the request of a representative.

In medium and large organisations safety representatives are more likely to work regularly with supervisors and might meet managers only at safety committees. In small organisations there is likely to be day-to-day contact between all parties.

Inspection

Union-appointed safety representatives can carry out **inspections** of the workplace every three months, if the employer is given reasonable notice in writing, or after a **reportable accident** has occurred. The inspection can include taking samples of harmful substances and checking records. Inspections help to indicate where controls are needed – to deal with work-related repetitive strain injury or respiratory problems, for example.

The safety representative has the legal right to inspect *any* document relevant to health and safety, except those that could threaten:

- national security
- trade secrets
- the privacy of individuals
- legal proceedings.

Consultation

Employers must consult safety representatives and employees about:

- the introduction of new measures and technologies that could substantially affect the health and safety of employees
- the arrangements for appointing **competent persons** (see pages 42 to 43)
- the provision of health and safety information for employees
- the planning and organisation of health and safety training for employees.

In good time

Employers must consult safety representatives 'in good time' about health and safety measures. This means that the employer/manager must allow enough time for consultation before making a final decision on any action to be taken. The process can be thought of as having three stages:

- the employer informs the safety representatives about what is proposed
- the safety representatives consult with employees
- the safety representatives report back to the employer.

This process allows the workforce to consider the possible impact of health and safety changes *before* they are made. In turn, this is likely to help to improve procedures and work practices and may also motivate workers to follow procedures more diligently because they have been involved in developing them.

Contacting enforcing authority officers

Safety representatives are entitled to contact enforcing authority officers directly for information. The officers are most likely to be an HSE inspector or a local authority health and safety enforcement officer. In some work sectors, such as catering, retail shops and offices, local authority environmental health officers are the enforcing officers with responsibility for health and safety. If there it is a formal complaint about conditions at a workplace, inspectors will have an expectation that the safety representative has already raised the matter with the employer and will check whether the complaint has been reported to the employer. Inspectors can, however, be contacted anonymously, or, if requested to do so, will keep secret the person's identity.

Main activities

In summary, safety representatives:

- carry out health and safety inspections in and around the workplace
- raise with managers health- and safety-related matters that have been identified by representatives or referred by staff members
- alert work colleagues to the risks
- remind employees of their obligations regarding their own health and safety and that of others
- investigate reportable accidents or incidents
- represent employees in consultation with Health and Safety Executive inspectors or other enforcing authorities.

Safety committees

Safety committees exist to improve health, safety and welfare measures at work. The committees review the measures designed to protect the health and safety of the workforce. In the process, they promote co-operation between employers and employees on health and safety matters, draw on the employees' considerable knowledge of working conditions, processes and procedures and help the employer to develop, promote, monitor and amend their health and safety management systems.

A typical committee includes managers, supervisors, safety representatives and other employee representatives.

If asked to do so in writing by at least two union-appointed safety representatives, an employer must set up a **safety committee** within three months of the request.

By working together, managers and representatives should agree:

- what they aim to achieve
- how often to meet
- how to organise the meetings – for instance, who chairs the meetings.

Committees typically:

- review statistics for accidents, notifiable diseases and safety audits so that reports can be made to the employer about unsafe and unhealthy conditions and the corrective action needed
- consider safety representatives' reports
- consider enforcement officers' reports
- liaise with the enforcing authority
- develop safety rules and procedures and safe systems of work
- monitor the effectiveness of employee training programmes
- monitor and review the health and safety information and publicity being provided in the workplace
- review risk assessments
- examine safety audit reports
- monitor all arrangements for health and safety and revise them whenever necessary.

Passing on the message

Safety committees can help one person's experience of ill-health from becoming a common occurrence.

A college lecturer damaged his voice box after filling in for absent colleagues. His managers arranged adjustments, such as the use of a microphone, laptop computer, projector and portable whiteboards so that he could carry on teaching, but less intensively.

When his voice eventually improved he told his safety committee about his experiences. As a consequence the committee encouraged local colleges to give lecturers advice about voice training and the use of teaching aids to protect their voices.

Gathering information

Representatives need to gather information before making a case to the employer about action on health and safety standards. Several internal sources of information can be used to identify health and safety issues that need attention. They include the organisation's:

- risk assessments
- regular inspections of the workplace
- safety audits
- accident investigations
- own employees.

Employees and supervisors are often an excellent source of information and can help safety representatives to identify all the relevant hazards, assess the risks and suggest appropriate controls that need to be introduced.

Work-life balance

An electricity generating company works closely with four recognised trade unions in the workplace. Safety representatives are encouraged to get involved in corporate-level initiatives. Information is shared openly and there are consultations with staff and their unions on key health and safety issues before management decisions are taken. As a consequence the company has:

- invested in additional health and safety training for managers, safety representatives and other staff

- provided staff with leisure facilities to help staff to achieve a good work-life balance

- provided an in-house training centre with a wide range of training resources to promote training and development with advice from the safety committee

- provided learning programmes for contractors and the family members of staff.

The partnership helps managers and unions to work together to improve the business, the health and safety performance and culture, with commitment at all levels in the company.

Working together

Everyone in the workplace needs to work together if a good health and safety culture is to be achieved. Managers, supervisors, representatives, safety committees, employees and contractors all need to take part in managing the risks in the workplace.

Key words and phrases

competent person – someone with the appropriate qualifications, knowledge and experience to identify the risks arising from a situation and the measures needed to control them.

information – verbal or written advice in a form that is easily understood by the employees to whom it is being addressed.

instruction – guidance or direction regarding a specific procedure or action.

reportable accident – an accident that must, by law, be reported to the enforcing authorities.

representative of employee safety – an employee elected by non-union employees to represent them on health and safety matters.

safety committee – a committee set up to deal with health and safety matters in the workplace.

safety representative – an employee appointed by a trade union to represent them on health and safety issues.

training – preparing a person to achieve a desired level of skill, knowledge or competence by the means of giving information, instruction and practice.

training needs – what sort of, and how much, training the workforce and/or individual employees require.

Foundations of co-operation

Employers and employees should work together to ensure good practice and legal compliance in health and safety matters.

Co-operation on health and safety issues indicates that everyone has accepted their responsibilities and is more likely to work safely. Such co-operation also helps to develop a positive health and safety culture, reduce accidents and ill health and their associated costs, meet customer demands and maintain credibility. The adopted system of co-operation could be part of the health and safety management policy.

There should be routine daily contact between employers (through the delegated managers and supervisors) and employees on health and safety matters. Team briefings should include regular items about health and safety in the workplace and there should be formal consultation with unions, where they are recognised in the workplace. A schedule of safety meetings can be drawn up for, say, every three months. Information on notice boards can provide an efficient way of distributing health and safety information.

It is a fundamental principle of health and safety that everyone is responsible for his or her own health and safety and the health and safety of others. Employers have their duties under the law and employees have their responsibilities. It is important that everyone accepts and follows his or her legal obligations. Communication and consultation with the workforce is essential for these duties and responsibilities to be put into practice. The next four pages outline the ways that this can be done.

Communication

Effective communication is necessary to ensure that everyone at work has the information they need to fulfil their legal responsibilities and to reduce accidents and ill health at work.

Managers, supervisors, safety representatives and representatives of employee safety could hold regular meetings to discuss the health and safety implications of work activities. Safety issues could be aired in a newsletter or on a prominent notice board, and there should be plenty of opportunities for employees to contribute their ideas and raise any concerns.

The benefits of effective partnerships

A large retail company has worked closely with unions for a number of years. Safety representatives are well trained and meet regularly with safety advisers and managers to discuss health and safety. All staff undergo minimum health and safety training. Two specific developments have had a real impact on health and safety:

■ a system of in-depth investigations of all serious incidents – all accidents, incidents, injuries are reported, recorded and followed up, and senior management and safety representatives investigate the more serious incidents and publish reports which are distributed throughout the company

■ an auditing system to monitor unsafe behaviour and influence safety behaviour – so that the partnership works and there is health and safety awareness.

In an emergency good communication may literally be a question of life and death, so there should be effective systems in place to ensure good communication between team members or between different teams.

When work practices change or teams change information should be provided for everyone in the workplace who might be affected. Several notable accidents have occurred because of failure in communication at a shift handover. In the 1983 Sellafield beach incident, for example, radioactive waste was accidentally discharged into the sea because of a breakdown in communication between people working on different shifts. One of the factors that was said to have contributed to the Piper Alpha oil rig fire in 1988 was also a failure to exchange information when a shift changed.

In the case of shift handovers, communication should ideally be face-to-face and two-way, with both 'participants' taking joint responsibility. It should be verbal and written, and based on an analysis of the information that incoming staff need. It should be given as much time as necessary.

Consultation

Consultation is a two-way process. Consulting employees involves seeking their views about health and safety issues, considering them carefully and feeding them into decisions. Workers must be consulted about health and safety matters that affect them before changes are made. Consultation can be carried out in several ways, such as:

- informally through day-to-day discussion with employees and their representatives
- formally by consultation meetings with union or employee representatives
- informally or formally through a health and safety committee
- formally through a safety committee and safety representatives.

Involving employees

Employees, particularly safety representatives can get involved in:

- the development or review of the health and safety policy
- taking on specific health and safety responsibilities
- delivering general health and safety messages, and designing and delivering training
- structuring a safety committee
- making health and safety plans and setting objectives
- purchasing equipment and materials
- designing new ways of working
- operating risk control systems
- problem solving
- undertaking inspections
- investigating accidents and near-misses

- spotting hazards
- auditing health and safety systems.

The Health and Safety Executive has developed a comprehensive process for involving workers in health and safety. It advises, for example, that it is good practice to pilot (or test) and improve new systems before they are rolled out more widely, and that employers should consider giving staff incentives to report health and safety incidents.

Motivating employees

Some employees need encouragement to appreciate the benefits of good health and safety practices. A clear health and safety policy and a strong and positive health and safety culture can help.

Fear

One of the biggest hindrances to staff motivation in health and safety is fear for job security or promotion prospects, fear of derision or fear of being blamed for an incident. Staff need to know that their comments about health and safety are positively welcomed and that expressing concerns or reporting incidents will not lead to punishment.

Opportunities to raise issues

Employees need opportunities to voice any concerns and to see that their comments have made a difference. Managers should work to ensure that people in the lower levels of the organisation feel secure talking about health and safety matters.

Managers should listen to people from the cleaner to the most senior manager. Getting to know employees as individuals can also be an important part in keeping them motivated – their lives outside work can suggest what motivates them.

Incentives

Systems of individual or team/department incentives can spur people on to make greater efforts. Some organisations find that days away from the usual workplace are a good way to bring employees closer together so that they provide mutual support. Research in many industries suggests that praise and recognition – from colleagues or managers – are powerful motivators.

Training and continuing professional development

The challenge of learning new skills and roles can be motivational. Many employees welcome the chance to undertake structured health and safety training and to gain a recognised award.

Additional responsibilities

Giving employees more responsibility for health and safety can be another effective way of keeping them interested in the subject.

Outside help

Bringing outsiders, such as consultants, into the organisation can play a major role in boosting employee morale. Implementing their recommendations can boost confidence in the organisation.

Discipline

Where an employee continues to flout health and safety rules, disciplinary procedures may need to be started as a form of motivation.

Handling conflict

Good consultation with employees reduces the risk of conflict in the workplace. Even so, managers, supervisors and representatives will sometimes come across situations where good health and safety practice and business demands seem to be at variance, and employees and managers cannot agree. Supervisors and representatives may be well placed to handle such conflict, whether it involves health and safety or not. Conflict can arise in a wide variety of circumstances, such as:

- where jobs are threatened, employers and employees may cut corners, so putting themselves and others at risk

- where some employees think that safety procedures and precautions are unnecessary, possibly because they are not properly trained

- when managers fail to accept suggestions from employees, and reports about safety risks seem to be ignored

- if one group of employees believes that another group is not working according to safety procedures

- where staff think that employers introduce precautions which are based on cost only

- if an individual feels guilty for causing an accident, while some employees believe that the blame for an accident has been wrongly placed

- whenever there is a fear of disciplinary action after blame for an accident has been decided.

Supervisors and safety representatives could identify and agree with employees and managers the causes of the conflict. Once these are agreed, possible solutions can be found. The advantages and disadvantages of the possible solutions should be considered, discussed and agreed with the people involved. Whenever a conflict arises act swiftly. Meet the individuals concerned and remain calm, showing interest and a readiness to listen to all points of view. Try to show sympathy with each of the parties involved, but be impartial.

Gather information and weigh up the evidence collected. If necessary, seek advice from others who may have more experience and knowledge of the subject being dealt with. Don't make accusations or jump to conclusions before you have all the information.

Agree a solution with the people involved and a time scale for the solution to be put in place or dealt with. If a solution cannot be found to the problem, then ask someone not involved to mediate between the conflicting parties.

Working with enforcement officers

It is important for managers, supervisors and representatives to co-operate with enforcement officers and to encourage employees to do likewise.

Normally either a manager or supervisor greets the enforcement officer. Sometimes the timing of the visit may be inconvenient, but it is worth spending time with the officer to discuss health and safety issues that could improve the organisation's performance. Ask for proof of identify: the officer should have a warrant card and identification. Try to arrange for safety representatives (or representatives of employee safety) to be available to discuss matters with the officer.

Accompany the officer during his or her inspection and provide information about any company safety rules. Co-operate with any requests, answer questions and provide the information asked for.

Introduce the officer to employees as appropriate and explain the purpose of the visit. Note any comments and advice that is given and, once the visit has finished, inform employees of its outcome.

Feature

Construction management

Construction sites are busy, potentially dangerous working environments where people from many different organisations often have to work alongside one another. The Construction (Design and Management) Regulations 2007, often abbreviated to the CDM Regs, place management duties on a range of people involved in a construction project to improve health and safety for everyone on the site.

In addition to duties under The Management of Health and Safety at Work Regulations 1999, the CDM Regs place specific duties on clients, designers, principal contractors, contractors and CDM co-ordinators. All parties involved in the project have a number of common duties, such as to:

■ liaise

■ consult and co-operate

■ co-ordinate their activities

■ share information about the project.

Clients

Any organisation having construction or building work carried out as part of its business must make arrangements so that construction work can be carried out, so far as is reasonably practicable, without risk to anyone's health and safety.

Clients must provide pre-construction information about the site, the construction work or anything affecting the site.

Where a project is notifiable clients must also provide additional information in a health and safety file and appoint a CDM co-ordinator and a principal contractor. (A project is notifiable to the Health and Safety Executive if the construction phase will be longer than 30 days or 500 person-days.)

Clients must also ensure that the principal contractor provides a construction phase plan.

Designers

Architects, engineers and quantity surveyors must avoid foreseeable risks to health and safety during construction work and related activities. They must not start work until a CDM co-ordinator is appointed.

Principal contractors

Principal contractors are usually the main or managing contractor for the work. They must plan, manage and monitor the construction phase in a way that ensures, so far as is reasonably practicable, that it is carried out without risks to health or safety. They must make sure that welfare facilities are sufficient, draw up site safety rules, take reasonable steps to prevent access by unauthorised persons to the construction site and give every worker a suitable site induction. They must also prepare and implement a construction phase plan and review, revise and refine it.

Contractors

Builders; civil engineers; mechanical, electrical, demolition and maintenance companies; partnerships and the self-employed must all plan, manage and monitor construction work carried out by them or under their control in a way that ensures that, so far as is reasonably practicable, it is carried out without risks to health and safety. Where the construction is notifiable they cannot start work until they have been given the name of the CDM co-ordinator and the principal contractor.

CDM co-ordinators

CDM co-ordinators must be appointed where the project is notifiable. They give suitable and sufficient advice and assistance to the client about the measures needed to comply with the regulations during the project. The CDM co-ordinator must notify the HSE about the project.

Specific requirements

There are a number of specific requirements in the regulations dealing with:

- safe places of work
- good order and site security
- the stability of structures
- demolition or dismantling
- explosives
- excavations
- cofferdams and caissons
- reports of inspections
- energy distribution installations
- preventing drowning
- traffic routes
- vehicles
- managing risks from fire
- emergency procedures
- emergency routes and exits
- fire detection and fire-fighting
- fresh air
- temperature and weather protection
- lighting.

4. Why should we create a positive health and safety culture?

What are the benefits of a positive health and safety culture?

Health and safety is seen by some as a burden on business, but this view is far from the truth. If you were to talk to organisations that have been prosecuted for a serious accident, had to pay compensation for personal injury or seen a sharp rise in insurance premiums because of damage to a building, they would say that their failure to protect the health and safety of their employees had resulted in personal loss and pain, financial loss, damage to property or all these consequences. The benefits of a good health and safety system are the best reason for adopting a strong health and safety culture in an organisation.

Key words and phrases

health and safety culture – the integration of health and safety awareness and controls into day-to-day workplace practices. Also the attitudes, beliefs and behaviours regarding health and safety within the organisation.

performance indicators – measurements used to help an organisation to define and measure progress towards the organisation's health and safety goals.

What is a health and safety culture?

A workplace culture can be characterised as being 'the way we do things here'. It is made up of things such as personal and organisational values – what is considered important – ethos, attitudes, levels of competence and ways of behaving.

A good **health and safety culture** exists in an organisation where health and safety awareness and controls are integrated into day-to-day organisational management practices. It is characterised by positive attitudes, positive beliefs and positive behaviour with regard to health and safety at work.

Good organisations *plan* for a positive health and safety culture. They encourage changes that improve health and safety procedures. They involve staff and management through consultation and communication: problems are discussed thoroughly and a solution is sought with everyone's agreement.

Benefits

The benefits to an organisation of a good health and safety culture are:

- reduced employee absence
- better recruitment and retention
- reduced insurance, damage and compensation costs
- safe reputation
- better productivity and efficiency.

Sickness absence

Sickness absence is costly for most organisations. If the absences are due to illness or accidents caused by work, then the time lost and extra costs caused can be controlled by adopting better health and safety standards: in short, the business could save a lot of money. Improving health and safety measures at work reduces the likelihood that people will need sick leave in the first place. Bringing them back to work sooner means less disruption in the long run.

By reducing the number of employees on sick leave, businesses can save money spent on the salary of the absent employee, overtime for other employees covering for the absent employee, the productivity losses incurred by the absent employee and the costs of hiring temporary cover. It also reduces the loss in productivity when a replacement employee or contractor needs time to learn the job of the absentee. It may also help to maintain good customer relations because customers have consistent employee contact. Reduced absence will also avoid unnecessary recruitment and training costs.

Recruitment and retention

Businesses with low employee turnover due to workplace illness or accidents avoid the costs of regularly finding new members of staff. Costs include advertising, the time spent interviewing candidates, temporary work placements and, possibly, additional training costs. There may also be costs from reduced productivity as a new staff member comes up to speed with the work required in the post. A positive health and safety culture will help to create better employee morale and motivation.

Insurance, damage and compensation

It is compulsory for employers to take out employer liability insurance to cover for injuries and ill health of employees while at work. Even so, insurance policies cover only a small proportion of the real cost of accidents and ill health (see pages 24 to 30).

It is worth bearing in mind that the cost of insurance premiums can increase because of a poor health and safety record, so investment in good health and safety systems and practice will eventually save money.

Reputation

Many organisations have established a positive reputation that has boosted profits. Accidents can destroy that reputation very quickly. Recovery of a reputation can take a long time and some organisations never recover. It comes back to the principle (mentioned on page iv) that prevention is better than cure.

It is not only *public* reputation that is important. The reputation of the organisation among its employees is also very important. High morale and strong motivation among employees is also good for business. Implementing a good health and safety system will prevent accidents and ill health at work, create a positive culture in the organisation and save time and money.

Productivity and efficiency

A healthy workforce with an enhanced sense of well-being can lead to good productivity and efficiency in the organisation. In contrast, sickness absence, long-term illness and work-related accidents and incidents have a negative impact on a business, leading to reduced productivity and profits.

A good health and safety culture can lead to better productivity from greater attendance at work, less down-time and fewer lost working days. Employees appreciate good working conditions and this could also lead to increased productivity and profitability.

How much does it cost?

Some companies have quantified the benefits of a positive health and safety culture. One saved £11 million through reduced sickness absence. Another saw a 40 per cent reduction in reportable injuries. Other examples include a reduction in the cost of health insurance by £200,000 a year; a 50 per cent reduction in civil claims; and the average absence period after injury reduced from 26 days to 4, with the savings at 12 times more than the cost of the improvements.

Achieving a good health and safety culture

There are a number of stages to follow in moving towards a positive health and safety culture. Managers need to assess the organisation's health and safety systems and identify where improvements need to be made. The assessment should be based upon all sources of information in the workplace – including supervisors, safety representatives and employees.

The next step is to find out how health and safety procedures, work practices and other health and safety information is distributed and communicated within the workplace. It is then important to find out the workers' levels of understanding of the organisation's health and safety policies and procedures.

Once these facts are known, managers can plan improvements and find the necessary resources. The plans should include suitable **performance indicators** and the dates for reviewing the plans to see if they are working.

Good communication about the plans is crucial to their success. The information needs to be given clearly and concisely to all the relevant people. Some will be specific to supervisors, safety representatives, representatives of employee safety or employees and it should be given at an appropriate time, level and pace for the target group.

Maintaining the culture change can be done through regular communication about health and safety issues and encouraging ideas on good practice, possibly through a safety committee.

Examples of a positive health and safety culture

- The managing director, chief executive or individual director of the organisation shows that he or she is serious about health and safety.

- Managers are clear about what to do and show their commitment by, for example, attending safety committee meetings regularly.

- Employees are involved in health and safety monitoring and are consulted about decisions on changes to health and safety procedures.

- There is good communication and everyone knows the aims for health and safety – for example, there are regular newsletter items about health and safety issues and the health and safety performance indicators are displayed on the notice board (such as the number of accidents or incidents recorded or the number of people trained in a particular period).

- There is a positive attitude to training and people are receptive to change.

- People talk about health and safety issues openly and positively. They question procedures and are sensible and understanding about how things can be improved.

What is the value of health and safety policies?

Health and safety policies are the main guiding principles for the organisation and control of health and safety at work. A policy includes the organisation's basic aims, objectives and arrangements for health and safety, the procedures to be followed and the standards to be achieved.

Key words and phrases

health and safety culture – the integration of health and safety awareness and controls into day-to-day work practices. Also the attitudes, beliefs and behaviours towards health and safety within the organisation.

health and safety policy – a written statement of the organisation's arrangements for and implementation of its health and safety management system and activities.

hierarchy of control – a well tested system of graded health and safety controls.

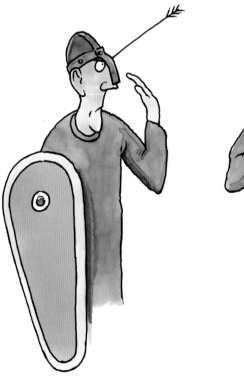

What is a health and safety policy?

A policy is the principle behind an action. A **health and safety policy** is a written statement of a company's general principles for the health and safety of employees at work. The policy also usually includes the organisational structure and the arrangements for carrying out the policy, including the communication of the policy to the employees.

In the UK employers with five or more employees must, by law, prepare and record a health and safety policy. It is good practice for *all* employers to prepare a health and safety policy, even if they have fewer than five employees.

The policy should be revised from time to time and the revisions brought to the attention of the employees.

The policy should describe the activities of the organisation, the resources provided for health and safety, the health and safety management systems and the products and services involved in the organisation.

The benefits of a health and safety policy

The advantages of having a health and safety policy include:

- recognising that a positive **health and safety culture** is important if the company is to achieve adequate control of workplace risks

- making sure that there is a systematic process for identifying risks

- aiming at continual improvements in health and safety standards

- recognising that accidents and ill health can result from bad management control and are not just the fault of employees

- helping to minimise financial losses from accidents and ill health

- helping to retain an exemplary record of good practice, without prosecutions or damaging publicity.

The development of a health and safety policy can help an organisation to focus on health and safety by systematically identifying the hazards and risks in its workplace, introducing controls and setting up monitoring procedures. In turn, this can assist employees to continue to improve health and safety standards.

Organisations that have well developed and 'living' health and safety policies are usually successful in achieving high standards of health and safety in the workplace. A 'living' policy is one that is part of the main management systems of the organisation and which corresponds to a realistic view of the organisation, not an idealistic one. It is integral to the day-to-day operations of the organisation and is monitored regularly.

In addition to helping employers to comply with legislation, a health and safety policy also helps to create a health and safety culture that satisfies employees, customers and shareholders. It may also reduce personal and financial losses.

Health and safety policy statement

To be effective, health and safety policies should be integrated into the organisation's general management systems. Policies vary, but they are generally structured along the lines described in the rest of this chapter.

Statement of intent

Among other elements, the statement of intent should:

- give a commitment to comply with health and safety law

- state the objectives of the policy – for example, a target for reducing the number of accidents in the workplace

- explain how the policy can contribute to the reduction of accidents and ill health in the workplace, and what impact this could have on business performance

- state that the hazards in the workplace must be eliminated or controlled and the risk they present must be minimised

- show how health and safety and other business objectives relate to each other

- state that the aim is continually to improve health and safety standards in line with the relevant good practice and not merely with the legal minimum standards (ambitious but achievable occupational health and safety objectives and performance targets should be set)

- name a senior manager as the person who is responsible for health and safety in the workplace

- commit financial and personnel resources to health and safety for protective and precautionary measures

- commit the company to planning, reviewing and developing the health and safety policy.

The policy must be signed and dated by a director or owner of the organisation. This is intended to show that the organisation is committed to health and safety matters. There should be a review at regular intervals – for example, every two to three years, and after changes in the organisational structure, work arrangements or processes and after any serious incident.

Organisation

Employers should set up a system to deal with health and safety matters. This usually involves a personnel structure designed to ensure the continual improvement of health and safety standards. The people designated implement the employer's decisions on health and safety policy and practice. It is important to name the post holders who are responsible for particular parts of the policy and its operation.

It is important for a senior manager to be named as the person with overall responsibility for health and safety in the workplace. He or she should also demonstrate commitment towards, and leadership in, health and safety by getting involved in the organisation of health and safety matters and by encouraging employees to have a positive attitude to working safely. Clear procedures and practices can be established by setting up a documented health and safety management system.

In large organisations, safety officers/advisers should be appointed. Training programmes should be put in place to ensure that all who have a responsibility for health and safety are competent to do the job they have been given.

The participation and co-operation of employees, safety representatives, representatives of employee safety, supervisors, managers and directors is necessary for the policy to work. All employees should be encouraged to participate in the health and safety management system. The people involved in the organisation of health and safety should be given clear responsibilities and there should be effective communication between employees, supervisors and managers. Safety and employee representatives should be recognised and safety committees set up, as appropriate (see pages 81 to 92).

The communication arrangements should include providing information and training for the workers in health and safety relevant to their work, and there should be procedures for receiving, recording and responding to all communications.

Arrangements

Employers must also make arrangements for the effective planning, organisation, control, monitoring and review of the preventive and protective measures in health and safety at work. The arrangements must take into account the nature and size of the activities and must be put into practice. The procedures and practices included in the policy must be designed to protect the health and safety of all people in the organisation by preventing work-related injuries, ill health, diseases and dangerous incidents.

This part of the policy states the practical measures for putting into practice the health and safety policy in the workplace. Risk assessment procedures should identify the hazards and risks in work activities that need to be controlled. The policy should also contain the measures to manage change in the organisation, deal with emergencies, arrange contractors and buy in services for health and safety purposes.

Priority should be given to those hazards and risks which are the most serious and harmful – see the **hierarchy of control** on pages 39 to 40.

It should also include the approach to such things as:

- accident recording and reporting
- the control of hazardous substances
- drugs and alcohol
- fire safety and the control of flammable substances
- first aid
- health surveillance
- ionising and non-ionising radiation

- lifting equipment and operations
- manual handling
- monitoring and inspection of the workplace
- noise and vibration
- personal protective equipment
- pressure systems
- risk assessment
- slips and trips
- stress
- training
- work equipment
- work at heights
- workplace standards in electrical safety, gas safety and welfare facilities
- workplace transport
- work-related upper limb disorders.

Legal requirements

Under the Health and Safety at Work etc. Act 1974 employers with five or more employees must have a written safety policy, which must be brought to the attention of employees. The policy should describe the activities of the organisation, the resources provided for health and safety, the health and safety management systems and the products and services involved in the organisation.

Why is it worth producing annual health and safety reports?

It is considered to be good practice to produce an annual commentary about health and safety matters. This is usually included in a company's annual report to shareholders. Some companies without shareholders also produce a similar document. Even so, a study of 250 companies with more than 250 employees found that only 26 per cent of them reported on health and safety. The study suggested that there was scope for improvement in the type and breadth of health and safety issues reported, particularly performance and target-related issues.

Key words and phrases

health and safety policy – a written statement of an organisation's general policy about its employees' health and safety at work, together with information about the organisational structure and arrangements for carrying out that policy.

performance indicators – measurements used to help an organisation to define and measure progress towards the organisation's health and safety goals.

Why include health and safety in an annual report?

Organisations try to show good corporate 'social responsibility' – they consider the interests of employees and customers by taking responsibility for the impact of their activities. The production of an annual report forms part of this. The perceived benefits include the following examples.

■ The report brings together key information which can be used by boards of directors to consider strategic health and safety issues.

■ It helps to encourage shareholders to support improvements in health and safety.

■ It enhances the organisation's public image.

■ It might help to enhance long-term company stability and sustainability by avoiding the costs involved in accidents and ill health.

■ It demonstrates the organisation's commitment to health and safety and shows good practice.

What should annual information include?

A good report about health and safety is likely to contain the following elements.

■ The **health and safety policy** (see pages 100 to 104).

■ Arrangements and the organisational structure for health and safety – for example, board-level responsibilities and the board's relationship with a safety committee.

■ Any national or international health and safety standards the company has adopted – for example, BS8800 2004 (dealing with occupational health and safety management systems).

■ The health and safety aims of the organisation.

■ The health and safety risks in the organisation determined by the risk assessments carried out.

■ The main hazards in the company, risk assessment arrangements and control measures used.

■ Health and safety audit arrangements.

BRITISH STANDARD   BS 8800:1996

Guide to

Occupational health and safety management systems

NO COPYING WITHOUT BSI PERMISSION EXCEPT AS PERMITTED BY COPYRIGHT LAW

BSi

- Arrangements for worker recovery after a work-based accident or illness.

- Worker involvement in the health and safety process.

- The structure of safety committee(s).

- Training provided.

- The causes of serious accidents and incidents and actions to prevent them recurring.

- The health and safety performance of contractors.

- Risks from travel outside the workplace.

- Organisational progress, as measured against the health and safety aims and objectives – see 'Performance indicators' below.

- How health and safety affects the business, whether positive or negative.

Performance indicators

Performance indicators are defined standards, limits and intermediate goals that are established to help an organisation to define and measure its progress towards the organisation's health and safety aims. In other words, the performance indicators help an organisation to check how well it is doing.

Examples of performance indicators that could be included in an annual report include the following.

- Accidents, incidents, ill health and sickness absence analysed under the headings of fatalities, major injuries, three-day injuries, total days lost – expressed per 100 workers, for instance – and those involving customers or members of the public.

- Management commitment, such as attendance at safety committees.

- Average number of health and safety training/refresher/development days per employee.

- Worker involvement, such as number of consultations.

- Risk assessments completed.

- Inspections, audits completed against target.

- Emergency response drills and exercises completed.

- Number of new occupational health cases.

- Costs associated with accidents and ill health.

- Number of enforcement notices received by the company.

An occupational health specialist discusses health and safety performance with a factory manager.

Commentary on the statistics

The statistics relating to performance can be meaningless without some explanation, so it is good practice to comment on them. The detail depends on the size of the organisation. The statistics could, for example, be compared with national targets and long-term trends in the organisation.

The report should also identify the priorities for improving health and safety management performance targets over the coming year.

5. How can we implement good health and safety standards?

How should we carry out risk assessments?

Risk assessment is one of the most important activities in a health and safety system. It makes a significant contribution towards the reduction in workplace accidents and ill health.

The process varies from a rapid visual assessment of a simple procedure, such as hammering a nail into a piece of wood, to a thorough written assessment of a large workplace operation, such as the bottling operation at a food processing plant.

Managers and staff might be involved in carrying out risk assessments. Supervisors and safety representatives are often in the best position to carry them out, liaise with the management team and/or safety committee and advise employees on the implementation of the findings.

Key words and phrases

competent person – a person with the appropriate qualifications, knowledge and experience to identify the risks arising from a situation and the measures needed to control them.

control measures (or **controls**) – the arrangements made, or precautions taken, to reduce risk.

hazard – a source of danger: any thing, condition or circumstance that could cause harm to people or damage to property.

hazard spotting – looking for and noting hazards in the workplace.

risk – a measure or scale of the likelihood that harm will occur from a particular hazard, and the severity of the consequences.

risk assessment – a systematic process for identifying workplace hazards and assessing the risks involved from those hazards.

safe system of work – a set of procedures for carrying out a task safely.

What is risk assessment?

A **risk assessment** is a careful examination of your work or workplace to identify hazards and assess the risks from those hazards. The aim is to prevent accidents and dangerous incidents and to reduce ill health from work activities.

The assessment involves identifying the hazards in a workplace or its associated activities, then assessing the risks involved, taking into account any precautions already in place.

The step-by-step process encourages organisations to assess every work activity. This enables the senior management team to identify the organisation's health and safety priorities and to allocate available resources to the measures that will have the maximum effect in reducing accidents, either by eliminating particular hazards altogether, or by controlling them so that the risk is at the lowest level that is reasonably practicable.

The assessment also helps employers (through their managers and supervisors) to comply with legal requirements.

As you are aware, a **hazard** is something with the potential to cause harm. Once the significant hazards have been identified in a workplace, the assessment must rate the likelihood that the hazard will actually cause harm – in other words, the level of **risk**. Any assessment of risk must also consider the:

- number of people who are at risk
- possible severity of any injury or illness
- the consequences of this harm.

A risk assessment is not a once-and-forever task. It should be a continual process of assessment and review. Circumstances can change frequently in the workplace and employers (through their managers) need to keep the assessment up to date to comply with legal duties of diligence and care.

Principles of risk management

Risk management aims to ensure that workers and the public are properly protected and that there is an overall benefit to society. This involves balancing benefits and risks, with a focus on reducing *significant* risks. Sensible risk management is neither about creating a totally risk-free society (as it is impossible to eliminate risk altogether), nor is it about generating a useless paper trail. It is not intended to scare people by exaggerating or publicising trivial risks, or to stop important business, recreational or learning activities where the risks are managed properly.

It is designed to prevent ill health and injuries – and all health and safety is about saving lives, not stopping living.

If you are involved in risk assessments and risk management, you should concentrate on the *significant* risks from hazards that cannot be eliminated and on the practical steps to *control* the risks that cause the real harm and suffering.

The responsibility for risk assessments

The responsibility for carrying out risk assessments lies with employers, but managers and supervisors usually have a pivotal role in carrying them out and implementing the actions identified as necessary. Safety representatives, where appointed, are also likely to be involved.

Employers can delegate the task to a **competent person**. Competence depends on knowledge of the business, experience of the industry and of carrying out assessments, the level of training undertaken, skills (for example, inspection, auditing and interpersonal) and technical knowledge.

Employers must make sure that an appropriate assessment is carried out of the health and safety risks to which employees are exposed through their work. Employers and self-employed people must also assess the risks from work activities to the health and safety of people who are not in their employment for example, members of the public.

According to the law, an employer with five or more employees must record the significant findings of the assessment.

In a small business with simple hazards – a wool shop, for example – the risk assessment could be so straightforward that it may not need any specialist skills or knowledge. In larger businesses and in those with a specific type of danger, such as a nuclear processing plant, an extremely detailed investigation may be required with the help of a specialist consultant.

In any business, it is often wise to seek advice from technical specialists – for instance, in assessing the risks from manual handling or display screen equipment. If you run a small organisation and you are confident you understand what is needed, you can do the assessment yourself. However, severe or fatal consequences can arise from an employer's failure to carry out risk assessments.

The extent of a risk assessment

Risk assessments may seem daunting at first, but they are in fact very simple. They are not rocket science, although they were used in developing the American space programme.

Failure to carry out responsibilities

A casual worker was seriously injured while unloading stones from a ship's hold. The crane operator's clothes got caught on a lever so that a grab closed onto the casual worker's head and almost severed his neck. The company had failed to make a proper risk assessment of the unloading technique and the use of the grab.

Regulations state that the risk assessment should be 'adequate' or 'suitable and sufficient'. These terms mean the same thing – that the assessment should not be overcomplicated, but should be thorough.

A single risk assessment may be all that is needed to cover all the work activities and hazards in some workplaces. However, some businesses may need to carry out separate assessments for particular hazards or groups of hazards (see 'Step 1' on page 114).

The level of detail largely depends on the level of risk. The greater the risk, the more detail is likely to be required. If an employer has a number of similar workplaces – for example, a chain of supermarkets or restaurants – then a *generic* or *model* risk assessment can be done for the same work activities in all the workplaces, with a site-specific risk assessment carried out for the *particular* hazards in each workplace. For jobs in which people carry out various tasks in different conditions at a variety of sites, such as gas engineers, building surveyors, structural engineers and tree surgeons, a *generic* risk assessment could cover a broad range of hazards and risk, but a *site-specific assessment* should also be carried out at each site.

The findings of any assessment must be followed up by an action plan designed to improve health and safety standards.

Failure to assess risk and follow safe procedures

A security guard died from carbon monoxide poisoning while working alone in a vacant building. There was no mains electricity, so a petrol generator was used to power the lighting, but no account was taken of the need to remove the fumes. As the guard was a lone worker, no one raised the alarm when he passed out from the fumes. The company had failed to assess and control the risks in a short-term job and had failed to follow its own procedures for employees who were working alone.

Carrying out a risk assessment

The precise details of how to carry out an assessment depend on the activities in your workplace and the type and extent of the hazards and risks. However, there are normally five steps involved:

1 identify the hazards

2 decide who is likely to be harmed and how

3 evaluate the risks by looking at the existing measures and deciding whether more controls are needed

4 record the findings, inform the workforce of the controls to be introduced and implement them

5 review the risk assessment and update if necessary.

What is likely to be involved in each of these steps is outlined below and on the following four pages, but it is worth considering the following general advice.

General advice for carrying out a risk assessment

- Walk around the workplace and observe all the work activities before starting the risk assessment. It helps to get a feel of the extent of the assessment to be done.

- Look at simple activities first. This gives you experience and confidence in doing the full risk assessment.

- Involve employees as well as the management team.

- Get advice, particularly if you or the organisation do not have the technical knowledge to carry out the risk assessment.

- Consider interruptions to work as well as the activities, because interruptions frequently lead to an accident.

- Ignore trivial hazards and insignificant levels of risk.

Step 1 – Identify the workplace hazards

You can use a number sources of information to identify the hazards in the workplace – *you* may be one of the sources.

- Look at the work activities that actually take place in the workplace. Walk around the workplace and concentrate on the *significant* hazards – those which could cause a severe injury or have a high risk that could affect several people.

- List the hazards in order of priority by hazard spotting.

- If your workplace has a number of hazards, consider assessing some of them in separate groups such as machinery, transport, electrical equipment and installations, manual handling and noise.

- Examine accident records and consider the manufacturer's instructions for machines and safety data sheets for harmful substances.

- Hold meetings to discuss the hazards in the workplace.

- Make sure that you include the tasks that are not done every day, such as maintenance and repair jobs, as well as long-term hazards to health, such as exposure to noise or vibration.

Step 2 – Establish who might be harmed and how

Everyone must be considered in a risk assessment – for example, office staff, machinists, cleaners, contractors, maintenance workers, visiting suppliers and representatives, security staff, people who share the building and members of the public. You should also identify groups of workers who may be particularly at risk – such as young people and trainees; migrant workers; employees with poor English, physical disabilities or learning difficulties; and pregnant women. Identify how they might be harmed – for example, railway workers might be struck by a passing train or by objects falling or being thrown from the train.

Step 3 – Assess the risks and decide on whether further controls are needed

Assess the risks that each hazard presents, including:

- the likelihood that harm will occur
- the nature of the injury that could result
- the severity of the harm
- who is likely to be affected by the hazard.

What are you already doing? Decide whether the existing precautions are adequate (and comply with current legislation) or whether more control measures are needed. It may be that the *existing* controls have already reduced the risk to an acceptable level.

Risk rating

Risk can be rated using a number of simple systems that help to determine the level of risk and action priorities.

One such system is based on assigning:

- a letter from A to C for the *severity* of harm that could result from a hazard
- a number from 1 to 3 for the *likelihood* that the hazard will occur.

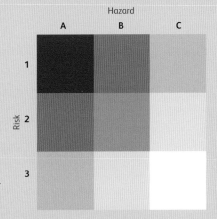

Severity
A – represents death, major, injury or major damage or loss of property or equipment.
B – represents an injury lasting over three days or damage to property or equipment.
C – represents a minor injury and minor damage to property or equipment.

Likelihood
1 – extremely likely to occur.
2 – frequently/often/likely to occur.
3 – slight chance of occurring.

Examples of rating
Using this system A1 represents a risk which is very high and unacceptable and requires urgent attention, while C3 represents a low risk where action can be left until more urgent issues have been attended to.

For more information, see the CIEH Level 2 Award in Principles of Risk Assessment and Level 3 Award in Risk Assessment Principles and Practice.

A1 – Unacceptable. Must receive immediate attention to remove or reduce risk or stop the work activity.

A2/B1 – Urgent. Must receive attention as soon as possible to remove/reduce hazard or risk.

A3/C1 – Must receive attention to remove/reduce hazard or risk.

B2 – Should receive attention to remove/reduce hazard or risk.

B3/C2 – Low priority. Remove/reduce hazard or risk after other priorities.

C3 – Very low priority. Remove/reduce hazard or risk after other priorities.

If the existing measures are insufficient to reduce the risk to an acceptable level, *additional* controls should be introduced. Always aim to do better than the minimum legislative standard: try to reduce the risk to as low a level as possible. This will help you to reduce the number of accidents and cases of ill health in the workplace.

However, do bear in mind that no workplace is completely hazard-free and risk-free. You are required to take control measures that are *reasonably practicable*. Try to find a less risky option, get rid of the hazard if you can, prevent access to a hazard, organise the work so that you reduce exposure to the hazard, provide personal protective equipment and provide adequate welfare facilities (see pages 293 to 295).

If the work involves staff in moving from site to site, you can identify the common hazards and their risks. At individual sites, you should carry out a hazard-spotting exercise for unusual hazards and assess the risk for those specific site-based hazards.

Make sure that your assessment covers, for example, the normal operation of a machine, and also its setting, maintenance, cleaning and repair. Bear in mind that the dangerous parts may be safe in normal use, but dangerous when accessible during maintenance, cleaning and so on.

When you consider which controls you should introduce, use a **hierarchy of control**.

As with all control measures, it is best to remove the risk by eliminating a particular hazard from the workplace. If this is impossible, substitute with something that will do the same job with less risk. If that cannot be done, control the level of risk by installing physical guards. Where a job must still be done, but none of the earlier measures mentioned is effective and the risk cannot be reduced to an acceptable level, introduce safe systems of work (see pages 121 to 126). The last resort is to provide personal protective equipment.

Whichever measures are introduced, all employees must be provided with adequate instruction, information and training.

Step 4 – Record the findings, inform the workforce of the controls to be introduced and implement them

If your workplace employs five or more people you must, by law, record your risk assessments. Even if there are fewer than five employees in your workplace, it is good practice to record the findings. (See below for guidance on the period for which records should be kept.)

The records provide a benchmark against which to measure improvements. They also help an organisation to demonstrate that it has gone through the process, complied with the law and is seriously committed to health and safety.

Employers must inform employees about the significant findings of a risk assessment: this might be a part of the job of a manager or supervisor.

The record should be kept clear and simple. It can be hand-written, typed or recorded electronically. It should include the significant findings of the assessment – for example, the hazards that are a serious risk to employees and others, the existing control measures, the extent to which the controls do actually mitigate the risks, and who may be exposed to the risks. You need to be able to show that a proper check was made and that you asked who might be affected. You also need to show that you dealt with all the significant hazards, taking into account the number of people who could be involved together with the reasonable precautions. You must demonstrate that the remaining risk is low and that you involved your staff or their representatives in the process.

A good plan of action often includes a mixture of controls, such as:

- a few cheap or easy improvements that can be done quickly, perhaps as a temporary solution until more reliable controls are in place

- long-term solutions to those hazards most likely to cause accidents or ill health

- long-term solutions to those hazards with the most severe potential consequences

- arrangements for training employees about the main risks that remain and how they are to be controlled

- regular checks to make sure that the control measures are being followed and have remained effective

- clear responsibilities – who must do what, who will lead each action and the timescale.

Set priorities and tackle the most important things first. As you complete each action, tick it off your plan.

The health and safety policy should include the main findings and actions taken. (See also pages 100 to 104.)

Step 5 – Review the risk assessment and update it if necessary

Review your risk assessments regularly because the nature of the work can change. The circumstances in the workplace sometimes indicate that the existing risk assessment is no longer valid. This is certainly the case where there are significant changes in work activities or there has been an accident. Look at what is already in place, consult employees, consider employee work habits and assess records – including those for injury and illness, workers' compensation costs, rates of employee turnover and records of training.

Decide on suitable adjustments to the assessment as appropriate. Ensure that the proposed changes are communicated to the management and the employees, then make sure they are implemented.

Who can do a risk assessment?

If your employer or manager delegates the risk assessment to you, it may be possible to carry it out without special training if you follow the five-step process outlined above. General guidance is provided on the Health and Safety Executive website, which includes examples of risk assessments in many types of small business. See page 382 for the web address.

If you are working for a small firm with few hazards, then the process is relatively straightforward. However, if you work for a large organisation or there are significant hazards and risks, it is advisable to obtain some training in risk assessment. You should also have a good knowledge of the workplace, its activities and processes and the control measures already taken.

Where work activities are complex or specific technical knowledge is required, it is recommended that a **competent person** from within the workforce undertake the risk assessment or be part of a team carrying out the risk assessment.

If outside consultants are contracted, it is always wise for someone who knows the business operation intimately to be involved as well: that person might be you.

Assessors need a sound knowledge and understanding of the workplace and the activities that they are assessing. They need to be able to gather information and arrange it clearly and logically. They need to be able to analyse this information and evaluate it so that it is valid and can be used to make reliable recommendations. They also need to be able to draw up a clear and concise report and communicate the findings of the assessment to those who have requested it and to those that it applies to, such as the employees. These skills make up what are called the competencies (or competences) required by risk assessors.

Legally required specific risk assessments

Every company should carry out a *general* risk assessment, but you may also need to undertake separate *specific* risk assessments, such as for specific sites – for example, where staff work at a different location every day – or for matters such as fire, manual handling and the control of hazardous substances. The legislation that requires a specific risk assessment gives guidance on what to examine. Some regulations also specify the length of time that the records of risk assessments have to be kept.

Here are some examples of specific assessments required by legislation.

- Asbestos – risk assessment records must be made for each employee exposed and must be kept for the time that the work is being carried out. Regular review is required.

- Display screen equipment – employers must carry out assessments (see pages 186 to 187). Self-employed people are not obliged to assess work stations, but must satisfy themselves that they are, so far as is reasonably practicable, not at risk from the equipment.

- Hazardous substances – work cannot begin until the risks have been assessed. Regular review is required.

- Lead – risk assessments must be recorded and the records kept for two years after they have been superseded or when work involving lead is stopped altogether.

- Manual handling – the specific requirements and the factors that must be taken into account are listed in the legislation (see page 205).

- Noise – the risk from noise affecting employees must be assessed according to the action values outlined on page 254. Assess the risk to members of the public according to what is reasonably practicable. Records must be kept until a new assessment is made.

- Personal protective equipment (PPE) – this risk assessment is for the use of PPE only, and not for the hazards and risks the PPE is protecting against, as this assessment should have been done in the general risk assessment.

Risk assessment examples

Example risk assessments are available from the Health and Safety Executive website. They are intended to improve standards by demonstrating what a risk assessment is, the sort of hazards you should be thinking about and the practical steps that can be taken to protect people. They are also intended to help you to save time and money. Examples include a hairdressing salon, office work in a manufacturing company, a contract bricklayers, an off-licence, a motor vehicle showroom, a butcher's shop, cleaning work in large retail premises, and chilled storage warehousing.

The example below suggests some of the things that should be included in a risk assessment, but is not intended to be comprehensive. Remember that each situation presents its own hazards and risks and certain controls should already be in place.

Ladders in a shop – example

Use
Retrieving goods from a height, changing light units and erecting display materials.

Hazards
Staff member falling, materials falling and hitting someone.

Someone bumping into or tripping over foot of ladder.

Who is at risk
Employees, members of the public and visitors.

Controls
Retrieving goods from a height
Existing – ladders are provided with securing hooks to stabilise the top of the ladders against a storage rack.

Proposed – set up a ladder register and ensure that the shift supervisor inspects the ladders every week and records the findings.

Changing light units
Existing – stepladders have stabilisers and wheel chocks used for this activity. No guardrails are provided on the stepladders.

Proposed – area to be cordoned off and a member of staff to warn employees and members of the public about the operation. Set up ladder register. New stepladders with adequate guardrails to be provided.

Erecting display materials
Existing – stepladders with stabilisers and wheel chocks used for this activity.

Proposed – area to be cordoned off and a member of staff to warn employees and members of the public about the operation. Set up ladder register. Where display materials are large or heavy, a **safe system of work** should be set up in consultation with the shift supervisor.

Records
Retained in the risk assessment register and kept together with the organisation's health and safety policy. Also held in electronic format on the organisation's computer system.

Review

Reviewed every 12 months and when work activities or equipment change significantly, or after an accident occurs.

Legal requirements

Under The Management of Health and Safety at Work Regulations 1999 employers and self-employed people must make a suitable and sufficient assessment of the risks to the health and safety of employees and others as a result of work activities.

Where there are five or more employees, the employer must record the significant findings of the assessment and make a note of any group of employees identified as being particularly at risk.

Risk assessments must be reviewed by the employer or self-employed person if there is reason to suspect that it is no longer valid or there has been a significant change in the activity assessed.

Risk assessment is also specifically required by other regulations, such as The Control of Asbestos at Work Regulations 2006; The Control of Substances Hazardous to Health Regulations 2002; The Health and Safety (Display Screen Equipment) Regulations 1992; The Ionising Radiations Regulations 1999; The Control of Noise at Work Regulations 2005; The Control of Vibration at Work Regulations 2005 and The Manual Handling Operations Regulations 1992. Information about these requirements is given in Part 6.

Why do we need safe systems of work?

A safe system of work is a set of procedures that helps staff to carry out tasks safely. It is the main tool for implementing safe working practices.

The procedures include information about the hazards involved in a work activity or work environment, together with the safety procedures that must be followed. Managers, supervisors and safety representatives are likely to participate in drawing up safe systems of work. Supervisors are most likely to be involved in explaining the instructions to all the staff involved in a particular activity.

Safe systems of work should be in writing and recorded as part of the company's overall health and safety management system.

Key words and phrases

competent person – someone with the appropriate qualifications, knowledge and experience to identify the risks arising from a situation and the measures needed to control them.

permit to work – a formal document that specifies the work that a named member of staff is permitted to do and the precautions to be taken.

risk assessment – a systematic process for identifying workplace hazards and assessing the risks involved from those hazards.

safe system of work – a set of procedures for carrying out a task safely.

Developing safe systems of work

A **safe system of work** should be based upon a systematic examination of the task, involving a **risk assessment** of the:

- equipment to be used
- processes involved
- environment where the work will be carried out
- people carrying out the task.

This should be carried out by a **competent person** with a sound knowledge of the task and, usually, hands-on experience of what is involved. It helps to take into account the experience and comments of several staff members who already do the work. Safety representatives should also be consulted for their views.

Priorities

For existing processes, safe systems of work should first be prepared for high-risk activities. Then safe systems of work should be prepared for medium-risk and low-risk tasks. You should also give a high priority to preparing systems of work for any task likely to be carried out by inexperienced or young workers, and for the tasks carried out most frequently.

Stages of development

The first step in preparing a safe system of work for a particular activity is to conduct a thorough **risk assessment** to determine:

- the nature of the hazards
- who is at risk
- whether the hazard could be eliminated by using other work procedures or equipment
- what controls would be appropriate to deal with the residual level of risk.

Preparing the document

Once this has been done, the safe system of work should be documented. It is likely to include:

- information about who is authorised to do what
- detailed information about the hazards and associated risks of the task
- specific information about the hazards and their associated risks in the particular working environment
- precautions to be taken before starting the task
- details about any collective protective measures (such as fences, barriers and warning signs)
- instructions about any personal protective equipment (PPE) to be worn while working
- clear instructions about how to carry out the task

- specific instructions about minimising the risks from the task, including, where appropriate, measures to protect particular groups of people such as members of the public, blind pedestrians, young children

- instructions about ensuring that the work area is left safe for others

- guidelines for correct waste disposal

- procedures for emergencies.

Examples of what might be included
- Authorisation – for example, authorisation required to undertake a particular technique/process or use equipment/machinery; in-company prohibitions on workers under the age of 18 (such as an in-house ban on the use of food slicers by young workers); procedures and personnel that provide authorisation; training/supervision required for task or certificates of competence required.

- Hazards associated with equipment/machinery/technique/process – for example, hazardous chemicals, radiation, biological materials, sharps, high voltage, swarf produced, speed of operation, possibility of infection or allergy.

- Hazards associated with the environment where the task is to be undertaken – for example, road, motorway, railway line, drain; pole, tree, scaffold, ladder; fume cupboard, local exhaust ventilation, bio-safety cabinet, radiation laboratory; presence of children, elderly people or people with limited mobility, sight or hearing in the vicinity.

- Precautions before starting work – for example, where to find information about particular hazards, such as material safety data sheets (MSDS), manufacturers' instructions, company safety manual, location-specific safety manual (such as for a laboratory); emergency procedures including information about nearest accident and emergency hospital; first aid equipment; associated documents such as inspection certificates (such as for lifting equipment); details about preparation of the area, materials and the people required before commencing task.

Concrete hose kills construction worker

A construction worker died after a concrete-hardened hose struck his head when a blocked concrete pump was cleared in an unsafe manner.

There had been a delay in delivering new concrete to the piling rig which the man was operating. As a consequence, the concrete already in the flexible rubber hose began to harden, leading to a blockage.

It was decided to use compressed air to blow the concrete clear, but the end of the hose was not restrained. The hose flew up and hit the man's head, causing his fatal injuries.

The Health and Safety Executive (HSE) prosecuted the company on the grounds that it had failed to carry out a formal risk assessment of the cleaning and unblocking of the rig, so there was no safe system of work. An HSE inspector commented, 'A risk assessment is the starting point for developing a formal safe system of work for operations. Once developed, clear instruction and training should then be given to those carrying out the work.'

A court fined the company £75,000 and ordered it to pay costs of more than £34,400 for failing to ensure the health and safety of its employees.

- Personal protective equipment to be used – for example, safety glasses, goggles, face shield; steel toe cap footwear, non-slip footwear, chemical-resistant footwear, chainsaw boots, gloves; laboratory coat/back-opening gown, apron, overalls; safety helmet, hair nets, ear defenders; respiratory protection.

- Step-by-step procedures for the task.

- Clean-up procedures – for example, removing swarf, decontaminating glassware, cleaning work benches, transporting and storing hazardous materials, removing animal carcasses.

- Waste disposal procedures – for example, for chemical, biological or radioactive waste; broken glass; wood dust; rinsing water.

- Emergency procedures – for example, specific instructions for what to do in the case of a chemical spill, power outage, explosion, injury to someone working at height.

- Procedures for lone or isolated working and after-hours working – for example, prohibited activity at specified hours; access out of normal working hours; buddy system where at least two people work together or in close proximity; regular contact arrangements for lone or isolated workers, such as foresters and agricultural workers.

Reviewing the document

When a draft document is complete, the safe system of work should be reviewed by a supervisor, manager and a safety representative, then signed and dated by them.

Implementing safe systems of work

Safe systems of work must be communicated to staff. This is often the responsibility of a supervisor. Ideally, the system should be explained face-to-face, perhaps with a walk through if appropriate. This may form a part of induction, job-specific and refresher training as well as being good operational practice. In some occupations where staff work at different sites each day, the supervisor may need to explain the safe system of work each day for the particular site and task. This may be known as *a toolbox talk* or *job briefing*.

A written copy of the system should also be readily available for reference. In some workplaces a notice of the safe system of work could be displayed next to a piece of machinery. Alternatively, the system could be in a ready-to-hand safety manual or job envelope.

Liaison with other workers

Where there is more than one employer on a site or in a building, the supervisor should ensure that other contractors and employees are clear what needs to happen to ensure that work is safe. This liaison with others is a legal requirement.

Keeping the system effective

No system is effective unless it is followed. Managers and supervisors must ensure that staff work in safe ways that conform to the appropriate safe system of work. From time to time the system should be reviewed as a matter of course and adjusted if necessary. It should also be reviewed if there are any accidents or incidents (near-misses), or if employees or safety representatives raise safety concerns.

Worker slipped on hot oil after improvising work system

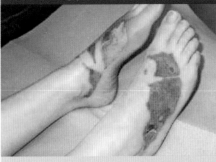

A supermarket was fined and ordered to pay costs because a catering worker was burnt by hot oil when improvising ways to empty a deep fat fryer.

The catering assistant had been emptying oil from a deep fat fryer into a plastic bucket when the bucket melted, spilling the oil onto her feet and the floor. She then slipped over and burnt her back.

Three months before the accident the fat fryer had been replaced with one without an integral filter and collection tray. The company was unaware of the change of design and failed to provide additional equipment for removing the oil safely, so staff improvised with the plastic bucket.

During the investigation it became apparent that there was no safe system of work in place for emptying the fryer. Poor training – where employees often trained one another, reinforcing unsafe working practice – and inadequate supervision also contributed to the problem. Although a risk assessment existed for fat fryers, the information was not passed on to all staff and was not reviewed when the new equipment was installed.

The council that instigated the prosecution commented, 'an extensive portfolio of policies, procedures and risk assessments are useless unless they are implemented at grass roots level.'

Types of safe system of work

Safe systems of work can be created in various ways and under various titles. These include:

- permit to work systems
- isolation and lock-off systems
- safe work instructions
- vehicle management plans
- safe work method statements.

An example of one of these systems – permit to work – is given below.

Permit to work

A **permit to work** is a formal document specifying the work that a designated jobholder is allowed to do and the precautions to be taken. Permits to work may be issued to help to control the risks in particularly hazardous situations or in non-routine circumstances. The permits are separate from certificates of competence and authorise named individuals or specific jobholders to carry out specified tasks, to work in specified areas or to work at specified times.

They might, for example, be issued for the use of certain powered equipment such as chainsaws, for working in confined spaces or on overhead electricity cables, for carrying out excavation work, working near railways lines or working at height. Non-routine work requiring a permit to work includes anything that creates non-typical health and safety risks. These might occur during annual or emergency maintenance or repair, deep cleaning, equipment installation and refurbishment or the use of specialised equipment not usually used in that work environment.

Employees working away from their own base – on another company's site or premises, for example – must abide by all permits to work being operated on that site.

Who can issue permits

The issue of permits to work should be tightly controlled. Only named, authorised and competent people should be allowed to issue permits to work. They might include managers and supervisors.

What should be specified

Permits to work should be written. They should identify the level of competence and any specialist skills of all individuals issued with a permit. They should list isolation and pre-work precautions, the prohibited activities (communicated to others as necessary), the plant and equipment required and the personal protective equipment (PPE) to be used.

The sequence of work to be undertaken should be stated, together with hazards identified and any residual risks. The controls should be clearly defined. Any emergency procedures for all foreseeable risks should also be included. Most permits cover work for 24 hours and need an authorising signature for extra time.

Communicating the permit requirements

Workers who are required to operate under the permit system should be briefed fully on the hazards and controls necessary. This should be done by a competent person such as a supervisor or team leader who must be familiar with all the details of the methods and sequence of work and all the emergency procedures. It is also advisable to explain what will happen after any emergency – such as instructions to stop work and leave the area untouched.

A notice explaining that a permit system is in operation should be displayed clearly at the work site or isolation point to remind everyone what is required.

Legal requirements

Employers and the self-employed have a duty under the Health and Safety at Work etc. Act 1974 or the Health and Safety at Work (Northern Ireland) Order 1978 to ensure the safety of people at work and anyone else affected by work activities.

The legislation specifically requires safe systems of work. The Management of Health and Safety at Work Regulations 1999 require risk assessments to be carried out and competent people to be appointed to assist in doing so.

How do monitoring, inspection and auditing help?

Information about the performance of a workplace is essential if an organisation is to manage health and safety successfully. Monitoring, inspecting and auditing can provide the information required. The key is to identify and collect the right information and use it to the best effect.

Key words and phrases

active monitoring – regular proactive measurement of performance against safety management standards and targets.

audit – a formal examination against a fixed standard by competent people who are independent of the area of work being audited.

competent person – a person with the appropriate qualifications, knowledge and experience to identify the risks arising from a situation and the measures needed to control them.

examinations – in a health and safety context, checks on equipment that are more thorough, but less frequent, than inspections.

inspection of equipment – checks on items of equipment to verify that they can be operated, adjusted and maintained safely.

inspection of the health and safety system – the assessment of the health and safety performance of a workplace, which enables any necessary remedial measures to be taken.

monitoring – regular, often daily, checks on what is going on in the workplace to help to deal with problems as they arise.

pre-use check – a check on equipment by an operator before using the equipment.

reactive monitoring – the reporting and investigation of incidents and accidents relating to health and safety.

risk assessment – a systematic process for identifying workplace hazards and assessing the risks involved from those hazards.

Checking the essentials

Managers, supervisors and safety/employee representatives all have a role to play in the monitoring, inspection and auditing of an organisation's health and safety. Monitoring is usually done by supervisors who then report to managers. Inspections can be carried out by safety representatives. Managers might organise audits as part of the health and safety management system. A health and safety consultant might be contracted to carry out the audit with the assistance of a supervisor and safety/employee representative. The audit report would then be considered by a manager.

Monitoring, inspection and auditing consider the factors responsible for causing accidents and ill health in the workplace. By looking at the human, organisational and environmental factors in the workplace and the work activities, the root causes of injury and illness can be identified so that hazards can be eliminated or controls applied that reduce the risk of accidents and ill health.

For monitoring, inspection and audit systems to work properly, there needs to be:

- proper financial and staff resources allocated to them

- commitment from managers, supervisors, safety/employee representatives and employees alike

- agreed inspection and auditing procedures

- adequate training and information for all involved in these systems

- regular reviews of the organisation's performance.

They can be carried out from a number of viewpoints such as the work environment, the particular occupation of the worker or the organisation's health and safety policy.

Monitoring

Monitoring can be either active or reactive. **Active monitoring** is the process of checking the day-to-day operation of the health and safety management system. It is the regular proactive measurement of performance against safety management standards and targets. It involves keeping an eye on what is going on and helps to deal with problems as they arise. Regular monitoring should help to identify the strengths and weaknesses of the system. Active monitoring includes methods such as safety inspections, tours of the workplace and surveys.

Monitoring can be impromptu or at set times: as you walk around the workplace you can check for variations in the ways tasks are carried out, spot hazards and discuss health and safety issues with employees, or you can arrange specific monitoring meetings. **Risk assessments** allow you to monitor the existing controls and to recommend improvements for implementation. **Reactive monitoring** is the reporting and investigation of incidents and accidents, whether these relate to people, processes, property or any combination of these. The process includes recording, investigating and examining information about accidents, ill health and complaints by employees about health and safety conditions.

The importance of keeping records

Apart from investigating incidents and accidents, much of reactive monitoring is about keeping and analysing records. So one of the indicators of a good health and safety culture is the quality and type of records kept by the organisation.

Examples of the types of records you should keep include those dealing with:

- training
- fire drills
- alarm testing
- electrical equipment testing
- plant and equipment maintenance
- operations or processes
- accident and incident investigations
- RIDDOR reports (see page 145 to 146)
- accident forms
- sickness and absence reports
- safety committee minutes
- inspections
- audits of safety systems
- work with hazardous substances – such as ionising radiation, lead and asbestos – or working with excessive noise or compressed air.

When records have been analysed, they can:

- demonstrate the company's history of safety management
- identify long-term trends
- be used to plan maintenance or identify training needs
- be used as evidence in case of litigation or prosecution
- to be used to monitor the effectiveness of control measures
- show the identified hazards and the control measures put in place
- be used by managers to conduct regular reviews of, for example, work processes/systems and health and safety performance.

Regulators, such as the Health and Safety Executive, can also use information gathered through The Reporting of Injuries, Diseases and Dangerous Occurrences Regulations 1995 to target health and safety issues – for example, the Better Backs campaign and the ladder safety campaign.

New beds saved injury and money

A National Health Trust recognised that its bed stock was old and that large sums of money were being spent to hire specialised mattresses and bed frames at short notice. Care staff reported patient dissatisfaction with the beds, and there was a high level of manual handling accidents and ill health among employees.

The trust established a multidisciplinary team to evaluate a bed management

contract. As a consequence, it replaced all the standard hospital beds with electrically operated beds that allow the patients and staff to move a bed up and down effortlessly.

Manual handling injuries to staff and pressure ulcers suffered by patients have reduced.

Inspection

The term **inspection** has various meanings. When used in relation to a specific item of equipment, the purpose of an inspection is to identify whether the equipment can be operated, adjusted and maintained safely, so that any deterioration can be detected and remedied before it results in unacceptable risks. The process of inspection is more thorough and formal than the routine checks that employees would do – for example, the pre-use check before starting work with a chainsaw.

In relation to the overall performance of the health and safety management system, an inspection is the assessment of the health and safety performance of a workplace, which enables any necessary remedial measures to be taken.

A **competent person** should carry out the inspection. He or she should be familiar with the working practices and the health and safety standards of the workplace. It is good practice for inspections to be carried out at least every six months, and records of the inspections should be kept for three years. Inspection reports should be given to the manager responsible for health and safety for any corrective work to be done.

What is included in an inspection of the system

An overall inspection of the health and safety management system does not necessarily have to cover all of the matters in the checklist below. Matters to be inspected could include checking that the:

■ safety policy is up to date and available

- safety committee minutes are available

- accident and ill health records are up to date and available

- training records are up to date and available

- first aid facilities are available and up to legal standard

- fire precautions include ensuring that the:
  - alarm test records are up to date and available
  - means of escape are clearly marked and visible
  - detectors are tested and records kept
  - fire extinguishers are available and records of testing available and up to date
  - training records available and up to date
  - fire drill records available and up to date
  - the storage of flammable substances is up to standard

- control of substances hazardous to health – records of assessments and safety data sheets available and up to date

- health surveillance records available and up to date

- display screen equipment risk assessments available and up to date

- manual handling risk assessments available and up to date

- records of disposal of hazardous waste available and up to date.

Other checks include:

- workplace
  - lighting
  - temperature
  - ventilation
  - cleanliness
  - storage
  - toilet and washing facilities
  - state of repair
  - fire escape routes

- equipment
  - guarding
  - maintenance
  - electrical equipment inspection and testing
  - pressure systems examinations and records
  - fire-fighting equipment
  - fire protection facilities

- lifting equipment examination and records.

You can customise your own checklist and compare the existing conditions observed against the relevant standards of health and safety.

The inspection report should note where unsatisfactory conditions occur and should make recommendations on any work that needs to be done to ensure that health and safety standards are maintained at a high level.

Examinations

Examinations, which apply only to equipment, are more thorough but carried out less often than inspections. The extent of a 'thorough examination' depends on an assessment of the risk, based on the type of equipment, where it is installed and how it is to be used. Examination is done so that deterioration can be detected in sufficient time for remedial action to be taken. Examinations must be done by a competent person.

Examples include the thorough examination of pressure systems or lifting equipment.

Auditing

An **audit** is a systematic, detailed assessment of the health and safety management system. It involves collecting information on the efficiency, effectiveness and reliability of the health and safety management system and measuring it against a fixed standard.

Auditing complements the routine inspection and monitoring of health and safety systems and goes deeper into the operation of the health and safety management system than monitoring or inspection. For example, if you wanted to audit a health surveillance system, an audit would try to find out whether:

- all employees exposed to risk are included in the health surveillance programme
- the people operating the health surveillance system are competent to do so
- proper records are being kept and are analysed
- the person responsible for health and safety in the workplace has seen the system records.

Auditing the health and safety management system helps to establish whether appropriate management arrangements are in place and helps you to make changes and improvements throughout the whole system. The conclusions and recommendations from an audit can help to:

- identify weaknesses in the system
- make improvements in the health and safety policy
- improve the organisation of the health and safety management system
- develop the planning of the system and the implementation of the policy
- continuously improve the performance measurement and the review of the system
- reduce accidents and ill health.

Carrying out the audit

An audit should be carried out by an independent, competent person, experienced in auditing health and safety management systems. Good practice is for an audit to be carried out every year. Audits of a small organisation can be done as a whole, but large organisations may have to audit parts of the organisation separately, by department, function (for example, maintenance) or hazard (for example, electrical).

The auditor should assess the records, question employees and observe procedures. The aim is to evaluate the:

- ability of the organisation's managers to produce and implement a health and safety policy to control health and safety risks
- communication and consultation arrangements for involving the organisation's employees
- training system and competence of employees
- health and safety risk control systems
- health and safety measures and procedures
- performance measurement system
- monitoring and inspection arrangements
- accident recording and investigation systems
- compatibility with the organisation's main management systems.

The audit can use a scoring system – for example, measuring the percentage compliance against a pre-set standard.

Example of the difference between an inspection and an audit

Inspection: light bulb missing.

Action: replace the bulb.

Audit: light bulb missing.

Questions: Is there inadequate lighting? Is there a system to assess lighting levels? Why has it not been followed?

Action: determine the root cause and put in place a system by which light bulbs are replaced when broken and lighting is inspected regularly so that lighting is adequate at all times.

Legal requirements

The Management of Health and Safety at Work Regulations 1999 require every employer to make arrangements for the effective planning, organisation, control, monitoring (including audits) and review of the preventive and protective measures for health and safety of his employees and others. The appropriate arrangements depend on the nature of the activities and the size of the business. Where there are five or more employees, the employer must record the arrangements.

The Provision and Use of Work Equipment Regulations 1998 says that every employer must inspect work equipment after installation and before being put into service for the first time to ensure that it has been installed correctly and is safe to operate. Employers must also inspect work equipment exposed to extreme conditions at suitable intervals and record the result of such inspections.

What is health surveillance?

Many organisations now actively promote the health of their employees in addition to taking preventive and precautionary measures. Some employers provide advice and assistance on topics such as smoking, diet and exercise. Others have introduced general health screening even if the employer is not required to do so. A programme of health surveillance is required by law in certain circumstances, such as where substances hazardous to health or radiation are involved.

Key words and phrases

environmental monitoring – tests to determine whether the work environment is safe and healthy for workers.

health surveillance – the systematic monitoring of the health of any worker who may be exposed to harmful substances or harmful work activities.

medical health screening – medical test to determine the health status of individuals at work.

What is health surveillance?

Health surveillance involves the systematic monitoring of the health of any worker who may be exposed to harmful substances or harmful work activities. The purpose of the surveillance is to identify adverse health effects or inadequate health and safety controls.

Types of surveillance

Generally there are two types of health-related surveillance at work – medical health screening and environmental monitoring.

Medical health screening allows early detection of specific work-related illnesses. It enables employers to prevent ill health and evaluate the need for changes that reduce the risks of disease.

Various techniques of medical health screening are used including:

- biological monitoring – testing employees for harmful substances in the body

- eyesight and hearing tests

- lung capacity tests

- chest X-rays

- manual dexterity assessments – for example, tests to determine whether a person has repetitive strain injury or back damage

- physical examination – for example, hairdressers can identify skin irritation by observing symptoms and reporting them to their supervisor

- interview.

Environmental monitoring can assist a health surveillance system by linking environmental results to medical results. Such monitoring includes:

- environmental sampling – for example, the measurement of harmful substances in the air

- the use of noise dosemeters – meters that indicate the level of noise to which an individual is exposed in the workplace

- the use of breathing zone air monitors – similar to noise dosemeters, but for measuring the amount of a harmful substance being breathed in by an employee.

Why monitor employee health?

The main aim of monitoring the health of employees is to protect them from harm, but individual privacy must also be considered. Health surveillance should be used only where it is likely to benefit those at risk, because it provides essential information on the effectiveness of control.

Health surveillance is normally used in order to:

- measure the body's absorption of toxic substances

- look for adverse effects on the body at an early stage

- identify from clinical and personnel records any work-related diseases in groups of employees

- identify and protect employees who have a greater risk of poor health than others before they start a job that may expose them to a harmful substance or other health hazard.

Health surveillance, such as eye testing, helps to identify employees who need protection from workplace hazards.

It is common for organisations to monitor the health of employees who wear personal protective equipment. The use of personal protective equipment is the only health and safety control in some circumstances where there are hazards that cannot be controlled by other methods.

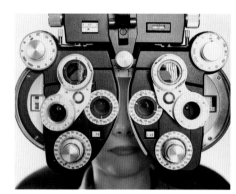

Employers can use health surveillance procedures to identify workers who may have adverse health symptoms and to find out whether the workplace health and safety precautions are adequate. If the measures are inadequate, then health surveillance should indicate which other measures need to be introduced. Some common symptoms of work-related illnesses are easily confused with non-occupational illnesses. Expert diagnosis is needed to pinpoint work-related causes. This can be a complex and lengthy process.

When to monitor employee health

Employers must ensure that their employees are provided with health surveillance appropriate to the risks to their health and safety that have been identified by a risk assessment. The following criteria should be used to decide whether health surveillance should be introduced:

- there is an identifiable disease or adverse health condition related to the work

- valid techniques are available to detect the disease or condition

- there is a reasonable likelihood that the disease or condition may occur under the particular conditions at work

- surveillance is likely to increase the protection of the health of the employees concerned.

Monitoring at different stages

Health surveillance can be done at different stages of an employee's employment – at recruitment or before transfer to a job with health risks, for example. It can also be done during work involving a risk to health and even after the exposure to the health hazard has stopped. Surveillance can also help to predict whether someone is likely to be at risk from developing work-related diseases from harmful substances used in the workplace. For example, where a person is susceptible to skin conditions, some substances can make the condition worse. Health surveillance may help to prevent this exposure occurring.

Information from monitoring health can set a baseline for later comparison with the results of surveillance carried out over a long period. For example, a hearing test at the beginning of an employment contract involving noisy work establishes the state of the employee's hearing abilities at that time. It can be used to compare with later hearing tests to establish whether there has been any deterioration in hearing ability.

The link between asbestos and mesothelioma was discovered in the 1960s, but increased health precautions and the gradual phasing out of the use of the material did not start until the 1970s. The HSE is campaigning to raise awareness of the dangers from asbestos among electricians, plumbers and others who are likely to encounter the material.

Surveillance after exposure has stopped is useful to detect long-term ill health effects such as mesothelioma (cancer of the lining of the lungs, usually due to asbestos exposure). This can help to detect the disease at an early stage, so that, should it occur, appropriate treatment can be given.

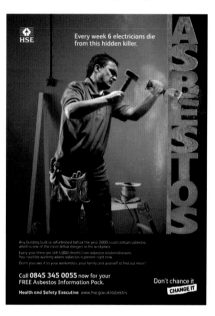

Biological monitoring

Biological monitoring is used to find out if a substance is being absorbed into the body. The technique is typically used to monitor lead or pesticide levels in the blood. Results can suggest whether existing controls are adequate and can help to identify employees who are over-exposed and need to be given additional protection or moved from the job.

Surveillance can also help to identify insufficient control of a harmful substance – for instance, where ventilation controls are inadequate to deal with airborne lung allergens, such as those in wool-processing workshops.

Harmful substances

Where harmful substances are in use, there must be a health surveillance programme. This is required by law for asbestos, lead and ionising radiation, for example. Employees working in compressed air or diving operations must also receive health surveillance.

Some important precautions

There are some issues which employees should know before they participate in a health surveillance programme and there should be certain safeguards for privacy in place.

- Employees should give their consent to participating in the programme, or it should be a clear, prior condition of employment that they must take part.

- Employees should be given information about the possible consequences of surveillance – for example, the possibility of discovering adverse effects. (Supervisors or managers can be trained to recognise the symptoms of some conditions that may indicate health problems in their particular workplace – for example, skin conditions such as redness, itching and soreness from substances which can damage the skin.)

- The programme must be under the direction of a competent person – for example, an occupational health doctor or occupational hygienist.

- The information obtained from the programme must remain confidential but should be available to the individual employee at any time.

- Details should be passed on to third parties, such as the Health and Safety Executive, local authority or court, only with the written consent of the employee.

- Employees cannot be dismissed because they are at a high risk of developing a work-related disease, unless there has been a detailed and thorough medical assessment and they have been given a full explanation of what has happened. Job redeployment should be considered first.

- There should be a system of quick referral for medical advice and treatment in the event that adverse effects are detected, so that treatment can be given at the earliest stage possible.

Health surveillance records

Sickness records are an important source of information in health surveillance and can be an early indication that something is wrong in the workplace. The details included in health surveillance records are likely to be:

- the name of the employee

- sex of the employee

- date of birth of the employee

- employee's address and other contact details

- employee's National Insurance number

- date the employee started his or her current employment

- current health surveillance details, including the type, frequency and results of tests

- details about the employee's previous jobs that involved exposure to harmful substances

- dates of previous health surveillance

- comments made concerning previous health surveillance

- the name of the competent person carrying out the health surveillance.

More detailed records can be kept if it is the advice of a competent person to do so.

Health surveillance records must be kept for at least 40 years from the date of the last entry.

Managing a return to work

Managing an employee's return to work after illness can help to create good relations with workers, reduce profit losses and increase productivity.

Organisations should record and monitor sickness absence, the reason for absence and the time taken off.

Managers or supervisors should keep in contact with people on sick leave and consider arranging to visit workers who have been off work for some time to discuss their progress and when they hope to return to work. When an employee is ready to return to work, managers should discuss the return and any circumstances or practices that could continue to have an adverse effect on the person's condition. (This should be based on the advice of suitably qualified occupational health staff.) Managers should ensure that employees returning to work after long-term sickness absence are not subjected to excessive demands during their planned return. This can be done through an informal interview at their home or on their return to work.

Taking it further

You can get advice and practical help about health surveillance from an occupational health adviser or from the Employment Medical Advisory Service which is part of the Health and Safety Executive.

Legal requirements

According to The Management of Health and Safety at Work Regulations 1999 every employer must ensure that employees are provided with health surveillance appropriate to the risks to them that have been identified by a risk assessment.

There are many sets of regulations that require specific health surveillance of employees who work with hazardous substances. Examples include The Control of Substances Hazardous to Health Regulations 2002; The Control of Asbestos Regulations 2006; The Control of Lead at Work Regulations 2002; The Ionising Radiations Regulations 1999; The Control of Noise at Work Regulations 2005; and The Control of Vibration at Work Regulations 2005.

Why must accidents and ill health be reported?

Recording and reporting accidents, ill health and dangerous occurrences can help organisations to reduce accidents and ill health in their own workplace and in others around the country.

There are legal requirements to report some types of injury and illness. The Health and Safety Executive analyses these reports and uses the results to help to shape national policy on health and safety at work and priorities for action. The 'Better backs' campaign, for example, was based on reported accident information.

Under social security legislation there are also requirements to keep records of accidents at work.

Key words and phrases

accident – any unplanned event that results, or could have resulted, in personal injury or ill health; damage to, or loss of, property, plant or materials; damage to the environment; or loss of business opportunity.

dangerous occurrence – a hazardous incident that arises out of, or in connection with, work and is specified in RIDDOR (see opposite).

reportable accident – an accident that must, by law, be reported to the enforcing authorities. Such accidents are those resulting in death, major injury, injuries that cause an employee to take more than three days off work and dangerous occurrences.

reportable disease – a disease that arises out of, or in connection with, work and is specified in RIDDOR.

responsible person – an employer, the duty manager, a self-employed person, the owner of premises or a vehicle, or the person in control of the premises at any one time.

RIDDOR – The Reporting of Injuries, Diseases and Dangerous Occurrences Regulations 1995.

Why report and record accidents and ill health?

There should be an effective system for reporting and investigating accidents and ill health in all organisations. The procedures should be clearly established in writing and all staff should be trained in the system. The principal objectives for the system should be to:

- enable prompt remedial action to be taken

- prevent a similar occurrence in the future

- ensure compliance with legislation – see pages 142 to 145 and 146

- comply with a company instruction, usually in the health and safety policy

- detect trends

- assist decision making, planning and resource allocation.

Failure to report and record

Many accidents and incidences of ill health go unreported and this can affect the health and safety performance of an organisation, as well as its compliance with the law. A failure to report accidents or ill health can starve the organisation of an essential source of information which could be used to shape changes in work practice.

Employees may be reluctant to report accidents or ill health for a number of reasons – for example, they may:

- think that the accident or incident is too trivial

- not appreciate the benefits of reporting accidents and ill health

- not relate ill health to work

- worry that reporting wastes time

- fear a reprimand by the manager or supervisor

- believe there is pressure from managers to keep down the number of *reported* accidents

- not want to admit errors for fear of appearing incompetent

- not want to fill in forms

- worry that they will lose pay or their job.

Encouraging good practice and legal compliance

Managers, supervisors and safety representatives have a crucial role to play here. They can encourage staff to report accidents by:

- removing any fear of reprimand for employees who do report accidents or ill health

- running appropriate training sessions and providing regular reminders

- setting up a reporting system that gives all reports of accidents and ill health equal importance

- investigating all accidents or incidence of ill health

- taking immediate remedial action and longer-term measures in the light of the hazards and their risks identified by investigations

- including accidents and ill health in safety meeting agendas

- informing employees of the outcomes of anything they reported.

Legal reporting requirements

Some accidents and ill health must be reported to the enforcing authorities. These are **reportable accidents** or **reportable diseases** as defined by The Reporting of Injuries, Diseases and Dangerous Occurrences Regulations 1995, sometimes referred to as **RIDDOR**.

Employers must report the accidents, diseases and dangerous occurrences specified in the regulations. Examples include:

- the death of an employee, self-employed person or a member of the public

- a major injury to an employee or a self-employed person

- accidents that result in a member of the public being taken to hospital

- injury to an employee or self-employed person that prevents them from doing their normal work for more than three days

- a reportable disease related to work

- a **dangerous occurrence** – an incident arising from, or in connection with, work and which is specified in RIDDOR, such as the collapse of a scaffold more than 5m high or the failure of a load-bearing part of fairground equipment.

How and when to report

Injuries, illnesses and dangerous occurrences specified by law can be reported via the Internet on the Health and Safety Executive website.

Accidents, dangerous occurrences and diseases specified in the regulations must be reported to the HSE without delay by the quickest means possible.

For most people the quickest and easiest way is to call the Incident Contact Centre on 0845 300 99 23. You can give all the information to the operator who will complete the necessary paperwork and send you a copy for your records. (The service is open during office hours and the Health and Safety Executive website gives information about when reporting is appropriate at other times.)

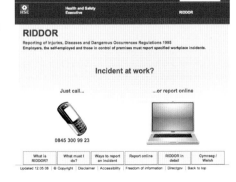

Alternatively, you can fill in a form on line at <http://www.hse.gov.uk/riddor/online.htm> or by email or by downloading the form, completing it and sending it by post to Incident Contact Centre, Caerphilly Business Park, Caerphilly, CF83 3GG. The form is F2508 (in English) or F2508W (in Welsh).

If a doctor diagnoses an employee with a reportable work-related disease, it must be reported by telephone or using the on-line forms – F2508A (in English) or F2508W (in Welsh).

What to report

Major injuries
Examples of a major injury include:

- any fracture other than to the fingers, thumbs or toes

- any amputation

- dislocation of the shoulder, hip, knee or spine

- loss of sight (whether temporary or permanent)

- a chemical or hot metal burn to the eye or any penetrating injury to the eye

- any injury resulting from an electric shock or electrical burn (including any electrical burn caused by arcing or arcing products) leading to unconsciousness or requiring resuscitation or admittance to hospital for more than 24 hours

- any other injury:
    - leading to hypothermia, heat-induced illness or to unconsciousness
    - requiring resuscitation
    - requiring admittance to hospital for more than 24 hours.

Over three-day injury
An 'over three-day injury' is one that is not a major injury, but results in the injured person being off work for more than three calendar days. This means three consecutive days, but does *not* include the day of the accident. Non-working days should be counted in the three consecutive days.

It is important to note that an accident includes physical violence to a person at work and should be reported if it results in death, major injury or an over three-day injury.

Dangerous occurrences
A dangerous occurrence is an occurrence arising out of, or in connection with, work and which is specified in RIDDOR. Examples of dangerous occurrences are:

- the collapse, overturning or failure of a load-bearing part of any lift or hoist, crane or derrick, mobile powered access platform, access cradle or window cleaning cradle, excavator, pile-driving frame or fork-lift truck

- electrical short circuit or overload attended by fire or explosion which results in the stoppage of the plant involved for more than 24 hours or which has the potential to cause death

- plant or equipment coming into contact with overhead power lines

- accidental discharge of a biological agent that is likely to cause severe illness.

Diseases
Specified diseases include:

- certain poisonings

- some skin diseases such as occupational dermatitis, skin cancer, chrome ulcer and oil folliculitis/acne

- lung diseases including occupational asthma, farmer's lung, pneumoconiosis, asbestosis and mesothelioma

- infections such as leptospirosis (Weil's disease), all types of hepatitis infection, tuberculosis, anthrax infection, legionellosis and tetanus

- other conditions such as occupational cancer, certain musculoskeletal disorders, decompression illness and hand-arm vibration syndrome.

Such diseases must be diagnosed by a doctor and the employee must be engaged in the work activities specified in RIDDOR.

Reporting an accident involving a member of the public

An accident involving a member of the public that arises from, or in connection with, work activities must be reported to the Incident Contact Centre (see page 142) if the member of the public is killed or is taken to hospital directly from the accident scene.

How do you determine whether an accident arises out of, or in connection with, work? You need to consider the following three issues:

- the way the business is run – how it is organised, supervised or performed by an employer, or any of its employees, or by a self-employed person

- the plant or substances used to carry out the work – for example, lifts, air conditioning plant, any machinery, equipment or appliance, gas installation or substance used in the premises or in any process in the workplace

- the condition of the work premises, or any part of them – this includes the state of the structure or fabric of a building or outside area forming part of the premises, and the state and design of floors, paving, stairs, lighting and so on.

Examples – reportable
The following three accidents are reportable because they arose in connection with work.

1. A shopper is injured using a shop escalator. The design or condition of the escalator is the cause of the accident.

2. A resident in a nursing or residential care home trips and falls over an obstruction, such as an electrical cable lying across the floor.

3. A member of the public who is visiting a factory is overcome by gasses that escaped accidentally from a process being carried out and is taken to hospital.

Examples – not reportable

The following three accidents are examples that may not be reportable.

1. A child falls off a safe piece of play equipment while being supervised by the parents.

2. Death by natural causes of a patient/resident in a nursing residential care home.

3. A person in an ice rink, using his or her own ice skates, falls while skating on the ice.

Who must make the report

The duty to report/notify accidents, ill health, deaths and dangerous occurrences falls upon a **responsible person**. That person may be the employer, the duty manager, a self-employed person, the owner of premises or a vehicle, the person in charge of the premises or the process at the time of the accident or incident. Supervisors may also be given the duties of a responsible person.

A reportable injury to a travelling employee, such as a postman, delivery driver, refuse collector or service engineer, has to be reported by that person's employer if the accident causing the injury happened while he or she was working away from base.

Accident records

Employers must keep records of accidents, ill health and dangerous occurrences at work. They can do this in several ways, such as by:

- using an amended accident book BI 510 (which has perforated, tear-out forms to comply with data protection legislation)

- keeping photocopies of completed F2508/F2508W forms

- storing information about each accident on a computer.

Accident records should be readily available to inspectors and the employee concerned. Safety representatives have the legal right to inspect and take copies of accident records.

Records of injuries/conditions, dangerous occurrences and diseases must be kept for up to three years. They should include the following information:

- name of the person who was injured or ill

- date and time of accident or illness notification

- location of accident

- details of any witnesses

- the activity, equipment or substances involved

- environmental conditions – for example, floor conditions, lighting, ventilation and space available

- what was being done and how

- the training, skill and general health of the person injured or ill
- previous similar incidents
- witness comments
- supervisor's comments
- any treatment given
- action taken in the short term and long term
- if and when notified to the enforcing authority.

Legal requirements

The Reporting of Injuries, Diseases and Dangerous Occurrences Regulations 1995 require that a **responsible person** must notify and send a report to, the Health and Safety Executive of accidents that result in a fatality or major injury, or when an employee is absent from work for more than three days as a result of a work-related accident. Certain specified diseases and dangerous occurrences must also be reported.

Separate legislation requires records to be kept of all accidents and incidents at work.

Why should we carry out accident investigations?

No one wants an accident to occur in their workplace and responsible employers do everything possible to ensure that none occurs. But what should *you* do if, despite all your best efforts, something does go wrong and an accident occurs? An accident investigation is an opportunity to find out what happened and to introduce changes aimed at preventing a similar accident.

Key words and phrases

accident – any unplanned event that results, or could have resulted, in personal injury or ill health; damage to, or loss of, property, plant or materials; damage to the environment; or loss of business opportunity.

incident (near-miss or **near-miss accident)** – an unplanned event that does not result in personal injury, death or damage, but has the potential to do so.

representative of employee safety – an employee elected by non-union employees to represent them on health and safety matters.

RIDDOR – The Reporting of Injuries, Diseases and Dangerous Occurrences Regulations 1995.

safety representative – an employee elected by a trade union members to represent them on health and safety issues.

safe system of work – a set of procedures for carrying out tasks safely.

Why investigate accidents?

A detailed investigation of an **accident** or a **near-miss** should be carried out as soon as possible, so that remedial action can be taken to prevent further accidents. The investigation should aim to establish the:

- sequence of events leading to the accident
- unsafe acts or conditions
- root causes of the accident.

Accidents and ill health can indicate that risk control measures have failed. A full investigation can reveal weaknesses in the controls that need to be remedied.

Organisations should investigate *all* accidents and incidents, as the information gained can help them to protect employees and others. Data obtained in the investigation can then be used to develop **safe systems of work** and safety strategies to ensure compliance with legislation. An investigation will also reveal whether company health and safety policy and procedures have been followed.

Staff morale can be damaged by an accident. An investigation followed by rapid implementation of corrective measures can help to restore confidence and commitment because it demonstrates the employer's determination to maintain high standards of health and safety in the workplace.

Who should be involved?

An accident should be investigated by people such as the organisation's safety officer/adviser, if there is one, a **safety representative** (or **representative of employee safety**), a manager and the supervisor of the job involved. You may be one of the people involved in drawing up the report. Employees who were involved in an accident, or were witnesses, may be reluctant to give as much information as they could for fear of being blamed. Including safety representatives/representatives of employee safety in the investigation team can give employees the confidence to co-operate fully. Witnesses include anyone who was hurt or who saw the incident and anyone who was, or might have been, involved in any part in a chain of events that could have contributed to the accident.

Whoever is involved in the investigation should be competent to do the investigation and should have the skill and experience to:

- explore the possible causes and question the people involved
- understand the relevant records and documents
- avoid bias, deal fairly with conflicting views and not make premature or unsound judgements
- gain respect and confidence
- recognise the significance of all the likely contributing factors
- have the authority to make recommendations.

People from outside the organisation may also want to investigate the accident – for example, a health and safety inspector from the Health and Safety Executive or an environmental health officer from the local authority.

If a civil claim for compensation is made against the organisation, the company's insurers will also need to carry out their own enquiries.

If a death occurs, the police may be called in. A coroner (England, Wales and Northern Ireland) or procurator fiscal (Scotland) may organise an investigation if there is likely to be an inquest (England, Wales and Northern Ireland) or a sudden death investigation (Scotland). Employers and employees have legal duties to co-operate fully with these officers.

What may be involved

An investigation is shaped by the circumstances of the accident, but there are many common features and steps you should consider.

Dealing with an accident

The safety and well-being of people at the scene of an accident are the first priority, but an accident investigation can help to prevent a recurrence.

The first priorities are to give first aid and make the immediate area safe. Someone should assess the scene of the accident to prevent further accidents happening. For example, if the injured person slipped on a wet floor, the area should be cordoned off; if the accident involved a machine, it should be switched off; or if a fire has broken out, people should be evacuated from the building.

If the injury is such that medical attention is needed, then an ambulance should be called. Someone should wait for the ambulance and direct it to the scene of the accident. Someone should note the details of the injured person if possible. If it is not possible, then the paramedics should be asked to inform the injured person to contact their employer when they can. If the accident comes within the scope of **RIDDOR**, a report must be submitted in accordance with the regulations. A report should also be submitted to the appropriate job holder in the company or organisation.

Investigating an accident – Step 1

The first step in the investigation is to gather information by inspecting the area where the accident happened, noting the physical and environmental conditions and any damage caused.

You should decide whether the condition of the premises or area where the accident happened is a factor in the accident. If not, does it involve equipment or harmful substances? Look at the work procedures if you suspect that they have not been followed. Were any controls not in place or tampered with? Were the work procedures adequate to prevent accidents happening?

Consider whether an employee or several employees contributed to the accident. Were they playing around? Were they competent to do the job? Had they been adequately trained, and are the training records up to date? Had the health and safety risks been adequately explained? Had they been given sufficient information to carry out the task? Was the employee under the influence of alcohol or drugs or under stress? Alternatively the investigation could be organised by looking at the typical factors involved in accidents such as occupational factors, environmental factors, human factors and the organisational factors (see pages 20 to 21).

Decide whether photographs or measurements of the position of relevant objects would be useful. Consider taking samples of substances or articles involved.

Step 2

The second step is to interview any witnesses, including the injured person if possible, and anyone else who could give relevant information.

Emphasise that the interviews are confidential. It is important not to attribute blame and to bear in mind that there is rarely only one cause of an accident. If a health and safety enforcement officer visits the premises to investigate the accident, he or she should be given as much co-operation as necessary to assist in his or her own investigation.

Step 3

The third step is to analyse the information gathered and to discuss possible conclusions with other members of the investigating team and, if necessary, to review the working procedures and risk assessment for the activity involved in the accident. Was the work procedure followed and was the risk assessment adequate? Did it foresee the accident? Were the controls identified by the risk assessment followed or not?

Step 4

The fourth step is to compile a written report containing all the facts and any proposals for improving conditions, procedures or policies in the health and safety management system. Identify any control measures that are necessary to prevent a similar accident. Set priorities and timescales for improvement and establish how changes will be monitored and success judged.

Step 5

Step 5 is to implement the recommendations of the investigating team. It is likely that a supervisor will be given the responsibility of implementing the action plan and reporting back to management once all actions have been completed. The measures taken will need to be checked to find out whether they have been successful in reducing the risk of accidents. It is a help to use a checklist covering the important points.

Example of an accident investigation

A worker suffers an electric shock from a defective electric drill. Once the worker has been treated and as soon as it is safe to do so, the drill should be inspected by a competent person who can determine whether the drill was faulty, and if so, what that fault was. An attempt should also be made to find out what led to the electric shock occurring. Was there a design fault in the drill? Was the drill over-used and poorly maintained? Was it due to someone interfering with the drill's safety controls?

The following list has suggestions for some of the questions that could be asked during the investigation.

- Why did the drill give the worker a shock?
- If the drill is found to be defective, why was the problem not found during the regular maintenance inspection?
- What was the condition of the area of the workplace in which the worker was working?
- Was the worker trained to use the drill?
- Was the worker told not to use the drill by a supervisor, manager or someone responsible for its maintenance?
- When was the drill last inspected and who inspected it?
- Was the supervisor or manager aware of the condition of the drill?
- Who was responsible for ensuring that the drill was maintained?
- Were the maintenance and inspection records being kept up to date?

Depending on the answers to these questions, the solutions could be one or more of the following actions:

- better maintenance procedures
- improved training and instruction
- clearer individual responsibilities
- better communication
- drill replacement
- drill repair.

If we look back to the cause of the accident, we can see that the unsafe act was using the defective drill and the unsafe condition was the defective or damaged drill.

Legal requirements

There is no legal requirement to investigate accidents or incidents, but there is guidance on investigating accidents that gives reasons for and benefits of doing so. (See *Investigating accidents and incidents – a workbook for employers, safety representatives and safety professionals HSG 245*.) The Management of Health and Safety at Work Regulations 1999 require employers to review their health and safety arrangements at intervals. Following an accident, employers should review their arrangements by investigating the accident and implementing the findings. An accident investigation would help to inform that review.

How do training, instruction and information help standards?

Training is an essential part of health and safety management and control. It prepares employees, through the means of information, instruction and practice, to achieve a desired skill, knowledge or competence. Training is very effective in reducing the likelihood of injury because the employee is made aware of the hazards, risks and controls involved in work activities. Trained employees make fewer mistakes and they often do a better job all round.

Managers, supervisors and safety representatives are often in a position to influence the type and extent of the health and safety training provided for employees, and some are qualified to provide the training themselves.

Key words and phrases

information – verbal or written advice, which should be in a style and at a level that is easily understood by the employees to whom it is being addressed.

instruction – guidance or direction regarding a specific procedure or action.

performance indicators – measurements used to help an organisation to define and measure progress towards the organisation's health and safety goals.

training – preparing a person to achieve a desired level of skill, knowledge or competence through the means of information, instruction and practice.

training needs – the type and extent of training the workforce or an individual employee requires.

What is training?

Training can be described as the process of preparing someone to achieve a desired level of skill, knowledge or competence. This is usually achieved by giving information, instruction and practice. Instruction is giving guidance or direction regarding a specific procedure or action. Information is verbal or written advice, which should be in a format and style that is easily understood by the intended listener or reader.

Why provide training?

One of the underlying causes of accidents is lack of training for employees and others who may be affected by work activities. So it is essential that employers provide well timed, good quality, appropriate and focused information, instruction and training for employees, and any others affected by the work activities. The benefits can include:

- a reduction in
  - accidents and ill health in the workplace
  - days taken off work because of sickness
  - costs of accidents and insurance

- an increase in
  - productivity
  - the hazards identified in the workplace

- an improvement in
  - the response to fire drills and emergency alarms
  - customer satisfaction
  - the organisation's reputation as a good employer.

Responsibilities for training

Employers must provide information, instruction and training for employees and people who may be affected by their business. Managers are usually accountable for this. They usually decide on the scope and type of training needed by the organisation.

Supervisors and safety representatives are in an excellent position to *influence* the provision of training. They can advise managers about the type and scope of the training and they can often plan and organise the training courses. Some may be able to run courses themselves.

To be able to run a training course yourself, you need to demonstrate that you have the appropriate knowledge of the subject and the skills to carry out the training. For example, if you would like to run a CIEH Level 2 Award in Health and Safety in the Workplace course, you would need to have achieved a CIEH Level 4 Award in Health and Safety in the Workplace, have a teaching qualification or group training certificate and have some experience of dealing with health and safety matters in your job.

Which level of training is needed?

You may be involved in assessing the organisation's or an individual employee's **training needs** – what sort of, and how much, training is required to enable employees to work as safely as possible.

There are several ways to identify the sort of information, instruction and training that is required. Risk assessments will help you to identify the major issues where technical knowledge, procedures, practical experience and so on would enable employees or others to achieve competence in relevant health and safety matters. You then need to match this information to the type of information and instruction that is most appropriate for employees and others who may be affected by work activities.

Legislation sometimes specifies the type and level of training, instruction and information to be provided – for example, for first aiders (see page 369).

New employees

Training should be given after someone has been appointed and when employees are exposed to new or increased risks.

The current knowledge, skills and experience of employees will also influence the type and level of training to be provided. For instance, a supermarket shelf-stacker who has received induction training on manual handling and who has been working in the shop for four years will not need a full course of instruction about manual handling, but may need a refresher course or, if the method of moving goods has changed, a training course that deals with the new method.

Training is very important in achieving competence and refresher training has an important role to play in maintaining that competence.

All training should take place during working hours because this is required by the law.

Instruction and training

The provision of instruction and training is a continuous process, not a one-off exercise. It needs to be provided for new and existing employees and those who take on new jobs and responsibilities. If you have the responsibility for instruction and training you must also take into account the impact of new processes, new ways of working and new equipment.

The type of training

When deciding what kind of training should be given, you must first decide whether training is the best or most appropriate way of reducing risks. Purchasing newer equipment with more built-in safety features might be a better solution, for example. Once you have identified who is to be trained, ask yourself whether training is the most appropriate method of improving the employee's knowledge? Would giving information or instruction be more appropriate?

Designing the programme

You then need to decide which subjects the employee needs to learn about, which skills they need to practice and who will run the training course. You can then create a programme of training yourself or devise it with the appointed trainer.

You need to decide who the target group is and what they need to know. You also need to decide on the most suitable training techniques to accommodate different learning styles – the way people learn most easily. Is the training going to use visual and physical training aids? Are you going to use interactive techniques to consolidate learning? Could you incorporate actual and relevant examples such as reporting forms, risk assessments and legislation. Finally, you need to break training into manageable segments.

Evaluation, monitoring and review

When the training has been completed, you need to evaluate the quality of training and decide whether it has fulfilled your expectations. You need to monitor the effect of the training on the job and on the health and safety standards of the workplace – the accident and illness rates, for example. From time to time you also need to review the whole training provision. This might be annually, whenever there are changes in processes or materials, after an accident or near-miss or at the request of the safety committee.

Methods of training

There are several methods of training and you must decide which is best in the circumstances. Examples include the following.

- One-to-one training – an experienced person, such as a supervisor, trains one person in a particular subject or skill.

Everyone throughout an organisation needs health and safety training.

- Learning from an experienced person at work – in the past this might have been referred to as the 'sitting by Nellie' method. The disadvantage is that bad habits can be passed on if the experienced person is not alert to the responsibility of helping the trainee.

- Mentoring, in which employees are 'paired up' with an experienced, and usually more senior, employee such as a supervisor.

- Formal training by a qualified trainer at the workplace or at a college or learning centre.

- Role-play where people engaged in a hypothetical situation play the part of the people involved – for example, if the scenario is an accident investigation, the people involved could be the injured person, the employer's safety officer, the local authority environmental health officer and the employer or manager of the workplace

- Report writing – projects where the learners are given a subject to study or investigate and are required to compile a report on their findings

- Study or discussion groups where the learners are given a scenario of an accident and asked to discuss the health and safety issues around the facts given in the scenario

- Distance learning courses – some educational organisations and publishers provide learning courses in a specially designed book, video, CD-ROM, DVD, internet site or pack of learning materials: the student studies at his or her own pace, rather than attending a training course with a tutor. Some of these could be interactive, involving the learner in answering questions to which the computer can respond with answers, or a tutor or adviser marks the answers and provides email or telephone support.

- Case studies – the learners are given a set of facts about a real or imaginary case involving health and safety and are asked to present a report outlining all the health and safety matters involved – for example, the legislation applying to the case, the interpretation of the facts and the conclusions, which could include the options for improvement of health and safety standards and any enforcement action that could be taken.

Evaluation

In deciding the type of training method, you should consider the capabilities of the employees and the cost and likely effectiveness of each method. The capabilities of the employees can be assessed during recruitment, at work and by discussion with them.

The cost and effectiveness of each type of training method can be gauged by experience and with reference to colleagues who have used the methods in their own training course. You can, of course, evaluate a training method by asking employees to give their opinion on the method, and managers should measure health and safety performance over time and decide whether the methods used were successful or not by comparing performance before and after the training courses.

All training programmes should be evaluated after they have taken place. You can do so by asking yourself a number of questions immediately and some time after the training, say six months later. The questions could include:

- to what extent were the identified training needs objectives achieved

- to what extent were the learners' objectives achieved

- what specifically did the learners learn or what were they reminded about that proved to be useful

- what commitment have the learners made about how they are going to implement what they have learnt when they return to work

- how successful were the trainees in implementing their action plans

- to what extent were they supported in this by their line managers?

When you have the answers to these questions you will be in a better position to assess whether the training programme has been successful. This needs to be measured against the company's health and safety **performance indicators** to see whether the training has improved the health and safety performance of the organisation

Information

Information can be verbal, printed (text and/or illustrations) or other forms of visual material, including computer-based material, video and DVD. It is important that the person who needs the information can understand it easily.

Information can be given to employees through the use of safety notices or signs, safety bulletins or newsletters, noticeboards or a network of safety representatives.

If you have responsibility for providing health and safety information in the workplace, you must decide first of all who needs information on health safety matters – for example, employees, visitors or members of the public.

Secondly, you need to identify what information should be provided – for example, precautions for reducing risks, emergency evacuation procedures or how to use work equipment safely.

Thirdly, you must decide when it is appropriate to provide the information – when staff start employment or their job changes, for instance.

Finally, you need to decide how the information is to be provided – for example, on a poster, in a leaflet, through conversation or presentation or by computer. The information must be easy to understand and the people receiving it need to know why they are receiving it.

Common types of health and safety information

Some of the information that is commonly distributed in the workplace includes:

- the health and safety policy (see pages 100 to 104)
- safety responsibilities
- safe systems of work (see pages 121 to 126)
- hazards in the workplace
- controls in place to protect employees from injury and ill health
- changes in procedures, equipment and so on
- where information, instruction or training can be obtained
- feedback on how well the staff have complied with health and safety work practices.

Induction course – what to include

The best time to give *general* health and safety training is before the employee starts work. This can be done in an induction course which is often carried out informally. Supervisors are often directly involved with induction training and they can ensure that the training establishes good working practices. The health and safety issues that should be covered include:

- fire safety – emergency evacuation procedures
- where to get health and safety information
- accident and hazard reporting procedures
- the organisation's health and safety policy
- first aid facilities
- employer/employee communication and representation, including safety representatives and safety committees
- information on who is the enforcing authority.

Records

You should keep records of the training given to employees. There should be enough information to identify the employee; the nature of the training completed, including refresher training; and a copy or details of any certificates obtained.

Legal requirements

Under the Health and Safety at Work etc. Act 1974 employers must provide information, instruction, training and supervision that ensures, so far as is reasonably practicable, the health and safety of employees at work.

The Management of Health and Safety at Work Regulations 1999 require every employer to provide employees with adequate and suitable health and safety training. The training should be after recruitment and when employees are exposed to new or increased risks because of new responsibilities, the introduction of new work equipment or new technology or the introduction of a new system of work.

The training must be repeated periodically and take place during working hours.

Several other pieces of legislation include specific requirements to train employees. For example, under The Control of Substances Hazardous to Health Regulations 2002 employers whose work exposes an employee to a substance hazardous to health must provide that employee with suitable and sufficient information, instruction and training. The same principle applies to legislation including The Provision and Use of Work Equipment Regulations 1998, The Ionising Radiations Regulations 1999 and The Control of Vibration at Work Regulations 2005.

6. How can we control specific risks?

The workplace

Work activities and equipment

Individual protection

Major hazards
Slips and trips

Slips normally occur when there is poor contact between footwear and the floor surface. Trips occur when feet are obstructed, so that the person loses balance. Every workplace needs to draw up a plan to prevent slips and trips. This chapter provides guidance on what to do.

Key words and phrases

ergonomic design – the application of scientific data about human mental and physical capacities and performance to the design of work systems.

reportable accidents (or diseases) – an accident (or disease) specified in RIDDOR that must be reported to the enforcing authorities, such as accidents resulting in death, major injury, 'over three-day injury' or dangerous occurrences, or certain diseases.

RIDDOR – The Reporting of Injuries, Diseases and Dangerous Occurrences Regulations 1995.

Hazards

Slipping or tripping over causes most of the major injuries at work.

Slips and trips are one of the main causes of injury at work and are the main cause of major injuries. They account for more than one third of reportable accidents every year. Most of the major injuries occur in the manufacturing and service industries. More than half of the accidents involving members of the public in workplaces are due to slips and trips.

The main slip hazards are liquid spills and wet floors, dropped solid materials, refuse on the floor, dusty floors (for example, in woodworking factories or workshops), loose rugs or mats, unsuitable floor surfaces, sloping floor surfaces and wearing unsuitable footwear.

Accidents can shatter lives

HSE

The main trip hazards are floors with holes or uneven surfaces, trailing cables, loose floor tiles and floorboards, holed and worn carpets or rugs, changes in floor level including steps and stairs, obstructions to the walkway, and floor fixings such as doorstops and electrical sockets near to floor level. Overcrowded workplaces can also create several tripping hazards, because the space for movement is restricted and overcrowded workplaces tend to be untidy.

Risks

The risk of slipping or tripping increases in a number of situations. Examples are given below.

- Areas with work equipment (such as a dishwasher, deep fat fryer or grill) that can leak or splash water, fat or another material so that the floor becomes slippery.

- Any floor where spilt liquids are not cleaned up immediately.

- Where there is no regular scheme of cleaning, so that rubbish or accumulated dust and dirt can cause someone to trip or slip.

- A haphazardly organised workplace with obstructions in work areas and along pedestrian routes, or routes with blind corners, twists and turns or narrow passageways.

- A badly supervised workforce, with some people rushing around and others unable to concentrate.

- Any workplace where staff are badly stressed.

- Poor lighting, so that people may not see a hazard.

Arm plunged into hot oil

A 16-year-old chip cook badly burnt her arm in boiling oil in a deep fat fryer when she tried to stop her fall after slipping on water from a leaking ice machine.

- Workers under the influence of drugs or alcohol. (There is a considerably increased risk that workers under the influence of drugs or alcohol will have an accident – see also pages 266 to 270.)
- Where the nature of the work influences risk – for example, hotel kitchens and fast food outlets with a lot of grease; anywhere that portable electrical equipment is used, especially if there are trailing electric cables; supermarkets where the throughput of goods makes it possible that some goods will fall to the floor.

Controls

A hierarchy of control comes into play here – see pages 39 to 40. In the first instance, try to eliminate slipping hazards from spills by putting lids on vessels, using tables with a lipped edge, and by preventing leaks. If floors do become wet or greasy, clean up frequently and consider installing floor drainage channels.

Risk assessment

It is essential to carry out a risk assessment of slips and trips in the workplace. The assessment could be carried out by managers or supervisors together with employees and safety representatives.

The assessment should enable you to identify the slip and trip hazards and the people who might be harmed – workers, visitors or members of the public. There may already be some controls in place, but a risk assessment will identify whether they are adequate. This will help you to identify and put in place any additional controls that would reduce the risk of injury. Findings should be recorded and the assessment reviewed occasionally – and certainly after any significant change in the workplace or its procedures.

Raised plinths in a retail shop

A member of the public fractured his arm in an electrical store when he tripped over an unmarked plinth. It was difficult to see because it was covered in a similar carpet to the rest of the floor. The retailer was prosecuted and fined when another member of the public tripped because the plinths were still not marked clearly.

Good housekeeping

Managers and supervisors should ensure that all work areas are kept tidy and that all pedestrian and traffic routes and stairs are unobstructed.

It is very important to stop floor contamination in the first place. Maintenance programmes should be introduced for floors, steps and stairs. Managers should set up a system of periodic inspections to identify hazards and why they are there. Suitable equipment needs to be provided to ensure that the cleaning schedules are achievable and that the cleaning methods leave floors as dry as possible. The cables to electrical equipment should be secure and should not create a tripping hazard.

Floors

Floor coverings need to be chosen carefully. The risk assessment will help to determine the type and quality of floor covering that is suitable. Special care needs to be taken if the floor gets wet or dusty as a result of the work activity – for example, behind the bar of a pub, in a restaurant kitchen or in a joinery workshop. It is important to provide flooring with sufficient surface grip.

When deciding on the type of floor covering in the workplace managers should consider a number of issues:

- where it is to be used – indoors or outdoors
- how it is to be cleaned
- how often it is to be cleaned
- how many people will walk over the floor
- whether it is used for pedestrians only, or for vehicles too
- whether there are any other legal requirements for the standard of cleanliness – for example, if the workplace is a food business then one of the requirements is that the floor must be capable of being cleaned
- how it can be maintained and repaired.

It is also important to ensure that employees' footwear, where it is provided, is compatible with the floor surface.

Do not choose a floor covering that is very smooth, just because it is easy to clean. Instead, opt for one with sufficient slip-resistance for your workers' safety, even if it needs a little more effort to clean. You can measure the slip-resistance of a floor covering with a device that registers the friction between the floor covering and a test pad. It is advisable to obtain specialist help to make the measurement and interpret the results.

Existing floors can be treated to improve the slip-resistance of the floor covering. For example, terrazzo floors can be roughened and coated with a non-slip material, concrete floors can be coated with resin containing abrasive particles, or flooring strips or squares can be stuck to the floor. Some treatments have to be repeated regularly due to excessive wear to the flooring, and, in particular, if the floor accumulates dirt which inhibits the slip-resistance of the treatment.

Tripping up on giving information

A new non-slip floor was laid in a catering kitchen, but after a few months it became very slippery and stained. After consulting the floor manufacturer, the employer discovered that the cleaners were not cleaning the floor in the recommended manner – simply because the kitchen manager had not passed on the correct information. The simple remedy was to give the cleaners the information they needed. They changed the cleaning method to the recommended one and the floor ceased to be slippery.

Stairs

Staircases must be constructed in accordance with current building regulations. This ensures that treads and risers are of the correct and consistent size and height, and that handrails are provided. The slip-resistance of stairs can be improved by applying non-slip nosings (strips on the edge of the tread) or by providing roughened-tread surfaces.

Cleaning and repairs

Cleaning procedures should be designed so that floors are cleaned regularly and properly and are left as dry as possible afterwards. While cleaning is in progress, barriers and warnings should be put in place to keep people from walking over the wet area. If possible, cleaning should be done out of normal working hours, or at quiet times.

Repairs to damaged, worn or defective floors and floor coverings should be done as soon as possible after they have been reported as defective. Similar precautions to those used for cleaning should be used when repair work is being carried out.

Slipping on workshop dust

A Health and Safety Executive inspector slipped on a workshop floor during a routine health and safety visit. Workers said they also found the walkways and working area very slippery and commented that visitors (such as staff from the offices) were often taken unawares by the slippery floor.

The painted concrete floors were contaminated with a fine dust, from graphite components, that could not be adequately filtered through the extraction system and was sometimes spilt when the filter bags were emptied.

The company improved the floor surface, so that it coped better with the conditions, and introduced local exhaust ventilation into a centralised ventilation system that had its filtration plant outside the workshop.

Lighting

The quality of lighting is very important in preventing slips and trips. Make sure that all parts of the workplace are properly lit. There should be no areas where dazzling lights or glare can obstruct someone's vision. Lighting should be included in the cleaning and maintenance schedules and programmes. Arrange stacked goods so they do not obstruct light and create shadows.

Footwear

Employers have a responsibility to provide proper personal protective equipment for the health and safety of workers. Protecting against slips and trips can come under this responsibility.

When choosing the design or range of footwear, managers and supervisors should consider the floor surface and the hazards involved in the work activities. The area of the sole in contact with the surface should be as big as possible and the tread should be well defined to give a firm grip in wet conditions. You should look at a range of footwear and test the shoes or boots for a sensible period in your own workplace. Choose the make and model that is most suitable overall for the circumstances. Avoid PVC and leather for anti-slip footwear, as micro-cellular urethane and rubber give better slip-resistance.

Footwear must fit properly and be replaced whenever necessary.

Planning work procedures

The planning and organisation of work activities can prevent slips and trips. Tasks should be designed so that workers are not exposed to unnecessary risk – for example, the moving of goods could be mechanised to avoid the need for workers to push, pull or carry goods on slippery floors. Ergonomic design of work areas can prevent workers creating obstructions, having to work around obstructions or having to walk across slippery floors.

Information and training

Managers and supervisors must ensure that employees are given adequate information and training. This should include the risk of injury, and the nature and extent of slips and trips in the particular workplace. It should also include the control measures necessary, particularly those that enable employees to prevent slips and trips, particularly information on methods for cleaning up spillages immediately.

Training, information and motivation improve safety

A major oil company halved its incidence of injury from slips, trips, manual handling and falls from a height by:

- training supervisors and managers in safety leadership

- creating awards and recognition programmes that reward excellent safety performance and reinforced good health and safety practices

- training supervisors in intervention techniques, including the observation of safe and unsafe behaviour, to help them to introduce changes in undesirable practices

- introducing and enforcing discipline procedures for breaches of safety.

Checklist for safety representatives

Check whether there is a significant risk from:

- work in progress – for example, goods receipt and dispatch, maintenance and cleaning

- leaking plant or machinery with fluids pooling on floors

- a build-up of floor contamination brought in on footwear in wet weather

- the use of temporary measures to control leaks, such as corrugated cardboard being put down or warning signs left in place for extended periods

- the age and construction of buildings, for example, leaking roofs, walkways exposed to the elements and the possibility of water or mud being brought into the workplace on wet clothing, shoes or vehicles

- cluttered walkways, build-up of waste materials, general untidiness, restricted pedestrian access, trailing cables.

It is worth talking to staff to identify 'difficult jobs' or to hear about incidences of falls not leading to injury ('near misses') and to examine records for evidence of slip and trip problems – sickness absence records, accident records, RIDDOR reports, for example.

Legal requirements

The Health and Safety at Work etc. Act 1974 (HSWA) requires employers to ensure the health and safety of all employees and anyone who may be affected by their work. This includes taking steps to control slip and trip risks. Employees must not endanger themselves or others and must use any safety equipment provided. Manufacturers and suppliers have a duty to ensure that their products are safe. They must also provide adequate information about appropriate use.

The Management of Health and Safety at Work Regulations 1999 build on HSWA and include duties for employers to assess risks (including slip and trip risks) and where necessary to take action to safeguard health and safety.

The Workplace (Health, Safety and Welfare) Regulations 1992 require floors to be suitable, in good condition and free from obstructions. People must be able to move around safely.

Under The Reporting of Injuries, Diseases and Dangerous Occurrences Regulations 1995 many accidents at work have to be reported to the Health and Safety Executive.

Work at height

About 35 people are killed each year as a consequence of work at height – the single biggest cause of death at work. About 4,700 people suffer major injuries.

Key words and phrases

access equipment – ladders, steps, trestles, cradles, mobile elevated work platforms and any other type of work equipment that enables an employee to reach to, or stand at, a height above their own height.

competent person – someone with the appropriate qualifications, knowledge and experience to identify the risks arising from a situation and the measures needed to control them.

fall-arrest system – a personal fall-protection system to arrest and restrict a fall by preventing the user from hitting the ground. An energy-absorbing device limits the forces on the body.

inspection of equipment – visual checks by a competent person on items of equipment to verify that they can be operated, adjusted and maintained safely.

platform – a horizontal surface raised above the level of the adjacent area, for a worker to stand on and work from.

safety harness – personal protective equipment that is attached to a reliable anchor point.

safety lines – ropes that stop the user hitting the ground in the event of a fall.

safety nets – nets used to catch people or objects that fall from a height.

safe system of work – a set of procedures for carrying out a task safely.

work equipment – equipment used at work including machines, appliances, apparatus, tools, installations, ladders, hoists and lift equipment.

work-positioning system – a personal fall-protection system to support the user in tension or suspension so that a fall is prevented or restricted.

What does work at height mean?

Work at height is any work where someone could be injured by falling.

According to legislation a place is 'at height' if a person could be injured falling from it, even if it is at, or below, ground level. 'Work' includes moving around at a place of work (except by a staircase in a permanent workplace).

Work at height usually involves the use of **access equipment** such as ladders, steps, trestles, cradles, tower scaffolds, scaffolding and certain types of lifting equipment. Access equipment is classed as **work equipment**, so the principles and standards applicable to work equipment (see pages 328 to 341) are equally relevant to access equipment.

A shop worker standing on a stepladder is involved in work at height, but a police officer riding a horse on patrol is not working at height as defined by the legislation.

Hazards

The hazards include:

- falling from a high place – for example, construction workers falling from scaffolding, warehouse workers falling from mobile platforms and cleaners falling from stepladders

- objects falling from a height and striking people – for example, bricks falling from a scaffold, tools falling from a platform or cartons falling from a storage rack

- being dislodged from, or crushed by, a structure that collapses – such as scaffolding that has not been erected properly

- contact with high-level lighting and other electrical equipment and installations when working at a height.

Risks when working at height

A number of factors need to be taken into account when assessing the risk of a work activity at a height, including the:

- time needed for the work to be completed

- complexity of the task

- weather conditions

- the place where the work is to be done, including the surface on which the access equipment is supported

- amount of working space

- provision of protective barriers, safety harnesses or safety nets
- provision of protection against falling objects
- manner in which access equipment is erected or installed
- competence of the worker including physical capabilities, training and experience.

The time involved to complete a task may increase the risk, because the longer a task takes, the greater the likelihood that an accident will happen. Complex work can be particularly risky, such as working on a scaffold with several ladders to climb to gain access to the area of work.

Bad weather can seriously affect work outdoors, particularly if it is cold, wet and very windy at the same time. The weather can also affect ground conditions – making it boggy, for example – increasing the chance that access equipment will become unstable.

Unsuitable equipment for the job – such as a chair used as a stepladder – increases the risk of a fall that causes injury.

Risk increases in any conditions where the access equipment is unsuitable, unstable, erected incorrectly or maintained in poor condition.

If working space is limited, or if a roof or other high-level structure is fragile or covered with moss or lichen, then there is a greater risk of knocking something to the ground, slipping over or falling through a weak supporting surface.

Risk increases if employees are unprotected by barriers, guard rails or a fall-protection system, such as a safety harness or a safety net.

The physical capabilities of the employee are also important: an employee's strength, suppleness, balance and confidence at heights, for example, all have a bearing on the risk that an accident will occur.

If there is no protection or inadequate protection against falling objects, there is a strong possibility that someone will be injured. Roof tiles from building work, display boards in shops, light fittings in a workroom and electrician's tools from high-level repairs are typical examples of objects that could fall and injure someone.

Controls

A risk assessment of the whole workplace must be carried out to identify the activities that involve a risk of falling from a height. This must be done *before* the work starts at any temporary workplace, such as construction and arboriculture sites. Where more than one employer is operating at a site, the person carrying out the assessment should prepare a short report about it for the site supervisor. (See also page 93.)

Once the risks and activities are known, you need to decide whether there needs to be permanent or temporary access to specific areas of the workplace.

Planning

Whatever work is to be done at a height, it must be properly planned, supervised and organised before the job starts. A simple hierarchy of control should be used:

1. avoid work at height where possible

2. use work equipment or other measures to prevent falls where work at height cannot be avoided

3. provide personal protection to minimise the distance and consequences of a fall, if other measures are not suitable.

1.   2.   3.

Avoiding work at height

The first question to be asked is: does anyone really need to work at a height? Consider ways to eliminate the hazard. For example, could goods be stacked and retrieved from storage racking from the ground by using fork-lift trucks, rather than by staff using ladders?

There are, however, many instances when work at height must be carried out. The risks must be assessed and appropriate work equipment selected and used.

Choice of equipment

When selecting work equipment for use in work at height, you should consider giving *collective* protection measures priority over *personal* protection measures and should take account of:

■ the working conditions

■ the risks to the safety of people at the place where the work equipment is to be used

■ the vertical distance for moving equipment into place and the space around the base of the equipment

■ the distance and consequences of a potential fall

■ the duration and frequency of use

■ the need for easy and timely evacuation and rescue in an emergency.

When planning a job involving work at height, consider the use of the following protective measures:

■ platforms

■ guards and barriers

■ safety lines or ropes

■ safety harnesses.

A **platform** in this context is a secure piece of equipment from which people can work safely, such as a scaffold, tower scaffold, mobile elevating work platform (MEWP), mobile platform steps or ladders with a platform. In selecting what is suitable, consider:

- the space available for the task

- the type of work to be carried out

- the time the job will take

- the risks when setting up the platform

- how difficult the platform will be to maintain

- how many people will use it.

A work platform must be capable of supporting the weight of the worker and any materials and tools being used. The platform must be stable and designed not to overturn or fall and there should be adequate working space on and around it. If the platform has a work area – for example, on a tower scaffold – it must have guard rails or barriers that are high enough and positioned in a way that prevents someone falling over or through the rail or barrier.

Protection against falls

When guard rails or barriers cannot be provided, a **safe system of work** needs to be designed and operated. This could be a **fall-arrest system** or **work-positioning system** and could involve **safety nets** or **safety lines** with **safety harnesses** and using secure anchor points. Although these measures will not *prevent* a fall, they minimise the risk of injury. Like the issuing of personal protective equipment (see pages 39 to 40), these measures should be the choice of last resort after every effort has been made to adopt other control methods.

Checks on equipment

Equipment used for work at height must be inspected regularly and maintained thoroughly. In addition to daily checks before use, a more rigorous or detailed **inspection** must legally be carried out by a competent person at appropriate intervals – see 'Mechanical lifting equipment and operations' on pages 342 to 350.

Workers must be given training in how to:

- assemble the system correctly according to the manufacturer's instructions

- wear the harness

- check equipment and recognise significant defects

- fall or land to minimise injury

- rescue themselves from a position at height and to assist others after a fall.

(Similar requirements apply to mechanical lifting operations.)

Scaffolding

Scaffolding should be erected on firm, level ground that is capable of supporting the weight of the scaffold, the people working on it and any materials or work equipment being used. It should:

- be secured to a permanent structure, if possible

- be wide enough for easy access

- have sufficient workspace and be provided with safe access.

Only competent people should design, erect, alter, dismantle and inspect scaffolding. The structure should be inspected and the inspection recorded:

- before first use

- at frequent intervals (not exceeding seven days)

- after severe weather

- after any significant alteration to the structure

- after any accident involving something substantial, such as a vehicle hitting the structure.

Tower scaffolding

Properly erected and maintained scaffolding helps to protect workers from falls, but it must be designed, put up, inspected and dismantled by competent people.

This type of work equipment can be erected easily and quickly, and can provide safe access. The rules for general access scaffolding outlined in the two previous paragraphs also apply to tower types, but there are other specific precautions to be taken.

You need to follow the manufacturer's instructions for setting up the equipment. It needs to be vertical, with the wheels locked. Safe access to the work platform needs to be provided – for example, via ladders on the inside of the tower. You may need to tie the tower to a rigid structure if the tower is sheeted or if any other significant loads are expected to be used. If workers have to move the tower, make sure that there are no overhead cables or holes in the ground and that there are no people or materials on the platform.

Mobile elevating work platforms (MEWPs)

Only fully trained competent people must operate this equipment. It should be used only on firm, level ground, with the outriggers extended and secured before the platform is raised. Safety harnesses provide extra protection against falls.

Ladders and stepladders

Ladders are one of the most common means of gaining access to high levels and are one of the most misused and abused pieces of work equipment.

If you want to keep full control of ladders, it is good practice to keep a ladder register. Each ladder should be marked with a unique identification mark. The mark should be recorded in a register which also has space for the details of inspections, defects and repairs. You could also record every time a person takes the ladder for use and returns it. If the ladder is destroyed, this should also be recorded. You should inspect ladders every three months. Every year you should thoroughly examine them by testing their strength, looking carefully at their physical condition and noting any defects.

Ladder use

Ladders should be positioned safely and tied in securely before they are used.

A system should be put in place so that the condition of ladders is checked before use. Ensure that, before using ladders, employees check for:

■ splits or wear

■ rot (wood)

■ corrosion and rusting (metal)

■ any other damage.

Ladders should be placed face-on to the work on a firm, level surface. The top and bottom of the ladder should be secured. Stepladders should be spread to their fullest extent.

Blocks or boards must not be put beneath the ladders or stepladders to extend the height: instead, a longer set of ladders or steps should be used. The top platform of stepladders should be used only if there is a handrail or a hold at least one metre above the platform.

The ladders should be placed in such a position to prevent workers from overreaching. There should be a handhold available to maintain three points of contact where possible, When climbing a stepladder, both hands should be used and the user should face the steps. Nobody should be allowed below the ladder or stepladder when work is going on. Tools should not clutter, or be left on, the ladder's platform.

The list opposite will help you to check the condition of a set of ladders. If the answer to any of the questions is no, then you need to take action – by marking the ladders, repairing or destroying them. The checklist could be kept as a record to show that the ladders have been inspected.

Fragile surfaces

Where the surface on which the access equipment is supported is fragile, there must be sufficient means of support or protection. Where there is still a risk that someone will fall, despite the measures taken, you must minimise the distances and consequences of the fall. This requirement also applies to the police, fire, ambulance or other emergency services when they are acting in an emergency.

The person doing the work must be made aware of the danger either through notices affixed on or near the fragile surface or by informing them personally.

Temporary access equipment

A competent person should inspect and maintain all temporary access equipment regularly. Any defective equipment should be clearly identified and not used. The people using temporary access equipment need to be trained adequately and be capable of using the equipment safely.

Condition check	Yes/No	Comments
Steps or rungs in place or secure		
Free from cracked, split, worn or broken parts		
Identification mark provided and clear		
Free from rusted or corroded metal parts		
Free from worn, frayed or damaged cord on stepladders		
Stable		
Free from bent hinges or spreaders		
Hinges secure		
Long enough to do the job safely		

Date   Inspected by

Falling objects and materials

No material or object should be stored at, thrown or tipped from height in circumstances where it could injure anyone. You can minimise the likelihood that materials will fall from heights by keeping platforms free from anything loose. Scaffolds can be provided with debris netting that will stop and hold any material, such as bricks, that could fall. Double sheeting or plywood sheets on the platforms prevent materials falling through the boards.

Waste materials must not be thrown from the scaffold: instead waste should be lowered in skips or buckets, or sent down enclosed debris chutes. Toe boards can stop materials being kicked from, or rolling off, platforms. Hoarding and protected walkways can protect workers, visitors and members of the public.

Where, despite all your reasonable preventive measures, there is a high risk that objects will fall – for example, during the demolition of a dangerous building in high winds – the vulnerable ground area must be clearly designated and marked. You could also create an exclusion zone where entry is strictly prohibited to site staff whenever work is taking place above.

Where you cannot prevent people working below an area where there is a high risk from falling objects, you must ensure that they all wear safety helmets.

Collapsing structures

Scaffolds must be erected, altered and dismantled following the guidance of the Health and Safety Executive given in *Health and Safety in Construction HSG 150*, or of any reputable industry body, such as the National Access and Scaffolding Confederation. Site workers or supervisors should inspect the scaffold every week and always after it has been altered or damaged or there have been strong winds.

If, after all reasonable precautions have been taken, the risk of a fall cannot be eliminated, you must do all that you reasonably can to minimise the distance and the effect of the fall.

Safe working practices indoors

Many accidents occur inside buildings where employees and members of the public are injured because of work taking place above ground level.

Many of the controls that apply to ladders and stepladders apply equally to work activities inside buildings – for example:

- retrieving items from storage and display racking in retail shops or warehouses

- cleaning, changing or repairing ceiling lights and their fittings in offices

- cleaning walls above head height in a food factory or catering business

- hanging up shop display signs or decorations

- cleaning windows.

Free-standing mobile platform ladders are the safest option in most of these situations. The ladders should be provided with guard rails around the platform that are sufficiently high to prevent someone from falling over or between the top rail and the platform. Single-section ladders should, ideally, be provided with hooks to secure the top of the ladder to racking.

Storage racking

Racking is a skeleton framework of fixed or adjustable beams designed to support loads without shelves. Safe racking should have the following characteristics – it should:

- be installed in accordance with the manufacturer's instructions

- be erected on sound, level floors

- be fixed securely to the floor

- have aisles wide enough for mechanical handling equipment to be manoeuvred easily

- have beam-connector locks in position at both ends of the beam (this prevents horizontal beams being knocked out of position by mechanical handling equipment such as fork-lift trucks)

- use column guards, boots or end protectors to protect the base of exposed beams from damage by mechanical handling equipment such as fork-lift trucks

- display maximum load notices on the racking: the weight indicated should never be exceeded

- incorporate coloured horizontal beams for high visibility

- have no physical damage

- use the correct type of pallet – this can be verified using calculations recommended by SEMA (Storage Equipment Manufacturers Association)

- have pallets in good condition.

Racking should be inspected regularly by a competent person to determine any damage that might affect its stability.

Free-standing mobile platform steps should be used in preference to ladders to retrieve goods by hand. Where ladders are used, they should be provided with hooks or some other method of fixing the top end to the racking. No one should be allowed to climb on the racking itself to retrieve goods.

See also information about storage systems for manual handling on page 203.

Key messages

- Carry out risk assessments before work starts.

- Make sure that all work at height is planned, organised and carried out by competent people.

- Follow the hierarchy of control for managing risks from work at height – take steps to avoid, prevent or reduce risks.

- Choose the right work equipment and select collective measures to prevent falls (such as guardrails and working platforms) before other measures which may only reduce the distance and consequences of a fall (such as nets or airbags) or which may only provide personal protection from a fall.

Legal requirements

The Work at Height Regulations 2005 (as amended) cover work at any height at which someone could be injured, unless appropriate preventive and protective controls are in place. Those covered by the health and safety requirements include instructors or leaders in recreational climbing and caving.

The regulations relate to the organising and planning of work at height; competent persons at work, or supervision by competent persons; the steps to be taken to avoid risk from work at height; the selection of work equipment; particular work equipment; the avoidance of risks from fragile surfaces, falling objects and danger areas; the inspection of certain work equipment and workplaces; and the duties of people working at height.

In many occupations the requirements of The Lifting Operations and Lifting Equipment Regulations 1998 are closely linked.

Musculoskeletal disorders

Musculoskeletal disorders affect about a million employees a year. They include what are popularly known as repetitive strain injuries or work-related upper limb disorders (WRULDs) and particularly affect the lower back and the joints in the lower and upper limbs.

Key words and phrases

display screen equipment – any alphanumeric (letters and numbers) or graphic display screen, usually as part of a computer system.

ergonomic design – the application of scientific data about human mental and physical capacities and performance to the design of work systems.

ergonomics – the study of the interaction between people and their work.

musculoskeletal disorders – conditions affecting the muscles, nerves, tendons, ligaments, joints, cartilage or spinal discs.

repetitive strain injury – a popular term for a work-related disorder mainly affecting the upper limbs.

work-related upper limb disorders (WRULDs) – conditions that result from prolonged and frequent activity that damages the muscle, tendon or joint involved so that it becomes painful and has a reduced function.

workstation – an assembly comprising a work surface, such as a desk, all the necessary equipment needed to carry out the assigned tasks, and the immediate surrounding area affected by the work activity at the workstation.

What causes musculoskeletal disorders?

Many ordinary work activities can lead to a musculoskeletal disorder – for example:

- entering information into a computer using a computer keyboard
- writing by hand
- working as a checkout assistant in a supermarket and handling goods through the automatic pricing machine
- laboratory work involving the repeated use of pipettes or the repeated staining of agar plates
- packing goods in a warehouse, including frequently folding cardboard boxes
- pot washing, dishwashing, preparing food, storage and cleaning in a kitchen
- constructing products on an assembly line
- pruning fruit trees or shrubs using secateurs
- plastering a wall
- butchering meat
- any job where a movement is repeated for a long time.

The health impact of musculoskeletal disorders

The symptoms can include:

- general aches and discomfort
- cramp-like pain
- pins and needles
- stiffness and restriction of joint movement
- loss of grip
- a burning sensation
- swelling of the joints or soft tissue.

The areas of the body most affected include:

- the tendons that connect muscles to bones
- the muscles themselves
- the nerves supplying the affected area, joints and ligaments.

If certain work activities are repeated for a long time, the repeated strain may result in a chronic or recurring injury. In turn, this may lead to permanent disability.

Examples of musculoskeletal disorders include:

- carpal tunnel syndrome – a condition that causes pressure on the nerves passing through the wrist
- epicondylitis – inflammation of the area where the bone and tendon join, which is often known as tennis elbow or golfer's elbow, depending on where the problem occurs
- lower back pain
- tendonitis – inflammation of the area where muscles and tendons join
- tenosynovitis – inflammation of the tendon or the tendon sheath.

Hazards

The hazards arise because of repeated actions such as:

- gripping
- squeezing
- twisting
- pushing
- pulling
- reaching.

It is important to remember that the actions themselves are usually not hazardous. It is the prolonged repetition of a movement, without sufficient rest, that is the hazard.

Risk

The severity of the risk from the prolonged repetition of a movement is increased by factors such as the:

- force applied
- regularity and length of time the action takes place, including the time allocated for rest and recovery
- posture of the worker while doing the job
- type of movement
- tool used in the work activity
- workplace design
- skill of the worker.

Force

Where an employee has to exert pressure on something while standing or sitting still – for example, fixing a component into an electrical appliance using a screwdriver – the manual force required may put an excessive demand on the fingers, hands or shoulders, so increasing the risk of injury.

Regularity and length of time

There is a high risk of injury in tasks where short bursts of repetitive movements are necessary – for example, a supermarket checkout operator or a data processing clerk may carry out thousands of movements in any working day.

The risk is reduced if employees are given sufficient time between the repeated actions for their muscles to recover their normal state of tension. This may mean that the rate of work needs to be appropriate to a particular employee, so that each person can carry out his or her assigned tasks in comfort and without the likelihood of injury.

It follows that, if you have a number of people on a production line, you will have to take care to select people with similar capabilities or to train them to work at a similar pace. So, it is important that the ergonomic arrangement of the job reduces the risk of injury to the lowest possible.

Posture

Some jobs cause staff to work in some very awkward postures – for example, working with their arms above their head, with arms outstretched, or bending down. Awkward posture might also occur in less obvious ways. For example, computer users might experience discomfort and injury because of an inappropriate chair, the inability to move the computer screen to an appropriate height or the use of a laptop across their knees.

Type of movement

The repeated twisting movement of the fingers, hands and wrists, when repeatedly turning or rotating dials, for instance, can lead to injuries, Similarly, employees may develop problems if they must repeatedly grip equipment or materials firmly – for example, a packer may need to manipulate cardboard or stiff paper around products to wrap them securely.

Tools used

Some tools can create severe strain on the upper limbs – for example, on the fingers and wrists when using scissors or cutters for a prolonged period. If the equipment also creates vibration, the employee may need to use greater force to keep control of it. Both the vibration and the intense gripping may lead to injury.

Workplace design

The design of workstations, workplaces, work procedures and work equipment is often for the 'average person', with no account taken of the individual user's size, shape or strength.

Injury is less likely where the height and position of chairs, work benches, tables and computer screens can be modified for the comfort of the individual staff member .

Skill of the worker

Untrained or poorly trained staff may not understand how to carry out their jobs in a safe and responsible manner, so increasing their risk of injury. Poor supervision may also increase the risk of injury – for example, where a worker develops his or her own method of doing the job and carries on unchecked, or where someone has been shown how to do a task by a colleague who is not competent to demonstrate the task correctly.

Controls

The control principles for musculoskeletal disorders are:

- carry out a risk assessment
- apply ergonomic principles to the job
- reduce the force used
- reduce the regularity and duration of the action
- improve posture
- provide effective training
- introduce job rotation
- organise regular breaks.

Risk assessment

You must carry out a risk assessment of all work activities to:

- identify the hazards present
- assess the level of risk for each hazard identified
- ascertain who may be affected
- apply the controls that are described below.

Organisations that fail to carry out risk assessments may be liable to pay compensation to injured employees. (For a more detailed description of risk assessments see pages 110 to 120.) For instance, a motor tester was required to test 130 heavy motors an hour, a task involving much twisting, turning, gripping and lifting at speed. She was diagnosed as having carpal tunnel syndrome, tenosynovitis and osteo-arthritis. The employer was held liable because it was known that the work carried a foreseeable risk of injury: it failed to give advice on the risks and consequences of repetitive strain injury and had no system of job rotation.

Ergonomic approach

Ergonomics is the study of the interaction between people and their work. **Ergonomic design** is normally defined as the application of scientific data about human mental and physical capacities and performance to the design of work systems. In the main, it involves designing tools, equipment, workstations and workplaces so that the job fits the person, rather than trying to make the person fit the job.

An ergonomic approach takes into account the size and shape of the human body. It is used to identify and control hazards.

Applying an ergonomic approach

You should take account of operating positions, working heights and reaching distances. Operators should not exert undue force, or stretch or reach beyond their normal range of movement in order to carry out tasks.

A small alteration is all that may be needed to make a task easier and safer – for example, providing an adjustable chair for a computer workstation or adjusting the height of a workshop machine so that the operator does not have to lean down to use it.

Generally speaking, the risk of musculoskeletal disorders can be reduced by using engineering controls, redesigning the task, training the workers or changing the job design so that a shorter time is spent on the task – for instance, by using job rotation.

If it is possible, organise tasks so they can be done sitting down. Workbenches and desks should have plenty of legroom. If employees have to work standing up, the workbench should be at a height that prevents them having to stoop or to stand on tiptoe. All equipment should be within easy reach.

Seating should be adjustable. Swivel chairs should be provided where the job involves twisting of the upper body – for instance, at a supermarket checkout. Seats should provide support for the lower back and footrests should be provided to staff who need them. Seating and workbench heights should allow employees to work with their hands at about elbow level or lower so there is no undue strain on the wrist, elbow and shoulders.

A number of different solutions to reducing risk to an acceptable level can be used. The following ergonomic principles need to be considered.

Reducing the force used

You should try to reduce the force needed to do the job by, for example, making sure that tools are maintained in good condition. If necessary, and where it is feasible, consider having the tool redesigned so that it can be operated more easily. Also consider redesigning the activity so that the stronger muscle groups are used or so that the task can be done with the tool held in either hand.

Reduction in the regularity and duration (repetitive movements)

Someone – it could be you – needs to analyse the job carefully to identify whether it could be done without the need for frequent movements. Consider the body movements, the individual's characteristics, the environmental conditions and the workstation design. Organise tasks so that individuals are not doing the same activity for long periods. Consider automating appropriate tasks to reduce the number of repeated movements.

Managers and supervisors should also consider whether it is appropriate to reduce the expected pace of the work activity, or even, where appropriate, to allow the employee to vary the pace. Small changes can lead to a significant reduction of risk.

Posture changes

If you redesign the work activity by, for example, introducing a tool or altering the tool being used, you can eliminate the action causing the problem. The tool can replace the awkward or repeated movement or, if the tool is altered to change the grip, the change in posture may avoid the repeated use of the muscles which are being affected. However, care must be taken to avoid replacing one bad posture with another.

Effective training

Employees need to be instructed in how to do their jobs correctly. The training should include the hazards and risks in the particular work activity and the controls that can be applied to eliminate the hazards or reduce the risk from them.

Job rotation

It is helpful to allow employees to rotate their jobs. You may have to train employees in more than one job, but this can have other advantages. For example, the workforce may be more flexible and there may be better job satisfaction in doing a wider variety of jobs. This rotation has the advantage of reducing the repetitive nature of a work activity and the length of time on a particular task.

Regular breaks

If you introduce regular short breaks, employees have an opportunity to recover from the exertion of the work activity. Tele-workers – people who work from home or on the move using information technology to keep in touch with their employer – are an emerging group that could be affected by musculoskeletal disorders. There are now about 2 million tele-workers in the UK and numbers are increasing. They may need to be reminded of their responsibility to ensure that they take enough breaks.

Height of beer barrel conveyor reduces back and shoulder pain

Workers at a beer factory had to use a chisel to remove the bung and the top from each empty beer barrel before it was washed for re-use. They experienced back and shoulder problems because of the forceful action required and because the work was at an awkward height, with the bungs on the sides of the barrels.

The brewery decided to take action to reduce the injury rate and lost time and to speed up production. Meetings brought together engineers, operators and an ergonomist to decide on a solution.

The conveyor was adapted so that the caps and bungs arrived directly in front of the workers at a more suitable height for both tall and short staff. The manual force required for bung removal was also reduced by providing better tools.

The cost of the changes were paid back in under three months because sickness absence was reduced. In the year after the changes there was no time lost due to musculoskeletal disorders or injuries. What's more, there was less need for overtime work and a reduction in conveyor belt breakdowns, because fewer wooden fragments from the bungs fell into the conveyor.

Display screen equipment

Display screen equipment includes desktop and laptop computers. Their use can lead to musculoskeletal disorders if proper assessment and adjustments are not made.

Most people use a computer at some stage in their working life and it is estimated that there are over 5 million *habitual* users of display screen equipment. They include word processing workers, secretaries and administrators, bookkeepers, data input operators, news subeditors, journalists, telesales/customer complaints/accounts enquiry/directory enquiry operators, micro-electronics assembly or testing operators or television editing technicians. About 400,000 people a year suffer from an upper limb disorder caused or made worse by work.

There are specific legal requirements for the use of **display screen equipment** – any alphanumeric or graphic display screen, regardless of the display process involved. In everyday terms, this usually means a computer made up of a screen, central processing unit (CPU) with a hard drive (with networks there may be no CPU), keyboard, printer and associated additional equipment.

Computer workstations often include a desk (workbench or other work surface) and chair; display screen equipment; any optional accessories such as a disk drive, modem, printer and document holder; and a telephone.

Hazards

Hazards usually involve repetitive work over long periods – for example, repeated finger movements with wrists in an upward position. If users sit upright in a rigid posture for a long time, they can eventually experience pain and discomfort in their hands, wrists, arms, neck, shoulders or back, or may develop eyestrain, headaches, general fatigue and stress. Some rare conditions can also occur such as photo-epilepsy (sensitivity to flickering light that may trigger an epileptic fit) and facial dermatitis (skin complaints affecting the face).

Risks

The use of display screen *equipment can* lead to musculoskeletal disorders and stress if the appropriate controls are not used (see below).

The risk of injury increases if the work procedure, workplace and work environment do not take account of the employee's individual requirements. The risk varies depending on the duration, intensity and degree of difficulty of the work being done.

Controls

The principles to follow in controlling the hazards and risks of using display screen equipment are:

- carry out a risk assessment
- assess the workstation design
- schedule regular breaks
- offer appointments for regular eye tests
- provide effective training.

Some examples of how these principles might be applied are outlined below.

Risk assessment

Employers must complete a suitable and sufficient analysis of workstations used in the business. This applies to the 'average' person working at the workstation and also to staff working at home. The responsibility for carrying out the assessment may be delegated to a supervisor or other staff member.

Whoever carries out the assessment must:

- be trained to do so
- be familiar with the legislation covering display screen equipment
- have the ability to assess the risks from workstations and draw valid conclusions
- be prepared to record the findings of the assessment with care.

Assessments should be:

- systematic
- appropriate to the likely degree of risk (a manager is likely to be at less risk than a data processing operator, for instance)
- comprehensive
- contain information provided by the employee and employer, such as ergonomic information.

If there are a number of identical workstations, one generic assessment could be carried out, provided that the workstation design allows the individual employee to adjust the chair height, backrest position and height, and the angle, brightness and contrast of the computer screen.

Any high-level risks identified need to be reduced to the lowest level that is reasonably practicable. Assessments should be reviewed if there is a change in the work activity relating to the display screen equipment. Working with portable display screen equipment requires a specific risk assessment.

Recording a risk assessment

The assessments need not be recorded in writing or on a computer if the assessment is simple and no significant risks are identified, or if no user is identified as being at risk. However, it is good practice to make a record so that you have a comparison for any future assessments.

Some solutions

Small adjustments to a workstation often result in greatly reduced risk. It is also usual for a combination of adjustments to be needed.

Posture

Postural problems can be solved by adjustments to the workstation and by training – for example, adjusting the height of the chair or by training the user about good posture, the correct hand position and how to adjust the equipment. If absolutely necessary, foot rests and wrist rests can help the employee to adopt the correct posture.

Advice may need to be given on such issues as positioning the mouse within easy reach, so it can be used with a straight wrist; sitting upright and close to the desk; and moving the keyboard out of the way when it is not in immediate use. Display screen users need to be reminded not to sit in the same position for long periods and to change their posture as often as practicable.

Eyesight

Visual problems can be sorted out by placing the screen at a comfortable viewing distance, by keeping the screen clean and by making sure that the screen is not affected by reflected light. Anti-glare screens can be used as a last resort to reduce eyestrain. Changing the size at which text is viewed and the colour of text may also making reading the screen more comfortable.

Employees who use display screen equipment have a legal right to request the employer to provide an appropriate eye and eyesight test by a competent person. This must be done as soon as practicable after the request is made: if the person is not yet employed, the test should be done before the person starts work. Further tests should be carried out at regular intervals to find out if there is any change in the employee's eyesight over time. All of these tests are at the employer's expense. Any glasses required to correct vision defects at the normal viewing distance from the display screen equipment must be provided free of charge to the employee by the employer.

It is important to note that the rights provided by the regulations are precautionary measures: there is no evidence that display screen equipment causes permanent damage to eyes or eyesight.

Stress

Stress is not caused by display screen equipment, but usually arises from an increased pace of work or pressure to meet deadlines. Fatigue and stress can be dealt with by giving the employee some influence over the pace of the work to be done. Perhaps the pace of the work can be decided after discussion between the employee, supervisor and manager.

Training in the use of the software is very important in avoiding problems of misunderstanding about how the software can be operated efficiently. If the operator is not trained correctly, mistakes can lead to more inputting than is necessary, in turn leading to stress and more mistakes.

Regular breaks

People who use display screen equipment must be allowed regular breaks or changes of work activity throughout the day to allow them to recover from the activity. The break or change may be in the form of a natural break, such as doing some photocopying, sorting out the post or assisting in the control of the office reception. Scheduled breaks are more likely to be needed if the work involves data entry or text entry because there is rarely an opportunity for natural breaks.

Information and training

All users of display screen equipment need health and safety training in the use of a workstation. If a person is to become a user, the training should be given before he or she starts work. The training should include:

- recognition of hazards, such as poor posture and the degree of risk that could lead to fatigue and pain
- the methods of control to reduce risk to an acceptable level – for example, comfortable posture and adjustment of the workstation components
- regular cleaning of the workstation
- the need to take regular breaks, whether natural or scheduled.

Employees need to be provided with information on the health and safety aspects of the workstation and the measures taken by the employer to comply with the legal standards.

For their part, employees should report any symptoms of ill health which may be related to the work they are doing.

Display screen equipment

Staff need to be able to sit at the correct height, with their eyes roughly level with the top of the computer screen and their forearms parallel to the desk top. To achieve this, chairs need to be adjustable, and staff may need to alter the height of their screens.

Ideal workstation design for seating and posture for typical office tasks

1   Seat back adjustability.

2   Good lumbar support.

3   Seat height adjustability.

4   No excess pressure on underside of thighs and backs of knees.

5   Foot support if needed.

6   Space for postural change, no obstacles under desk.

7   Forearms approximately horizontal.

8   Minimal extension or bending of the wrists.

9   Screen height and angle should allow comfortable head position.

10   Space in front of keyboard to support the hands and wrists during pauses in keying.

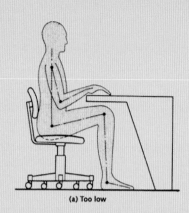

(a) Too low

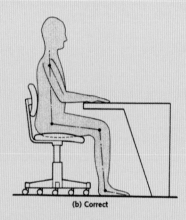

(b) Correct

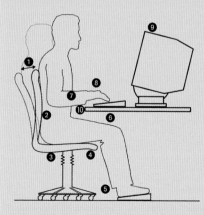

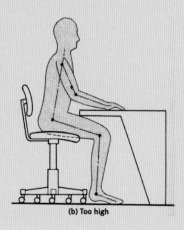

(b) Too high

Supermarket checkouts

The employees who work at supermarket checkouts handle thousands of items every day, repeating similar movements throughout the day. This can lead to, or aggravate, musculoskeletal disorders, particularly in the shoulders, elbows and wrists.

The aim of any control is to reduce undesirable physical loading and operator dissatisfaction and to reduce the risk of injury from, or the development of, musculoskeletal disorders.

Repeating movements throughout the day at a supermarket checkout can cause or aggravate musculoskeletal disorders.

A basic supermarket checkout unit is made up of a place for the operator to sit or stand, the method of delivering the goods to the operator, a recording method for the price of the goods, a cash receptacle, ancillary equipment such as weighing scales and an area for the goods to be returned to the customer. There are, of course, variations including laser scanners and credit card swipes.

The best way to control risks involved with supermarket checkouts is to apply an ergonomic approach which emphasises the need to ensure an acceptable fit between the operator, the equipment and the tasks performed.

Workstations

There should be sufficient room for operators to move and change posture without restriction. The seat and backrest heights should be adjustable and the backrest should be in good repair. Footrests should be available. Operators should be able to reach goods easily and the design of the checkouts should minimise the need for twisting and bending.

Workstations with a moving belt that delivers goods to the operator are generally preferable to systems that involve the operator in unloading and moving goods by hand. The scanner and the cash drawer should be directly in front of the operator, allowing for plenty of knee room. The scanner should be positioned so that the operator does not have to twist from the goods delivery point to the scanner.

Work organisation

Operators should be allowed adequate rest breaks, and job rotation should be considered. A second person could help by packing bags. Opening a sufficient number of checkouts prevents long customer queues – benefiting the consumers and taking a little pressure off the checkout operators.

Work environment

Poor environmental conditions may increase the likelihood that operators will complain about symptoms. Cleanliness, temperature, ventilation, noise and lighting are all important to employees' sense of well-being.

Training

Operators are unlikely to suffer injury if the work is performed properly at a well designed checkout. Staff should be trained to vary sitting and standing postures, to use both hands for scanning and to request breaks before they become fatigued. Supervisors should observe operators at work and advise them of any poor practices and how to improve what they are doing. Operators should be encouraged to report any symptoms such as shoulder or wrist pains.

Management controls

Supervisors and managers should respond quickly to complaints and reports of symptoms. Equipment should be maintained regularly and assistance should be given wherever possible to ease the workload.

Legal requirements

The Management of Health and Safety at Work Regulations 1999 require employers to assess risks (including risks from repeated movements) and where necessary to take action to prevent musculoskeletal disorders.

The Manual Handling Operations Regulations 1992, amended 2002, require employers to avoid the need for employees to carry out manual handling operations – including repeated and awkward lifting – which involve a risk of their being injured. Employees must make full and proper use of systems of work provided for their use by the employer.

The Workplace (Health, Safety and Welfare) Regulations 1992 require workspaces, workstations and seating to be suitable, in good condition and designed to prevent injuries and ill health.

The Health and Safety (Display Screen Equipment) Regulations 1992 require employers to make a suitable and sufficient analysis of display screen equipment workstations to assess and reduce the health and safety risks to operators.

Employers must plan the work to provide breaks or changes of activity. They must also provide employees with eye and eyesight tests on request and at regular intervals and must provide adequate health and safety information and training about the use of the workstation.

Employers must also meet the standards specified in the HSE Approved Code of Practice L26 *Work with display screen equipment*.

Display screen workstation checklist

Display screen equipment

1. **Monitor**
   Can you tilt the monitor and swivel it easily?
   Is the monitor at the correct height for you?
   Is the screen flicker free?
   Are you able to adjust the brightness and contrast of the screen?

2. **Keyboard**
   Is the keyboard separate from the screen?
   Is there enough space in front of the keyboard for you to rest your hands?
   Can you easily see the characters on the keys?
   Can you raise the keyboard?

Furniture

3. **Desk**
   Is the desk surface area large enough for the monitor, keyboard and all your other equipment to be where you want it?
   Is the desk at the right height for you?

4. **Footrest**
   Do you need a footrest?

5. **Document holder**
   Do you need a document holder?
   If you have one, is it adjustable?

Work Environment

6. **Lighting**
   Is the lighting suitable for you?
   Do you have control over the lighting?
   Are there any reflections or glare from the screen?

7. **Space**
   Have you enough space around your workstation?

8. **Noise**
   Is there any work equipment near you that distracts you?

9. **Temperature and humidity**
   Is the temperature and humidity around your workstation comfortable?

Training

10. **Use of the workstation**
    Have you been trained in the use of the workstation?
    Have you been trained in the use of the software?
    Do you know what to do if the workstation is not suitable for you?
    Do you know about the arrangements for eye tests and eyesight tests?
    Do you have any other comments?

Manual handling

Manual handling occurs in almost every workplace in the world. At any one time someone is moving objects as part of their everyday work activities. It could be an administration assistant moving a small pile of papers from one side of the desk to another. It could be a shop assistant stacking packs of bottles, or a checkout assistant moving goods from the conveyor to the scanner. It could also be a builder lifting bags of sand and cement to tip them into a mixer, or it could be any number of actions that involve moving something from one place to another.

This common activity causes more than one-third of all injuries lasting over three days that are reported each year in the UK. Over one million people suffer from musculoskeletal disorders (often back pain) that are caused, or made worse, by their current or past work.

Key words and phrases

competent person – someone with the appropriate qualifications, knowledge and experience to identify the risks arising from a situation and the measures needed to control them.

hierarchy of control – a well tested system of graded health and safety controls. The sequence helps organisations to determine their most effective health and safety controls.

load – any movable object, including a person or animal.

manual handling or **manual handling operation** – any transporting or supporting of a load (including lifting, putting down, pushing, pulling, carrying or moving) by hand or by bodily force.

musculoskeletal disorders (MSDs) – conditions affecting the muscles, nerves, tendons, ligaments, joints, cartilage or spinal discs.

safe system of work – a set of procedures for carrying out a task safely.

What is manual handling?

British legislation defines **manual handling** as any transporting or supporting of a load by hand or by bodily force. This includes lifting, putting down, pushing, pulling, carrying or moving any object. A **load** is anything that can be moved, including a person or an animal. The load can be light or heavy, small or large.

The occupational significance

More workplace injuries arise from poor manual handling than from any other activity. There are more than 3,500 major injuries a year, plus over 38,000 injuries that keep employees away from work for more than three days. Bad though these figures are, they do not present the full picture because many injuries go unreported while employees suffer in silence.

Manual handling contributes significantly to injuries known as **musculoskeletal disorders**. Most injuries involve a strain or sprain to the back: other injuries affect the muscles, nerves, ligaments, joints, cartilage, spinal discs and tendons. In addition, there may be cuts and bruises to the hands or feet or even bone fractures.

However, many injuries are difficult to link to any single activity or accident because they are cumulative – the problems develop gradually, perhaps over a considerable period and perhaps without being noticed at first. It is often difficult to make a full recovery from a manual handling injury and cumulative injuries may lead to temporary or permanent disability, leaving the sufferer with a limited range of movement that is very painful.

Even slight strains can lead to other problems. For instance, suppose that an injured person continues to work but, as a consequence of the injury, loses grip of a box of bottles of chemicals. Vapours from the spilt chemicals could cause breathing problems affecting other staff, or the floor could become slippery so that other staff slip over and hurt their backs. The falling box could land on someone or become jammed in machinery.

Typical hazards

When considering manual handling, it is helpful to do so under three main headings:

- the manual handling load
- the manual handling task
- the work environment.

The manual handling load

The size, shape, weight, texture and contents of the load itself can all affect the ease with which an object can be handled and could give you initial problems in designing a safe procedure for moving it.

The manual handling task

The task itself can also be a hazard. Some of the issues that need to be considered include the frequency of the operation and whether the task involves stretching, twisting the body or bending forward.

A task involving two or more people can also be a hazard because there could be a misunderstanding between them that leads to an accident. Good co-operation and communication between employees working on the same job is essential.

Even the use of personal protective equipment (PPE) has hazards. Some types of PPE, such as breathing apparatus, have a potential to restrict movement so that employees find it more difficult to lift a load.

The work environment

The workplace itself plays a major part in creating or eliminating hazards for staff involved in manual handling activities. The materials used in the construction of the building, the way equipment is laid out and installed, the standards of cleaning and maintenance and even the routes that are possible through the workplace can all affect the safety of staff and visitors.

Take flooring and the ground surface as examples. There may be different levels to negotiate. The flooring might be a special non-slip material, but it could become unsafe to walk on when wet or splashed with grease. If there are holes in the flooring, or rubbish is left lying around, the number of hazards increases. Work outdoors often poses particular problems where the ground is uneven or potholed and where there is debris or tools lying around.

The temperature of the workplace is also important, together with the ventilation and humidity. A high temperature and humidity can cause sweating that makes it difficult for workers to maintain a steady grip on a load. A low temperature or increased ventilation can lead to cold hands which can also make it difficult to handle materials. This is also the case when working outside – for example, scaffolders handle cold, steel poles which are heavy and sometimes awkward to lift.

If you are cold, you are more likely to strain a muscle, so draughts and strong air movements can also cause problems. Draughts affecting a workstation, for example, can be uncomfortable and can lead to muscular problems, especially for sedentary workers, such as data processing operators, when they are asked to carry out one-off manual handling tasks. Strong air movements can blow litter around and may even move light sheets of wood or plastic, making manual handling operations more hazardous.

Low lighting levels in the workplace or as the sun goes down can make it difficult for someone to see where they are going and to negotiate obstructions and steps.

Risks

The typical risk factors associated with manual handling operations are discussed below under the headings already identified:

- the manual handling load
- the manual handling task
- the work environment
- personal capabilities.

The manual handling load

Factors to consider when assessing risk include:

- size
- shape
- weight
- texture
- content.

Size

A load that is large and difficult to get your arms around is likely to involve a high risk, while a smaller load which is easy to pick up and hold is likely to be a much lower risk.

Shape

There is likely to be a low risk from a load with a regular shape, such as a rectangular box. There is also likely to be a low risk of injury if a load has easy-to-grip handles or handholds, such as cut-out handles on a cardboard box or a bag with rope handles. In contrast, a sack of gravel or stones intended for a dry stone wall can be difficult to grip and lift safely because of their awkward shapes.

Staff need to be trained to be aware of the centre of gravity of each load when assessing the lifting operation. If it is not taken into account, the risk of injury increases because the load could unexpectedly tip away from the body, causing strain.

Weight

Lightweight loads are likely to be a low risk for most people, provided that they lift them safely. If a load is heavy, it is likely to create a higher risk of injury for most people.

Texture

The texture of a load can affect the level of risk of injury. If it is rough, sharp or splintery and is liable to dig into someone's hands, it is more likely that the people holding it will loosen their grip, or drop it. Similarly, a load with sharp edges or a slippery surface creates a higher risk of injury to most people.

Content

If the contents of a load are loose inside a container, there is an increased risk that the contents will shift position while the load is being moved. This may tip the load unexpectedly, causing a loss of control that may cause a leak or spill. Where the contents of a load are toxic, corrosive, hot, cold or alive, the risk of injury is obviously much greater.

The manual handling task

Factors to consider when assessing the risk associated with the task include the:

- space available
- number of movements
- type of movements
- number of people involved
- use of personal protective equipment.

Space available
If the space in which the load can be moved, or in which the worker can move, is restricted, there is an increased risk of injury.

Number of movements
Risk also increases with the number of times a similar load has to be moved. Repeated lifting of small-size and medium-size loads can lead to strain on muscles, ligaments or tendons. A cumulative effect can lead to a long-lasting injury.

Type of movement
If someone has to twist, bend down or stretch to move a load, the likelihood of injury increases. For example, if you have to stretch to your fullest extent with your hands right above your head to get something from a high shelf, you are more likely to injure yourself than if you stretch just above your head height to retrieve something.

Number of people involved
The greater the number of people involved in handling a load, the greater the risk of poor communication. If one person misunderstands what the rest of the team members are doing, someone could get seriously injured, particularly if the load is heavy.

To avoid misunderstandings between workers lifting a load, it is best to keep the number of people involved to a minimum. However, there are many situations where a load has to be lifted by two or more people. In such cases, training and communication are crucial in reducing risk of injury.

Personal protective clothing
Clothing designed for personal protection can restrict movement and mobility. For example, if staff wear gloves to protect against splinters from wooden crates, they may have reduced sensitivity to the security of their grip on the load and may be more likely to let the crate slip.

The work environment

There are higher risks if the immediate environment is badly lit, the floor or ground are holed, uneven or slippery, or there are sudden changes in floor or ground level. The temperature, humidity and ventilation can also influence the levels of risk (see above).

Personal capabilities

An individual's state of health, fitness and strength can affect the ability to perform a task safely, although there is no evidence to suggest that there is a close link between the incidence of injury and these factors. That said, the lifting of excessive weight in relation to a worker's capabilities can lead to the injury of the employee and colleagues.

People who, with the appropriate training, are capable of lifting loads are often attracted to jobs in which manual handling is involved: self-confidence and motivation are also significant factors in personal capability.

Controls

By law, employers must make a 'suitable and sufficient' risk assessment of all manual handling operations. Such a risk assessment may be a part of the responsibility of managers and supervisors and may also involve safety representatives. Whoever carries it out needs to be a **competent person** and may need specific training.

During the assessment always consult the employees who carry out the manual handling operation. The flow diagram (left) summarises the assessment of manual handling.

There are many other manual handling assessment charts available – for example, from the Health and Safety Executive website (see page 382). Some are specific to certain types of manual handling such as the pushing and pulling of wheelchairs or the lifting of people.

There is no legal requirement to record the assessment, but it is good practice to do so. A generic assessment is acceptable, but specific assessments may be necessary for special manual handling operations, such as dealing with a toxic or corrosive substance.

Implement any new methods of handling and any other controls you identify. Update an assessment when significant changes are made to the operation or the workplace.

Hierarchy of control

When planning to implement measures to reduce the risks identified, consider the **hierarchy of control**:

- elimination or avoidance
- substitution
- controlling risks at source
- safe working procedures
- training, instruction and/or supervision
- personal protective equipment.

First of all, try to eliminate the manual handling task altogether. Ask yourself whether staff really need to carry out a manual handling operation in the first place, or could the task be reorganised so that the load does not have to be moved at all? If moving the load is unavoidable, is there a feasible substitute process? Can the goods be moved in another way – perhaps by automating the process or using mechanical help? For example, could

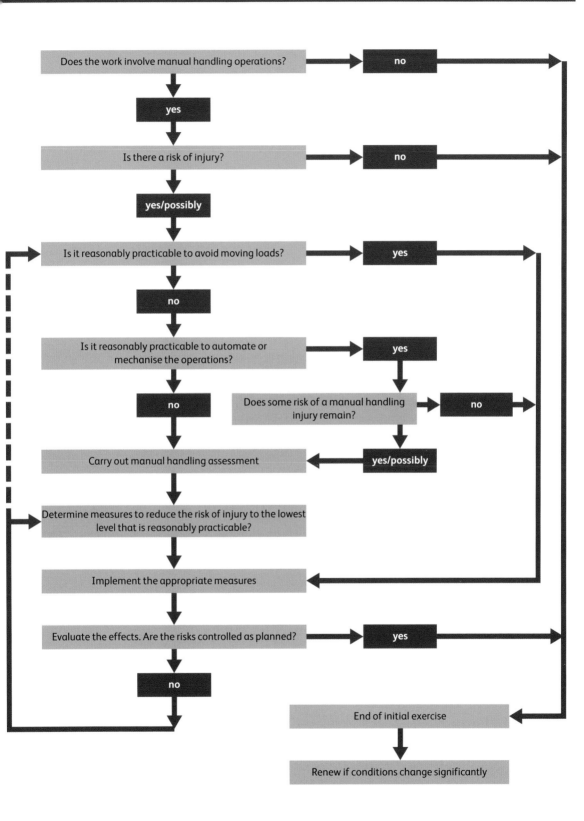

retail goods be moved in a wheeled cage rather than carried to the shelves? Could goods in a warehouse be stacked on pallets which could be moved and lifted using a fork-lift truck? Might a powered conveyor belt be a more suitable system of handling loads? Of course, you'll also need to assess the hazards and risks presented by any mechanised or automated process. For example, might a fork-lift truck run over someone's foot, or might a conveyor belt trap someone's hand?

Once the assessment has been done, any actions required to reduce risk from the new procedure should be implemented.

Lowest level possible

The aim is to reduce the risk to the lowest level that is 'reasonably practicable' (see page 378 for an explanation of 'reasonably practicable'). All workers should be trained in general handling techniques and practices. However, manual handling tasks that are unavoidable should be carried out by workers who are trained for the particular task and are physically capable of undertaking it. In all manual handling operations the solution is to fit the job to the person and not the person to the job.

In deciding whether someone is suitable to do a manual handling operation a number of factors must be taken into account:

- the physical suitability of the employee to carry out the operation
- the clothing, footwear or other personal effects worn
- knowledge and training
- the results of a relevant risk assessment
- whether the employee is within a group of employees identified by the assessment as a group especially at risk
- the results of any health surveillance (see pages 134 to 139).

Each staff member needs to be comfortable while lifting or carrying a particular load and should not have to struggle with it. Bear in mind that capabilities may vary at different times – for example, a woman who is usually confident and competent to lift a particular load may not be so while she is pregnant, and she may face a greater risk of back injury.

The manual handling load

If a load is an awkward shape, managers should consider redesigning the container or buying different containers so that workers can handle them more easily. Provide cut-out handles in cardboard boxes. Add some form of handle wherever possible or provide a means of gripping the container easily. Make sure that two or more people deal with heavy or awkward-shaped loads. If the load can be split into smaller loads, the risk may be reduced.

The staff selected should be trained how to carry out the operation, have agreed who should give the instruction to lift, and should be supervised and monitored. There must be a **safe system of work**, based on the risk assessment. The system should ensure that staff work as a team and communicate well.

When assessing the risk from the manual handling operation you should consider:

- how quickly the job must be done

- how many loads are to be moved

- how big the loads are.

Choose a balanced approach between these three factors so that you can minimise the risk. Where possible, eliminate any sharp edges and ensure that packaged loads are secure and cannot move about inside their container.

Special loads

Special loads need special attention – for example, gloves or eye goggles may need to be worn if the load contains a toxic or corrosive substance. Everyone involved must be specially trained for the task, and it is particularly important to emphasise the procedures to follow if something goes wrong.

Marking the weight

If possible, loads should be marked with the approximate weight of the load. For example, the Health and Safety Executive campaigned to reduce the large number of manual handling injuries in the parcel delivery industry. Drivers collecting parcels often do not know how heavy they are before lifting them. It helps to know the weight of the parcel when employers assess the risk of injury from manual handling.

Businesses have a general responsibility towards the health and safety of everyone who handles their parcels. Encourage staff to mark parcels to the nearest kilo on the same side as the address, or to ensure that individual parcels are not too heavy by packing loads as two or more lighter parcels.

The manual handling task

When planning manual handling there are a number of factors you need to consider:

- whether there is sufficient space

- the frequency and length of rest breaks

- how the task is carried out

- the use of personal protective equipment.

Space

The space where the manual handling task takes place must be large enough to allow the member of staff to manoeuvre the load easily and without restriction of movement.

Rest breaks

When staff have to handle a large number of loads, provide regular rest breaks to allow them to recover from the physical exertion. Alternatively, vary the work pattern. This change of activity avoids harmful repetitive work.

Redesigning the task

If you notice that staff have to bend down, reach or stretch frequently when moving loads, you need to consider redesigning the task so that they do not have to carry out these types of frequent movement.

Such a redesign might involve the use of mechanical aids such as levers, portable hoists, trolleys, sack trolleys, pallet trucks, roller conveyors or chutes, for example. Using mechanical aids can improve productivity by making it easier, quicker and safer for workers.

If the loads are large and need to be moved frequently over considerable distances, manual handling should probably be excluded. Powered work equipment, such as fork-lift or reach trucks, should be used.

Use of personal protective equipment

Protective clothing can provide essential protection to staff when they have to work with unavoidable hazards. For example, gloves must be used if the load is hot, has sharp edges or would otherwise be very uncomfortable to handle.

The work environment

The workplace must be well lit and the temperature and humidity of the workplace should be as comfortable for staff as it can be, depending on the loads being handled.

In a cold storage business, for instance, the temperature of the walk-in freezers should be at -18°C or colder to preserve the food, so staff must be provided with appropriate warm clothing.

As the temperature of the workplace cannot be altered in many industries, the protective clothing can have the dual purpose of protecting against the cold and allowing manual handling to take place without any increased risk due to the cold. However, the cold can present other risks such as icy surfaces and the fogging up of spectacles, for example. These hazards need to be dealt with in the manual handling assessment.

Floors need to be in good condition, without holes, tripping hazards, uneven surfaces or inconspicuous changes in level. There should be a non-slip surface where necessary – for instance, in a catering kitchen.

Outdoor work areas must be kept clear of tripping hazards. Tools and materials should be kept in an organised way so that they do not cause an obstruction or fall on anyone. Designated areas for different tasks and storage and work exclusion zones may need to be established. Workers need to be trained and supervised to put sharp tools, such as forks and saws, in a safe place when they are not in use, but so that they are still to hand when needed.

Training

Being able to lift a load correctly is a fundamental necessity for workers in order to prevent them from risking serious injury. An employer has a duty to train employees in good manual handling techniques. Once trained, employees should be able to recognise poor handling techniques and carry out manual handling techniques without risk to their health and safety.

Storage systems

The method of storage largely depends on the shape and fragility of the article being stored. For example, long thin articles are normally stored on horizontal racking and boxes are stacked.

General features

Storage areas should be specifically designated and clearly marked. The layout should be carefully designed to avoid tight corners, pillars, uneven surfaces, changes of gradient and awkwardly placed doors. The design of traffic and pedestrian routes should be considered with regard to handling methods (see also pages 210 to 211).

Where many small items are to be lifted mechanically, they can be placed on pallets or battens which are then lifted by a pallet-truck or a fork-lift truck onto a storage rack. The driver must ensure that the load is uniformly distributed over the deck area of the rack.

A typical racking system consists of a steel framework, either fixed or adjustable, to support loads without the use of shelves. The design of the racking depends on the type of material being stored – for example, pallet racking in a food warehouse, tyre racking in garages and drum racking in chemical storage areas. One of the most common types is the adjustable pallet racking, a system of upright frames connected by horizontal beams to provide pallet storage levels, which can be adjusted vertically.

Safety standards

Racking should be installed by competent persons and the safe working loads, heights and widths should be set by the designers and manufacturers of the system. The standards of construction of the racking should meet those recommended by the Health and Safety Executive guidance for storage racking.

Mattress injuries

A company ended up in court after several workers suffered back injuries and shoulder, knee and wrist problems from lifting heavy mattresses on their own. One worker had even stacked double mattresses in a pile 2.4m high. The company had failed to carry out a manual handling risk assessment.

Manual handling checklist

This checklist can be used during the first stage of assessing manual handling tasks.

Load
Which loads are being moved in the workplace – eg. bags, boxes, drums and sacks?
Who moves the loads – one or more than one worker?
What is the weight and shape of the load?
Is it awkward to carry?
Is it difficult to grip?
Is the load wet, hot or cold?
Does the load have sharp edges?
Is the load potentially unstable?

Task
How are the loads moved?
How often are loads moved?
How far are loads moved?
To what height do the loads need to be lifted?
Is there handling while seated?
Does the procedure involve carrying, stooping, twisting, reaching, bending sideways, pulling or pushing?

Environment
What are the environmental conditions where the manual handling operations take place?
Is it hot, cold or humid? Is it windy or dusty? Is it noisy or is there vibration nearby?
Is it well lit?
Is there enough space to manoeuvre the load? Are there obstructions in the way?
Are the floors non-slip, in good condition and even?
Are there steps or different ground levels that need to be negotiated?

Who is at risk?
Is there a need for unusual strength?
Is training required?
Does personal protective equipment need to be worn?
Are there any workers who may be at a greater risk than others – eg. pregnant workers, young people or people with a medical condition or history?
Does the accident book show injuries that could be associated with manual handling?

Positive action

People involved in medical and residential care often need to lift people or to help them to move. As a consequence, they often suffer back and other injuries. One NHS Trust estimated that about one-sixth of all time lost at work was due to manual handling injuries associated with patients. Three priorities were chosen to reduce this lost time:

- risk assessment – risk assessors were trained to focus on ergonomic assessment

- the purchase of lifting equipment, particularly patient-lifting aids

- general staff training on manual handling.

Following the implementation of these three priorities there was a dramatic fall in lost working hours from 6,720 hours to 200 hours. The cost of absenteeism fell from £800,000 in 1993 to £10,000 in 2001.

Another NHS Trust was concerned about the number of back problems among ambulance staff, often resulting in early retirement. The Trust adopted five actions aimed at reducing the personal, professional and financial cost of musculoskeletal injuries:

- purchase of equipment that reduces the risk of injury

- ergonomic design of vehicles and manual handling procedures

- training on manual handling techniques

- medical treatment and rehabilitation for staff

- awareness and behaviour therapy as part of rehabilitation.

The Trust worked in partnership with the vehicle manufacturers to introduce automated tail lifts on ambulances and manual pumps on stretchers to try to eliminate risks in those areas. The number of shifts lost to ill health fell from 4,000 to 2,000 in two years.

Legal requirements

The Manual Handling Operations Regulations 1992, as amended, require employers to avoid the need for employees to carry out manual handling work involving a risk of injury. Employers must make a 'suitable and sufficient' assessment of all manual handling operations to reduce to the lowest reasonably practicable level the risk of injury. They must also provide employees with specified information about the loads to be carried and must review (and where necessary, change) arrangements regularly. Employees must make full and proper use of any system of work provided for their use by the employer.

Feature

Safe handling techniques

As a manager, supervisor or safety representative, you need to understand the basic techniques for manual handling because you may need to advise employees about safe lifting and handling methods and procedures.

Keep a close eye on employees when they are lifting loads. Some indications of poor practice to watch out for include staff who:

- attempt to lift awkward or heavy loads without asking for assistance or without using mechanical aids, such as trolleys

- are out of breath or sweating after a manual handling task

- lift a load from the floor, or from a low position, with straight legs and a curved back

- are very tired after manual handling tasks

- have a poor posture after lifting loads.

If they are not following safe procedures, talk with them about the risks associated with poor manual handling and explain how they could improve the way they handle goods. Arrange for training or refresher training, or, if appropriate, give an immediate, simple, informal demonstration of ways to lift that avoid injury.

The basics

There are some common stages to all manual handling operations:

- assess the load and plan the lift

- position the feet with care and secure your grip (feet slightly apart and one in front of the other is a more stable stance than feet close together)

- bend the knees, keeping the arms and back straight

- lift smoothly, using the legs to take the main strain and keeping the load close to the body

- use the feet to move the load from one position or place to another

- put the load down with care, using the legs to take the strain and keeping the back straight.

Stages of lifting

Before you start any manual handling operation, plan what you are going to do. Assess whether you can lift the load easily and without hurting yourself. Check that you can take the load to the desired place easily. If necessary, get help or use equipment.

Your body position is very important before, during and after the lift. The position of your feet, the position of your back, how you grip the load and the position of your legs and shoulders are all crucial to a good lift.

Make sure that you start the lift by positioning yourself in a stable and comfortable posture. Your feet should be apart, with one foot slightly in front of the other. Hold the load in a secure hook-shaped grip. Bend your knees with your back as straight as possible.

Lift in a smooth movement, avoiding any sudden or jerky movements Your arms should be straight and you should keep the load close to your body. Keep your head up when handling a load, and look ahead.

Use your feet to move to the load's destination and to manoeuvre around obstacles, rather than twisting your body or reaching.

When you put down the load, reverse the procedure if the load is to be put back on the floor. If you are using a table, put the load down first before sliding or pushing it into its final position.

Workplace transport

The use of vehicles in workplaces accounts for the death of about 45 people every year. In addition, more than 1,800 people a year receive major injuries from being hit, run over, crushed or struck by a vehicle or thrown from one.

Key words and phrases

competent person – someone with the appropriate qualifications, knowledge and experience to identify the risks arising from a situation and the measures needed to control them.

mobile equipment – any work equipment that operates while it is travelling or is moved between work locations.

safe system of work – a set of procedures for carrying out a task safely.

traffic – vehicle or pedestrian movement.

traffic route – a defined or non-defined route used by vehicles or pedestrians in a workplace.

vehicle – includes cars, vans, heavy goods vehicles, fork-lift trucks and reach trucks.

work equipment – apparatus used at work including machines, appliances, tools, installations, ladders, hoists and lifting equipment.

workplace transport – any vehicle or piece of mobile equipment used by employees, self-employed people or visitors to a workplace, excluding vehicles on a public road.

What is workplace transport?

Workplace transport is the term for any **vehicle** or piece of **mobile equipment** used by employees, self-employed people or visitors to a workplace. Examples include fork-lift trucks, compact dumpers, tractors or mobile cranes. It does not cover vehicles travelling on a public road or by air, rail or water transport. However, a goods vehicle loading or unloading on a public highway is regarded as workplace transport.

Hazards

The hazards from workplace transport include being struck or crushed by a vehicle or the load it was carrying while the vehicle is moving or being unloaded. The reversing of vehicles often causes injury or death, as well as damage to vehicles, equipment and buildings, particularly loading bays. Manoeuvring through junctions and negotiating sharp bends, crossings, corners, steep gradients, roadworks and other work activities is also hazardous. Vehicles can also overturn and crush the driver or anyone nearby.

Sometimes people fall out of, or off, a vehicle, or fall from loading bays or while sheeting a load on a vehicle. Injuries also occur when people are trapped or become entangled in dock levellers – machines used to bridge the gap between the loading dock and a vehicle trailer to allow access for lift trucks and rolling containers – or vehicle tail-lifts.

Risks

The main risks involved in workplace transport occur because of inadequate training, information, instruction and supervision of the people who operate and work with or near the vehicles. Without specific training, instruction and information, the risk of injury and damage is high. Recent research has showed that while training is essential to provide individuals with the necessary skills to use workplace transport safely, the way in which individuals subsequently choose to perform a task is more heavily influenced by the attitudes and beliefs of the drivers.

Poor management control also often leads to unsafe **systems of work** and lack of maintenance and repair. Low staffing levels may prompt employees to cut corners – literally and metaphorically – so that they can meet tight deadlines. This often leads to accidents.

Controls

The main control measures that can be taken to make workplace transport safer include:

- risk assessment
- good layout of traffic routes
- pedestrian protection
- safe parking
- procedures at loading bays
- construction of roads and routes

- competent maintenance
- driver selection and training
- good practice.

Risk assessment

Identifying the hazards and assessing the risks involved with workplace transport are the first steps in dealing with the hazards that may exist in your workplace. This could involve managers, supervisors and safety representatives in consultation with employees. (See pages 110 to 120 for more details about risk assessments.)

If you are involved in the risk assessment, consider the potential dangers by looking at the vehicles, the routes they follow and the behaviour of employees, visiting drivers and pedestrians. Think about suitable precautions to reduce the risk of injury from these hazards: has a speed limit been imposed on traffic routes, for example? Once measures have been identified and put into practice, record all findings.

Traffic layout

Pedestrian and vehicle routes need to be clearly marked, both inside and outside workplaces.

Safe routes need to be planned and made easily identifiable. Make sure that it is clear whether a route is for vehicles or pedestrians, or both, and indicate traffic routes clearly by marking or signposting the direction of flow. Routes need to be wide enough to allow two vehicles to pass side by side. If the traffic flows are heavy, consider introducing a one-way system.

Avoid traffic routes that pass vulnerable facilities, such as a fuel tank. If that is impossible, provide protection around it, such as fencing or barriers. Avoid sharp bends and junctions if possible: otherwise keep them to a minimum.

Clearly signpost any road junctions, areas where there is low headroom and any dangerous installation, such as tanks of flammable liquid. Forward visibility needs to be good enough to allow drivers to see and avoid hazards. Speed limits could be introduced: they are usually between 5 and 10 miles an hour. Traffic-calming features could also be used to reduce vehicle speeds.

Any doorways or entrances should be wide enough for two vehicles to pass one another. Allow for varying heights of vehicles. An unloaded vehicle may be greater in height than a loaded vehicle.

Pedestrians

Pedestrians are best protected by providing them with separate routes. In areas where vehicles and pedestrians do mix, provide barriers or guard rails – for example, at the entrance or exit to a building where the pedestrian access leads straight on to a traffic route. It is also important to provide separate entrance and exit doors for both pedestrians and vehicles (See photograph opposite above.)

Pedestrian routes, including doors, should be separate from vehicle routes and doors wherever possible.

Inside buildings, where vehicles and pedestrians mix, mark the routes on the floor to show pedestrians and drivers where the vehicle and pedestrian routes are. The points where traffic routes cross, or where pedestrians and vehicles cross, should be marked clearly and drivers should be able to see in all directions.

Where members of the public have access to the workplace, they should, wherever possible, be kept away from any work activities or separated from them as much as possible. Make sure that the separate pedestrian routes are clearly signposted, with plenty of warning signs about hazards from the work activity.

Parking

Provide parking areas for all vehicles used in the workplace. If members of the public visit the premises, their parking areas should be separate from those provided for workplace vehicles. Parking areas should be clearly marked, well lit and in a position where those using the parking areas are not put in danger from work activities nearby.

Take, for example, the car park of a large supermarket. The direction of traffic flow needs to be clearly marked and the car parking spaces need to be clearly defined. The area should be well lit to enable customers to find their way around safely. The routes to and from the supermarket should be well marked with pedestrian crossing points well signposted and protected, possibly by using pedestrian islands.

Loading bays

Adequate space is needed outside loading bays to allow delivery vehicles to be manoeuvred. There should be a safe system of work for loading and unloading.

There should be enough space outside loading bays for vehicles to be manoeuvred safely. The loading bay should be well marked and well lit. Where there is a risk that people could fall off the raised area of the bay, guardrails should be fitted. There should also be a separate exit door from the loading bay for pedestrians.

It is important to design a safe system of work for the loading and unloading of goods.

Construction of roads and routes

Roads should be constructed so that they can support the type and amount of traffic that operates in and visits the workplace. In permanent premises, this probably involves the use of concrete or Tarmacadam. At temporary sites where routes are across fields or other soft surfaces – such as at festivals or agricultural shows or where trees and other plants must be protected – a temporary load-bearing road surface should be laid so that vehicles can move about the site easily and without causing compaction and other damage. Slopes and cambers should be avoided and the roads should be well drained, where possible.

Whether permanent or temporary, roads must be suitable to carry the type and amount of traffic safely.

Routes through buildings should have a floor or surface suitable for the purpose for which it is used. This is usually concrete of an appropriate thickness. All routes should be kept clear of anything that could obscure a driver's vision and cause any pedestrian to slip, trip or fall. All traffic routes should be adequately lit. Be careful where lights are positioned so that large vehicles do not block them.

Maintenance

All workplace vehicles are regarded as **work equipment** and must be designed, constructed and maintained to be suitable for their intended purpose. The construction of vehicles is subject to strict legal standards and controls.

The type and frequency of necessary vehicle maintenance varies. For instance, the driver of a vehicle needs to make basic visual checks on things like the brake lights, brakes and tyres before travelling, while a garage mechanic needs to make precise checks on the performance of the brakes, the integrity of the brake pipes and the efficiency of the brake system. In general, the type and use of the vehicle, together with the manufacturer's instructions, determine the frequency of preventive maintenance checks.

However, all vehicles must undergo specific checks by a **competent person** at appropriate intervals. These include the systems controlling braking, steering, signalling and windscreen washing, any special system used – for example, the lifting chains on a fork-lift truck – as well as viewing mirrors and tyres.

Driver selection and training

Someone must be responsible for ensuring that new staff are competent. This may be the responsibility of a supervisor. Thorough checks should be made on the qualifications and experience of new drivers. Organisations should also ensure that existing employees have the skills and experience needed for safety and that they maintain their skills.

Training for fork-lift use

A car manufacturer wanted to reduce the number of accidents involving fork-lift trucks so it:

- modified the trucks to restrict their speed and give the driver better visibility

- reduced the number of fork-lift trucks in the workplace

- introduced systems to control vehicles in designated areas

- fitted rail guards outside doors to canteens and rest areas

- painted floors to mark out pedestrian and vehicle areas.

The modifications were carried out only after consultation between the management, trade unions and employees. The resulting safer work environment reduced the risk of injury.

If work is contracted out, make sure that the contractor's drivers are competent to drive. The best way to do this is to ask for proof that they have been trained or instructed to a standard you are comfortable with. For example, ask to see certificates of training for a fork-lift truck driver and evidence of any refresher training courses taken.

(Employers need to provide health and safety information about the workplace and a site plan to contractors and drivers who visit the site.)

Training

When employing new drivers, assess how much training, instruction and information the driver needs before taking up his or her duties. Drivers should be capable of operating a vehicle safely. He or she should have a mature attitude and be able to do their work responsibly. Assessing maturity and responsibility is a matter of personal judgement, taking into account the person's previous experience and record. The type and level of training should concentrate on the driver's areas of inexperience.

It is good practice to introduce a planned programme of initial and refresher training for all drivers to make sure they are, and continue to be, competent in their work. It is also good practice to record all training activities, particularly the formal training and instruction which needs to be done to prove competence for, for instance, fork-lift trucks.

General training should cover the workplace traffic routes, instruction on how to use the vehicle safely, the hazards and risks associated with the vehicles and the controls needed to prevent accidents. It is also essential to reinforce the message that drivers must not attempt to control a vehicle under the influence of drugs or alcohol.

Specialist training must be given for particular vehicles that have been assessed as severe risk. For example, training on how to operate reach trucks should be done by a qualified instructor who is trained and authorised to instruct others in the use of that particular type of lift truck.

There are four recognised accrediting bodies that ensure these instructors are competent to instruct, test and certificate drivers:

- ConstructionSkills – a partnership between CITB-ConstructionSkills, the Construction Industry Council (CIC) and Construction Industry Training Board Northern Ireland (CITB (NI))

- RTITB

- Association of Industrial Truck Trainers (AITT)

- LANTRA (the Sector Skills Council for the environmental and land-based sectors).

Good practice

Reversing vehicles

Avoid the need for vehicle reversing by, for instance, setting up a one-way system. If reversing cannot be avoided, set up well marked reversing areas and prohibit pedestrians from going into the reversing areas, or employ someone to direct reversing manoeuvres. Consider fitting reversing alarms to vehicles, marking the floor with white lines to guide drivers into the correct position and fitting barriers to protect loading bays.

Access to vehicles

Employees must be trained how to get into and out of large vehicles safely, and there may need to be purpose-designed walkways or ladders to provide access to particular vehicles.

Aim to avoid anyone having to climb onto a large vehicle such as a petrol tanker. Where this is unavoidable, restrict access to the vehicle. The employee allowed onto the vehicle must be trained to follow safe procedures for access and the activities that take place on the vehicle, such as dipping – measuring the level of liquid present in the tanker.

The means of access to a vehicle must always be safe – for example, there may need to be a purpose-made walkway with a handrail or ladders specifically designed for access to particular types of vehicles, such as petrol delivery trucks.

Loading and unloading

Any loading and unloading operation (deliveries) should ideally be done away from passing vehicles and pedestrians. It must not be undertaken on a gradient that could make the operation unsafe.

When employees or subcontractors are loading a vehicle, they must ensure that the:

■ brakes are applied

■ vehicle is stable

■ weight is distributed evenly on the vehicle and the load is stable

■ weight of the load is within the legal maximum for the vehicle

■ load is secure before transporting.

Before unloading a vehicle, employees or subcontractors must ensure that the:

■ brakes are applied

■ load is stable.

A **safe system of work** should be agreed between the site manager and the driver well in advance of operation. For example, the keys to the vehicle could be kept by the person in charge of the loading and unloading (not the driver) to avoid the vehicle being driven away before the operation is finished. Train the staff on safe techniques for loading and unloading. Managers should consider giving a supervisor the authority to refuse permission for unloading or loading if there are any safety problems.

Tipping loads

Drivers need to be given any appropriate special instructions by the site manager before tipping a load and there should be good communication between them during the tipping operation. The driver should check that the load is evenly distributed in the vehicle and that precautions are taken so that the whole of the load discharges smoothly and safely. The driver must also be trained and experienced in the tipping operation.

Sheeting of loads

The sheeting of loads is done to prevent the load from falling or flying off and hitting people or other vehicles. Large loads can shift position during travel and could fall off the lorry. Systems must be in place to prevent this movement or falling. Secure, strong curtains, for example, are used on brewery lorries to prevent kegs and barrels from falling off a lorry during transit.

Mechanical sheeting systems powered by electricity, pneumatics or hydraulics are the safest option because they can be operated from the ground. Where mechanical systems cannot be used, manual sheeting systems should be designed so that drivers and other employees do not have to climb on top of the vehicle. For example, sheeting platforms with handrails can be constructed and placed on each side of the vehicle.

Bakery safety improvements

One bakery company halved the number of accidents associated with reversing within two years of introducing a closed-circuit television system. Drivers used a video monitor in the cab that allowed them to see more easily where the lorry was going when reversing. The new system also reduced the costs associated with reversing accidents to one-quarter of the original level.

Overturning

Vehicles overturn for a number of reasons – for example, when travelling on steep slopes, on slippery surfaces or on soft ground or when they are overloaded, unevenly loaded, travelling too fast around a corner or carrying loads at a dangerous height.

Drivers must wear seat belts, follow safety procedures and be trained to spot dangers in advance. There is a legal requirement for many types of vehicle to have rollover protection – for example, some grass cutters and tractors – but drivers must still wear seat belts if they are to be effective.

Legal requirements

The Road Vehicle (Construction and Use) Regulations 1986 (as amended) cover all aspects of vehicles including weights and dimensions, safety items and environmental standards. The specific guidance for the safety of transport at work is in the Health and Safety Executive document HSG 136 Workplace transport safety – Guidance for employers.

The Provision and Use of Work Equipment Regulations 1998 require lift trucks that need a seated ride-on operator to be fitted with a restraining system, such as a seat belt, if a risk assessment indicates a risk of the vehicle rolling over and the operator falling from the operating position and being crushed between the truck and the ground. The regulations also require operators to be trained to use the equipment safely.

Under The Workplace (Health, Safety and Welfare) Regulations 1992 employers must organise workplaces to ensure that vehicles and pedestrians can move about safely.

Workplace transport checklist

Workplace
Vehicles and pedestrians kept apart?

Layout
Crossing points on vehicle routes?
Parking for employees?
Parking for customers?
Any sharp bends or blind corners?
Is a one-way system needed?
Are routes wide enough?
Do the routes have well constructed, even surfaces and are they well maintained?
Are the routes free from obstruction?
Are the routes marked?
Are signs necessary?
Are any special facilities needed, such as mirrors on blind bends?

Vehicle
Does the vehicle have parking brakes?
Has the vehicle got a horn, lights, reflectors and reversing lights?
Are the seats provided with seat belts?
Is the driver provided with adequate protection against adverse weather or hazards?
Is it easy to get on and off the vehicle?
Does the driver need protection in case the vehicle turns over or if the load, or parts of it, fall off?
Is the vehicle included in a maintenance programme?
Are reversing alarms and rear view mirrors fitted to the vehicle?

Driver
Does the driver carry out basic safety checks before using the vehicle?
Has the driver passed the required tests for the vehicle he or she is driving?
Is there a planned programme of training and testing drivers, including refresher training?
Does the driver follow the vehicle routes?
Has the driver been trained in loading and unloading?
Is everyone using the site, including contractors, aware of the site safety rules?
Loading and unloading
Is loading and unloading done away from passing vehicles and pedestrians?
Are vehicles stabilised during loading and unloading?
Is the load stability checked before unloading and during loading?

Parking
Do drivers use the parking areas provide for their vehicles?
Are the parking brakes used?

Reversing
Is there a designated reversing area?
Is it practicable to prohibit pedestrians from entering the reversing area?
Is there someone present to direct the reversing of vehicles?

Stress

Stress can be described as an adverse reaction that some people have to external pressure. Many employees find it difficult to admit that they are experiencing stress as a result of their work and may be reluctant to report the problem for fear of stigma. Other people openly doubt that stress really exists. However, stress has overtaken musculoskeletal disorders as the biggest stated cause of working days lost through injury or ill-health. Statistics indicate that the health, education, local and central government and financial services sectors have the highest incidence and prevalence of work-related stress.

Key words and phrases

stress – an adverse reaction to external pressure.

Duty and balance

Whatever your own views on the issue, you need to be aware that stress is very real for some people and can make them ill. What is more, employers have a legal duty to ensure that employees are not made ill by their work activities.

Some employers are moving towards introducing the concept of a work-home life balance: the employer encourages employees to adopt healthy lifestyles and tries to ensure that the workplace makes a beneficial contribution to the health of the workforce. This can contribute to the control of stress in the workplace.

Recognising stress

If you are to deal effectively with the causes of stress, you need to know how to recognise the symptoms of stress, how it affects the individual, and what the effect might be on the business.

The symptoms of employee stress vary but may include:

- lack of concentration
- changes in a person's normal behaviour or mood
- raised blood pressure
- frequent headaches
- poor relationships with other staff
- being irritable
- showing indecisiveness
- drinking or smoking more than normal
- loss of appetite or weight
- backache
- ulcers.

Some people can suffer sleeplessness, indigestion and fatigue. In severe cases, stress can lead to mental problems – such as depression or even a nervous breakdown – or to heart disease. However, you also need to recognise that there is a difference between stress and pressure. Some external pressures can have positive effects, helping us to be more productive. Some people actually thrive under short-term added pressure, and our bodies are designed to meet these short-term demands.

Risks

Employees are more likely to be affected by stress if the work activities are poorly organised, if there is an ineffective manager or if the views and interests of the staff are usually ignored by managers.

If even a few workers suffer from stress, other employees can be affected and this may ultimately affect the organisation's prospects. For example, there may be increased absence because of sickness, poor work performance, poor timekeeping or an increase in customer complaints. Employees suffering from stress are more likely to be involved in accidents. There may also be a financial impact – for instance, if staff claim personal compensation for workplace stress.

Finding out if there is stress in the workplace

Find out what the level of stress is, if any, in your workplace. First of all, speak to the staff about the pressures of work and how they are coping. Find out if staff are regularly late for work and if the rate of absenteeism has increased. Low morale, a low rate of work and productivity and increased staff turnover may indicate stress in the workforce.

Involve the staff in identifying whether stress exists in the workplace. Their involvement could include surveys, questionnaires, discussions and suggestions about improvements in work practices.

The triggers for stress

The issues that can lead to employee stress are generally signs of poor management. Features of a workplace that often generate low morale and subsequent poor performance include:

- poor communication between the management and employees
- an employer's expectation that employees will work late without pay and will take work home
- blame – if things go wrong, the employer blames the employees without first examining the circumstances
- insufficient appropriate training in health and safety
- managers who ignore health and safety rules
- poor organisation of work activities
- bullying and harassment in the workplace
- uncertainty about the company's prospects
- job insecurity
- inadequate support from managers and colleagues
- conflict between different parts of the organisation
- individuals' inability to cope with the pressures of work, or with pressures outside work
- boring and repetitive tasks
- the feeling that staff have no power or influence in the workplace.

Controls

One of the first things to do is to carry out a risk assessment for stress in the workplace. This could include looking out for the work activities that could lead to stress and examining the current methods of dealing with stress, if such methods already exist. The assessment could be part of your job.

Organisational controls

Managers and supervisors should listen to employees' ideas and to talk them through. It may be appropriate for managers to consider asking staff to contribute to designing the way they carry out their work, bearing in mind the safety and production targets. This can improve motivation, safety and work performance.

Communication within the business should also be reviewed. Introduce new ways of keeping employees informed about any alterations in their work activities – for example, set up weekly update meetings or a newsletter.

Make sure that the work environment is well controlled and does not contain any hazards which might increase the risk of stress – for instance, a noisy machine near to staff who need sustained concentration.

Supervisors might be able to organise the work more efficiently by making sure that individuals are suited to the job – for instance, by matching their skills, experience and temperament to a particular job. Train workers to become more competent, so that they increase their efficiency and confidence and take responsibility for, and ownership of, the job they do.

Introduce a system that identifies any bullying or harassment in the workplace, and ensure that managers and supervisors are not themselves inadvertently bullying staff or putting undue pressure on them. Clear and thorough procedures for grievances or complaints can help you to deal with these issues.

Supervisors could also create a team atmosphere by introducing regular meetings to discuss the work and how it is going. Encourage staff to make suggestions on how the work can be done better. Make sure that everyone knows what is expected of them and that there are clear objectives and targets in their work activities. Where possible, vary the work by moving people between jobs (but not against their will). Managers could consider varying working hours of employees and, where appropriate, supervisors should advise managers to do so.

Try to keep an open mind about what staff say about work pressures, and do not brush the issue aside. If an employee complains about stress, you should tackle the cause of the problem: involving him or her in the investigation and any decision-making will help.

Where the causes of stress cannot be controlled, consider moving the employee to other suitable work and suggest counselling. If the employee takes sick leave, keep in touch with him or her to find out how he or she is progressing.

Training and assistance

Give as much support to individuals as possible – offer encouragement, treat staff with respect and ensure that they are well trained for the job they are doing.

Where employees do suffer from stress offer them counselling for example, to help them recover from the illness. Don't overlook your peers and superiors: they may suffer stress, too. For example, stress management courses should be available for supervisors and for members of the management team.

Call centre problems

Staff at call centres are prone to stress. The staff need a high level of concentration, but the work of dealing with the public can be exhausting. There are usually very tight time targets for handling each call, the work is often highly repetitive and there is rarely flexibility in what the worker can say and what they can do to follow up the call. Many workers also have to work long and anti-social hours. Some have been known to 'burn out' after only a few months.

A survey of workers at one call centre showed that stress was made worse for 66 per cent of workers whose telephone calls were constantly monitored. Only 15 per cent of those questioned felt that background noise levels were comfortable and high noise levels made listening and speaking difficult for 82 per cent. A total of 66 per cent had experienced pain in the hands, wrists and back.

The company has now introduced controls, including:

- introducing regular rest breaks

- implementing good communication and consultation procedures between staff and managers

- bringing in flexible working arrangements

- training staff specifically to deal with stressful situations such as calls from aggressive clients.

Time will tell whether levels of self-assessed stress have reduced.

Management standards for work-related stress

The Health and Safety Executive has introduced management standards for work-related stress. The standards aim to help employers to manage stress, reduce its impact and help the overall performance of the business. The standards present a set of conditions that help organisations to achieve high levels of health, well-being and organisational performance. Employers can use the standards to assess how well their organisation performs. If the standards fall short, the employer can then introduce measures to improve performance. The standards are based on six key sources of occupational stress:

- demands

- control

- support

- relationships

- role

- change.

Occupational health
Hazardous substances

Around 10,000 people die each year from work-related ill health. Many of these deaths are due to exposure to substances hazardous to health. The substances can enter the body and react with it, causing immediate poisoning, or can gradually build up in concentration in the body, leading eventually to long-term illness or death.

Chemicals are the most commonly used hazardous substances in the workplace. They are the main focus of this chapter. There are also other substances that can cause ill health or harm, such as dust and biological agents, or are classed as 'dangerous', such as flammable materials and explosive atmospheres (which are discussed on pages 323 to 327).

Key words and phrases

acute – in the context of health, an immediate effect on health.

asthmagen – a substance that cause sensitisation of the human airways, often leading to medical conditions such as asthma.

carcinogen – a substance that can cause cancer.

CHIP (or CHIP3) – abbreviations for The Chemicals (Hazard Information and Packaging for Supply) Regulations 2002.

chronic – in the context of health and safety, a persisting and life-threatening illness that may take a considerable time to develop, usually after prolonged or repeated low-level exposure to a hazard.

competent – in relation to health and safety at work, a description of someone capable of carrying out work in a safe and healthy manner appropriate to the level of responsibility.

COSHH – the common abbreviation for one of the main pieces of legislation dealing with hazardous substances: The Control of Substances Hazardous to Health Regulations 2002 and amendments.

dose – in the context of hazardous substances, the amount of a harmful substance absorbed into the body.

DSEAR – the common abbreviation for The Dangerous Substances and Explosive Atmospheres Regulations 2002.

hazardous substance – any substance that is defined as being toxic, very toxic, harmful/irritant or corrosive, or is a biological agent or dust of any kind present in the air at above a defined concentration. The phrase includes substances that have been assigned a workplace exposure limit (WEL).

health surveillance – the systematic monitoring of the health of an employee who may be exposed to harmful substances or harmful work activities.

hierarchy of control – a well tested system of graded health and safety controls.

mutagen – a substance that may cause inherited genetic damage.

personal protective equipment (PPE) – anything designed to be worn or held by someone at work to protect against one or more workplace hazards.

REACH – an abbreviation for a European Community Regulation on chemicals and their safe use (Regulation (EC) No. 1907/2006), which deals with the Registration, Evaluation, Authorisation and Restriction of Chemical Substances.

safety data sheet (SDS) – a document that must be provided by product manufacturers or suppliers to give vital information for using the product safely. Also sometimes referred to as 'COSHH sheets' or material safety data sheets (MSDS).

toxicity – a measure of a substance's potential to cause harm.

workplace exposure limit (WEL) – the maximum concentration of an airborne substance, averaged over a specified time, to which employees may be exposed by inhalation under any circumstances.

Types and states of substance

A **hazardous substance** is one that is defined as being one or more of the following:

Hazardous substances include biological agents such as these Aspergillus mould spores that are responsible for causing the respiratory disease farmer's lung.

- harmful or irritant

- toxic

- very toxic

- corrosive

- a biological agent

- a dust of any kind above a defined concentration in the air.

The term hazardous substance includes substances that have been assigned a workplace exposure limit (WEL) – see page 226.

Hazardous substances can be in the form of a:

Hazardous substances include gases and fumes.

- solid

- liquid

- gas

- vapour

- fume

- dust

- mist.

To save repetition, the word *chemical* is used throughout the chapter to cover all these forms. If there are any specific issues about the hazards, risks and controls applicable to a chemical in the form of fumes, gases or dust, they are outlined separately.

The use of chemicals

Virtually every workplace uses at least one chemical in its day-to-day activities that is hazardous to human health. Such chemicals include bleach, disinfectant and detergent in cleaning products used in many businesses; acids and alkalis used in hospital laboratories; clothing dyes in the textile industry; flour in the baking industry; solvents in the printing and the motoring industries; adhesives in offices; diesel in public transport vehicles; pesticides on farms; chlorine in swimming pools; and paints and cement in the construction industry.

Some substances that are hazardous to health are produced for commercial, industrial or domestic use in containers that are labelled with information about the safe use of the product. Other hazardous substances are *by-products* of processes, such as flour dust in a bakery and wood dust in a sawmill, or are *waste products*, such as incontinence pads from a nursing home.

The production, use and disposal of substances hazardous to health are strictly regulated. Many chemicals must not be used in particular circumstances because they are so dangerous. Where there is no alternative and such chemicals must be used, strict controls must be followed.

Hazards

Hazardous substances can have one or more of the following effects:

- irritant – they irritate the skin or eyes, for example
- corrosive – they weaken or destroy metal and other material
- toxic – they are poisonous when consumed
- flammable – they catch fire easily
- explosive – they cause an explosion
- allergenic – they cause an allergic reaction such as asthma or difficulty in breathing
- carcinogenic – they can cause cancer
- mutagenic – they can cause genetic changes in the next generation (mutation)
- pathogenic – they can cause disease (the term is applied to micro-organisms, such as harmful types of bacteria and viruses)
- radioactive – they emit radioactive particles and can cause cancer or radiation sickness.

Risks

The level of risk from substances harmful to health depends on the **toxicity** and **dose** of a chemical. Toxicity is a measure of a chemical's potential to cause harm, while the dose is the amount of chemical that is absorbed into the body.

The effect on health depends on the chemical's concentration and the time that an organ or tissue is subjected to the substance. Some substances have an *immediate* (or **acute**) effect on health, such as a skin rash. Other symptoms, such as a malignant tumour, usually arise from repeated small doses that accumulate in the body and eventually cause harm or early death. These are referred to as **chronic** effects.

A number of factors are considered when assessing the risk from these substances. They include:

- how the chemical gets into the body (see pages 11 to 13)
- the effect on the body
- how quickly the body responds to the substance, because people react at different rates and to different extents
- how often and for how long the exposure occurs
- whether the employee is working directly with the substance, or whether it is being used in the immediate surrounding area, or somewhere farther away in the workplace

The orange-coloured areas on the X-ray of these lungs are scarred fibrous tissue and inflammation resulting from lung silicosis, a form of pneumoconiosis.

- whether the employee is in the area where there has been an accidental release or spill

- if the person is wearing contaminated clothes or has come into contact with contaminated surfaces

- if contamination is passed from contaminated clothes on to people's skin.

An increased risk of exposure to hazardous substances occurs if:

- containers leak

- liquids are spilt

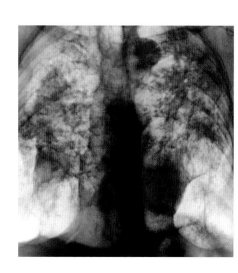

- large amounts of the substance are split into smaller packages

- substances that react with each other are mixed accidentally (and create dangerous vapours or gases, for example).

Limiting the risk

Some substances are designated a legally enforceable **workplace exposure limit** (WEL) in the workplace. This limits the concentration of hazardous substances permitted in the air. (The WEL replaced the previous occupational exposure standard and maximum exposure limit.)

The workplace exposure limit is the maximum concentration of an airborne substance, averaged over a specified time, to which employees may be exposed by inhalation under any circumstances. Some of the substances with a WEL are arsenic, cadmium, hardwood and softwood dusts, cyanides, flour dust and petroleum fume. Where a WEL is specified, it cannot be exceeded in the workplace.

Controls

Employers must, by law, operate strict controls over substances hazardous to health. The general obligations are specified in The Control of Substances Hazardous to Health Regulations 2002 (as amended), often referred to as COSHH.

The Control of Substances Hazardous to Health Regulations

Under **COSHH** employees must have specific information about the controls necessary to reduce the risk of harm from the particular substances used or produced in their workplaces. A specific requirement of the law is to ensure that exposure to **asthmagens**, **mutagens** and **carcinogens** is reduced to a level that is as low as reasonably practicable.

There must be adequate control of exposure to the substances hazardous to health. Adequate control means not exceeding the WEL, but keeping to the limit or below. Employers must apply eight principles of good practice:

1 design and operate processes and activities to minimise the emission, release and spread of substances hazardous to health

2 take into account all relevant routes of exposure – such as inhalation, skin absorption, injection and ingestion – when developing control measures

3 control exposure by measures that are proportionate to the health risk

4 choose the most effective and reliable control options which minimise the escape and spread of substances hazardous to health

5 provide, in combination with other control measures, suitable personal protective equipment in circumstances where the adequate control of exposure cannot be achieved in other ways

6 check and review regularly all elements of control measures for their continuing effectiveness

7 inform and train all employees on the hazards and risks from the substances with which they work and the use of control measures developed to minimise the risks

8 ensure that the introduction of specific control measures does not increase the overall risk to health and safety.

To implement these principles, employers must:

- assess the risk
- decide what precautions are needed
- prevent or adequately control exposure
- ensure that staff continue to carry out control measures
- monitor the exposure
- carry out appropriate health surveillance
- prepare plans and procedures to deal with accidents, incidents and emergencies
- ensure that employees are properly informed, trained and supervised.

COSHH risk assessment

The first step in the process of control is to carry out a COSHH risk assessment. Employers have a duty to carry out a suitable and sufficient assessment of the risks created by work that involves any substance that is hazardous to health. *Any* work that is likely to expose someone to substances hazardous to health should be assessed in an appropriate way. The aim is to evaluate the risks to health that could develop from work activities involving the substances.

The assessment helps organisations to decide:

- the control measures necessary to protect employees
- whether exposure monitoring and health surveillance are needed
- what information, instruction and training need to be provided.

Every substance used at work must be assessed for safety: in this workshop the dust from cutting wood and MDF is a hazard. The findings of the assessment should be explained to staff and information given about any necessary precautions, such as wearing personal protective equipment or limiting exposure time.

It also enables employers to comply with the relevant legislation and demonstrate that they have considered all the factors relevant to the safety of the work.

The assessment must be reviewed regularly and whenever the assessment is thought to be invalid or if there has been a significant change in the work. Most assessments need to be recorded and the findings communicated to the employees who are affected.

You might question whether you need an assessment for every substance in the workplace, including, for example, correction fluid. The answer is: yes. You need to do an assessment for every hazardous substance. Do bear in mind, however, that an assessment of common substances that are low risk will be short and easy to complete.

Competence

Anyone who carries out a COSHH assessment must have the necessary information, instruction and training, and must be **competent** to do the job. The person who does the assessment needs a knowledge and understanding of the regulations and the approved code of practice. He or she should know the workplace, the employees, the systems of work, the processes and procedures and also the available control measures.

The assessment

The steps to be taken in a COSHH assessment include the following:

- identify the substances hazardous to health in your workplace

- find out how the substances can enter the body (see material safety data sheets on page 229)

- identify the potential effects of the substance

- study the working processes and procedures where hazardous substances are involved; look at the existing controls and decide whether they are effective or not

- find out who is at risk

- decide what the risk is where people may be exposed

- estimate the exposure level and how long it may last

- choose the steps to take, using the **hierarchy of control** (see page 230)

- prepare for unplanned events, such as the accidental release of harmful substances, making sure that the workplace is organised so that employees can control any deterioration in, or failure of, a system that leads to the release of a harmful substance

- decide whether you need to monitor the quality of the air in the workplace and whether employee health surveillance should be introduced

- make sure that employees are properly informed, trained and supervised.

The significant findings must be recorded and communicated to employees.

Sources of information that could assist in the COSHH risk assessment include:

- material safety data sheets (see below)
- audits and inspections carried out for the specific purpose of COSHH or other general health and safety purposes
- informal discussion with staff
- purchasing records
- monitoring records of substances generated by the organisation, such as dust and compound chemicals (those of two or more elements that are chemically united)
- accident records
- health surveillance records.

Safety data sheets

These are documents that must be supplied with a hazardous substance (usually dangerous chemicals) by the manufacturer or supplier. They provide all the information necessary to devise procedures to use the substance safely. They can provide a great deal of information towards a COSHH risk assessment.

Safety data sheets include:

- general information about the manufacturer or supplier
- specific information about the product including workplace exposure limits where they exist
- the hazards associated with the substance
- advice on the handling and use of the substance
- the personal protective equipment to be used
- how to store the substance
- how to dispose of the substance safely
- advice on emergency procedures, if a spill or a fire should occur
- advice on first aid for the effects of inhalation, ingestion and eye and skin contact.

Another important source of information about hazardous substances is the container label or the packaging in which the substance is supplied. This information must by law include:

- the name of the chemical or chemicals in the formulation of the product
- the hazards involved in handling the container and using the chemical
- the precautions needed when handling the chemical.

The container itself must be suitable to prevent contamination and leaks. Some chemicals have to be provided with child-resistant openings to prevent young children swallowing the contents. Some have a tactile danger warning (a small raised triangle) for blind and partially sighted people.

Assessment failure

A painter went to hospital complaining about a throbbing pain in the tip of his right index finger. He always wore gloves at work and had not had any previous problems, but he had been using a new cleaning fluid at work. The fluid contained hydrofluoric acid which is used, for example, in the production of plastics, electronics and computer chips; for metal cleaning; and in household products, such as rust removers and heavy duty cleaning products. Hydrofluoric acid is corrosive and can cause severe chemical burns. It is also highly irritating to the respiratory system and is very toxic if swallowed. Clearly the COSHH assessment had not been adequate to prevent the painter from being injured.

Hierarchy of control

There is a specific hierarchy of control for substances hazardous to health:

1. the first choice is to eliminate the substance from the workplace

2. the second choice is to substitute it with a less hazardous substance

3. the third choice is to introduce plant, processes, procedures and systems of work to prevent exposure to the substance

4. the fourth choice is to use general or local ventilation or an enclosure

5. the fifth choice is to limit the number of people exposed to the substance and the time they are exposed

6. as a last resort, use personal protective equipment (PPE).

First of all, if a substance is hazardous to health and there is an unacceptable risk from it, you should either eliminate it from your work procedures or substitute a new substance which does the same job but with no, or less, risk to health. It is important to note that if you substitute the hazardous substance, you must take into account all of the possible hazards presented by the substitute. If it is not possible to substitute the hazardous substance, you could change the method of working, so that the operation creating the exposure is not necessary.

The method of working can be changed to control exposure to the hazardous substance (particularly carcinogens) by:

- using processes that minimise the production of the hazardous substance

- partially enclosing the process and using local exhaust ventilation
- using local exhaust ventilation alone (receiving and capturing)
- using general ventilation so that the substance is diluted to such a degree that it is harmless
- restricting the number of employees exposed to the substance
- restricting the time that employees are exposed to the substance
- labelling containers clearly
- designing a safe system of work for handling the substance.

If the method of work cannot be changed so as to achieve adequate control, you must use personal protective equipment to control exposure to the substance.

All control measures including engineering control, PPE, systems of work and supervision should be checked and maintained at suitable intervals.

Monitoring and health surveillance

Health surveillance is the systematic monitoring of the health of an employee who may be exposed to harmful substances or harmful work activities.

In certain circumstances, you should monitor the airborne concentrations of substances hazardous to health. This *environmental monitoring* is the continuous or repeated measurement of hazardous substances in the work environment to evaluate exposure and possible danger to workers, visitors or members of the public. The measurements obtained are used to decide whether the workplace exposure limit for the substance has been exceeded or not. If it has, then action must be taken to reduce the levels of the hazardous substance in the workplace to an acceptable level. Whether monitoring is necessary depends on the substance, the control measures used and the level of the substance in the air.

You can use personal sampling equipment to measure the occupational exposure of individual employees. This should be done at least every 12 months for continuous processes or where an employee is exposed to the hazard regularly. A competent person should do the monitoring.

Records must be made and kept, by law, for 40 years for individuals and 5 years for employees in general.

Where people work with certain substances or processes (see page 136), employers must keep the employees under suitable health surveillance and, by law, must keep those health records for at least 40 years.

Dealing with accidents, incidents and emergencies

Plan for emergencies by designing emergency procedures to be followed in the event of a spill or an adverse reaction between chemicals. Organise safe systems for disposal and cleaning up, and make sure that there is sufficient personal protective equipment available and facilities for decontaminating people.

Information, instruction and training

According to COSHH and The Dangerous Substances and Explosive Atmospheres Regulations 2002 – usually known as **DSEAR** – employers must provide appropriate information, instruction and training so that employees recognise the health hazards and understand the risks in their workplaces and take suitable precautions. The information could include:

- what the hazard and its risks are and how serious they are
- any control measures necessary, why they are needed and how to use them
- whether personal protective equipment is provided and why
- any environmental monitoring or health surveillance being carried out and arrangements for access to the employee's own records.

Where it is felt that there is no competent person in the workplace to carry out a COSHH assessment properly, consider contracting a health and safety consultant to advise managers and supervisors or to do the assessment.

Carcinogenic and mutagenic substances and biological agents

The controls for **carcinogenic** or **mutagenic** substances and biological agents are stricter than those for other substances hazardous to health. They are often necessary in hospitals, laboratories, clinics and veterinary surgeries.

The risk assessments must include, for example, the hazards, control measures, operational instructions and procedures, use of personal protective equipment, monitoring procedures, health surveillance procedures and consultation arrangements with employees.

Good practice

Handling and storing

Employees who use hazardous substances must be made aware of the risks and know how to protect their health and safety.

Several good practices can be followed when handling or storing hazardous substances. They include:

- good housekeeping standards
- the provision of safe storage (see safety data sheets above)
- the safe disposal of hazardous waste (see safety data sheets above)
- appropriate employee facilities for washing, changing and for storing clothing

- banning staff from eating or drinking in work areas
- good personal hygiene standards among staff
- the provision of warning signs
- the use of closed and labelled containers.

Welfare facilities

The employer must provide adequate washing facilities so that employees can avoid contaminating themselves or their clothes. Storage for clothing should be provided where there is a risk that the employees' own clothing will become contaminated.

To prevent staff from swallowing substances hazardous to health, there should be a ban on eating and drinking while using hazardous substances or anywhere that is not specifically designated for meals and breaks. Where possible, facilities for eating and drinking should be set up in an uncontaminated area.

Maintaining safety controls and equipment

Employers must take all reasonable steps possible to ensure that everything provided for the protection of employees is used or applied properly as intended. Employers must also ensure that control measures in place are maintained adequately and that, where engineering controls are provided, they are tested regularly and examined. For example, local exhaust ventilation should be examined at least once every 14 months, depending on the substance being controlled. If respiratory protective equipment is provided, it must be examined and tested at regular intervals. Records of the examinations and tests of equipment and PPE must be kept for at least five years.

Hazard warning panel

Panels such as the one shown should be displayed on road vehicles carrying a hazardous substance. The background is orange and the lettering is black, except for a section showing a coloured hazard warning diamond symbol on a white background. The panel carries the following information:

- emergency action code – commonly known as the HAZCHEM code – which is designed to be used with emergency action scale cards that are carried by the emergency services. The cards indicate the action necessary in the first few minutes of an incident

- substance identification number (based on a list produced by the United Nations), sometimes with the chemical name included with the identification number

- the telephone number that brings into operation the Chemsafe scheme organised by the UK Chemical Industries Association

- hazard warning diamond that shows that the contents of the vehicle are dangerous and the broad nature of the hazard

- manufacturer's name and logo.

Legal requirements

Under The Control of Substances Hazardous to Health Regulations 2002 (as amended) employers must assess the risks to health created by work with any substances hazardous to health. They must prevent or control exposure to substances hazardous to health; maintain, examine and test control measures; monitor workplace exposure; arrange health surveillance; provide information, instruction and training for people who may be exposed to substances hazardous to health; and make arrangements to deal with accidents, incidents and emergencies.

The Dangerous Substances and Explosive Atmospheres Regulations 2002 – DSEAR – cover substances including petrol, liquefied petroleum gas (LPG), paints, varnishes, solvents and dusts which, when mixed with air, could cause an explosive atmosphere – for example, dusts from milling and sanding operations. There is more about these substances and the regulations in 'Flammable and explosive substances' on pages 323 to 327.

The Chemicals (Hazard Information and Packaging for Supply) Regulations 2002 – often abbreviated to CHIP or CHIP3 – require suppliers (manufacturers, importers, distributors, wholesalers and retailers) to provide information about the dangers of chemicals and to package them safely. Since 2004 biocides and plant protection products also have to be classified and labelled according to CHIP.

Suppliers must identify the hazards of the chemical. This is known as 'classification'. They must give information about the hazards to their customers. Usually this is on the package and, if supplied for use at work, in a safety data sheet (SDS). They must also package the chemical safely.

A new European system of information on hazardous chemicals came into force in 2007. Known as REACH, for short, it is Regulation (EC) No. 1907/2006 and deals with the registration, evaluation, authorisation and restriction of chemical substances.

The aim of REACH is to improve the protection of human health and the environment through the better and earlier identification of the properties of chemical substances. The REACH Regulation gives greater responsibility to industry to manage the risks from chemicals and to provide safety information on the substances.

Manufacturers and importers are required to provide information on the properties of their chemical substances, to help employers to organise safe systems of work, and to register the information at a central database run by the European Chemicals Agency (ECHA) in Helsinki. The Regulation also aims to progressively substitute the most dangerous chemicals when suitable alternatives have been identified.

Feature

Asbestos

Asbestos is a soft mineral rock consisting of tiny fibres that can be released into the air when it is cut, damaged or deteriorating.

Its heat-resistant properties meant that the substance was frequently used in the past for insulating boilers and pipes; for making fire blankets, brake linings and clutches; and in building materials, such as wall or ceiling boards.

Such uses have now stopped, but it is estimated that there are still two million industrial or commercial buildings (about three-quarters of commercial buildings) containing asbestos in the UK and more than two million domestic premises.

The inhalation of asbestos fibres is now a recognised factor in several lung diseases. For example, asbestosis is a form of fibrosis causing scarring of the lung tissue which results in profound shrinkage of the lungs. The symptoms include breathlessness, a dry cough and cyanosis (blue fingers and lips due to lack of oxygen in the blood).

Asbestos is also a carcinogen (cancer-causing substance) and can cause lung cancer. It can be recognised in the sputum and by X-rays.

The main types of asbestos are:

- chrysotile – white asbestos
- amosite – brown asbestos
- crocidolite – blue asbestos.

Asbestosis occurs only after heavy occupational exposure to asbestos over a number of years. Typically, the time between exposure and the development of symptoms is 20 years or more.

Mesothelioma, which is relatively rare, can occur after short exposure to low doses of asbestos. It is the name given to malignant tumours which develop in the pleura and peritoneum.

The carcinogenic potential of asbestos is related to the physical size of the fibre and not to its chemical composition. The harmful fibres are generally longer than 5 micrometres with a diameter of less than 3 micrometres.

When working with asbestos the following hierarchy of control should be used.

- Enclose completely the area or equipment where work is being carried out.
- Put in place safe systems of work.
- Test local environmental ventilation every six months.
- Provide personal protective equipment.

The COSHH Regulations do not apply to asbestos, which is covered by The Control of Asbestos at Work Regulations 2006 – see page 235.

Duty holders – employers in occupation of premises and the owner or managing agent of a property – must identify the materials containing asbestos, assess the materials' condition, prepare a written register and create an asbestos management plan. (The plan must consider the implications of the asbestos for 50 years from the creation of the original asbestos plan.)

Unless they can prove otherwise, the duty holders should presume that materials contain asbestos and treat them accordingly.

Duty holders must decide on priorities for action. A survey of the building is not a legal requirement but it can provide invaluable evidence on which to base the asbestos management plan.

Accredited or certified asbestos surveyors should be employed to advise duty holders on the asbestos management plan. The asbestos surveyors should have experience of surveying commercial premises, have used the Health and Safety Executive's guidance on the surveying, sampling and assessment of asbestos-containing materials, and have professional liability insurance.

The surveyor should draw up an asbestos register, giving materials a risk score, depending on their type, location, condition and surface protection, and should make recommendations for any remedial work necessary.

Asbestos in good condition should be left in place, but duty holders must inform others of the materials' location and condition, carry out regular condition checks, revise the asbestos plan and record changes as necessary.

Materials in poor condition should be sealed or enclosed, or removed by licensed removal contractors, using the hierarchy of control.

Licensed asbestos removal contractors should provide written evidence of their knowledge of working with asbestos-containing materials and supply references for work of a similar nature.

They should be able to demonstrate financial stability and be able to supply sufficient trained and medically examined workers to undertake the work. Contractors should provide copies of their health and safety policy, risk assessment and plan of work.

Employers must protect all workers, not just employees. Most at risk are plumbers, electricians and cablers because they could regularly encounter asbestos.

Duty holders also have to assess other health and safety risks to asbestos surveyors, such as working at height, in remote locations or confined spaces, or working with chemical, electrical or biological hazards.

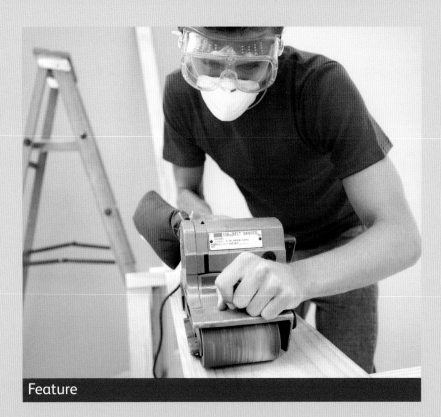

Occupational asthma

Occupational asthma occurs when workers who breathe in a chemical or biological substance at work develop a hypersensitivity that triggers a constriction of the airways.

The symptoms include severe shortness of breath, wheezing, coughing and chest tightness that can stop the employee from doing the simplest tasks. The difficulty in breathing means that many sufferers find it difficult to climb stairs or even move around. Some sufferers are unable to work again.

Short-term high exposure or lower-level exposure for an extended period can lead to asthma. Up to 1,800 people a year suffer from occupational asthma.

The most common substances that cause asthma (asthmagens) are flour or grain,

isocyanates in paint in motor vehicle repair workshops and wood dust. Vehicle paint sprayers are 80 times more likely to develop occupational asthma than other workers. More than 50 paint sprayers a year report starting to suffer from asthma, but the true figure is probably 150 annually.

Employers must assess the risk of breathing in the asthmagens and prevent exposure. The presence of asthmagen in the workplace air can be reduced by local exhaust ventilation (LEV), provided that it is maintained and kept in good working order. Operators need to be trained to use the controls correctly and supervised.

There are some common themes running through occupations where employees are at risk of developing asthma.

In the case of vehicle paint sprayers, they

should never spray outside the paint spray booth. They should measure the clearance time of the spray and not enter until that time has passed. They should wear air-fed breathing apparatus while spray mist is still in the air.

Bakers should avoid raising clouds of flour. They could, for instance, start mixers on a slow speed until wet and dry ingredients are combined and flour or icing-sugar dust is unlikely to become airborne. They should also use either dust extraction or respiratory protective equipment for dusty tasks, avoid cleaning floors with a broom or compressed-air equipment and instead use wet methods or a purpose-made industrial vacuum cleaner.

People working with wood should use dust extractors and take similar precautions to bakers, such as using respiratory protective equipment for dusty jobs (especially when sanding and cleaning), and cleaning using wet methods or an industrial vacuum cleaner.

Health surveillance also has an important role in protecting employees. Employees who are exposed, or likely to be exposed, to an asthmagen should be placed in a health surveillance programme together with those employees who do develop asthma.

Radiation

We are all exposed to natural low-level radiation from the Sun, soil, food and our own bodies every day. Radiation can give us many benefits and we rely on radiated energy for heating, lighting and technology such as medical and dental X-ray machines, smoke detectors, skin tanning equipment, nuclear power generation, CD players and laser printing. However, high levels of radiation can harm our health and the quality of our environment, so there are tight legal controls on its use and levels of personal exposure.

Key words and phrases

classified person – an employee who is exposed to an effective dose of radiation that is over a legally set level in any one year.

dosimetry – the calculation of the dose that is absorbed into body tissue and other matter as a result of exposure to ionising radiation.

effective dose – a dose of radiation to the whole body.

equivalent dose – a way of expressing a dose of radiation to one part of the body in relation to exposure of the whole body.

ion – an electrically charged atom or molecule resulting from the loss or gain of one or more electrons.

ionising radiation – electromagnetic waves (such as X-rays and gamma rays) or particles (such as alpha and beta particles) that break atoms and molecules into ions.

non-ionising radiation – part of the electromagnetic spectrum (including ultraviolet, visible and infrared light and electricity power frequencies, microwaves and radio) that leaves atoms and molecules intact.

radiation – energy emitted or transmitted either as electromagnetic waves, or as subatomic particles.

radiation employer – an employer who carries out work with ionising radiation.

What is radiation?

Radiation is energy that travels either as electromagnetic waves, or as subatomic particles. It is categorised as ionising or non-ionising radiation according to the effect it has on physical matter, such as the cells of the human body, at a molecular and atomic level.

Diagram of the electromagnetic spectrum

GAMMA RAYS   X-RAYS   ULTRA VIOLET   VISIBLE LIGHT   INFRA RED   MICROWAVES   MOBILE PHONE   TELEVISION   RADIO

Ionising radiation

Ionising radiation is the short wavelength part of the electromagnetic spectrum that occurs as electromagnetic rays – such as X-rays and gamma rays – or as particles, such as alpha and beta particles.

It arises naturally from the radioactive decay of naturally radioactive substances, such as radon, and can also be produced artificially. The practical uses of ionising radiation include medical and dental diagnosis and treatment, scientific measurement, research, teaching and power generation.

There are also radioactive forms of some chemicals – such as uranium, iodine, strontium and polonium (historically called radium F).

Ionising radiation gets its name because it is powerful enough to break molecules and atoms up into charged particles called **ions**. Exposure to ionising radiation can kill, or lead to cancer or genetic damage.

Non-ionising radiation

Non-ionising radiation is the long wavelength part of the electromagnetic spectrum which includes ultraviolet light, visible light, infrared light, microwaves and radio frequencies. (See diagram of the electromagnetic spectrum above.)

Common sources of non-ionising radiation are the Sun, sunbeds, lasers (in barcode readers and printers, for example), ultrasound machines, microwave ovens, radios, electrical supply equipment and telecommunications systems.

Non-ionising radiation leaves molecules and atoms intact, but agitates them so that they vibrate, causing heat. Overexposure can cause skin burning or blindness or lead to cancer.

Hazards and risk

Ionising radiation

Any tissue in the human body can be damaged by ionising radiation. The body attempts to repair the damage, but sometimes the damage is too severe or widespread and can result in cancer.

Low-level, or 'chronic', exposure over a long period can result in permanent damage to human DNA (the genetic information in our body cells). This can result in:

■ sterility

■ genetic defects (mutations) in embryos

■ direct damage to a child in the womb, leading to, for example, a smaller head or brain size, poorly formed eyes, abnormally slow growth and mental retardation.

The symptoms of short-term high-level, or 'acute', exposure usually appear soon after exposure. Radiation sickness can cause premature ageing or even death. If the dose is fatal, death usually occurs within two months of the exposure. The symptoms of radiation sickness include nausea, weakness, hair loss, skin burns or diminished organ function. Patients receiving radiation treatments sometimes experience acute effects because they are receiving relatively high bursts of radiation.

Radioactive substances

Some substances have particular forms that emit ionising radiation and can cause illness if they are consumed. For example, radioactive iodine contributes to thyroid cancer, while ingesting strontium can contribute to bone cancer.

Risk from ionising radiation

The level of risk from ionising radiation depends on factors such as the:

The dangers from consuming the radioactive form of some chemicals were widely publicised following the death in London of the former Russian spy Alexander Litvinenko.

■ source of the radiation

■ distance from the radiation source to the employee's normal work position

■ period of exposure

■ amount of the radioactive substance being handled or present

■ effectiveness of shielding – for example, employees working with X-rays protect their critical body organs from radiation by wearing personal protective equipment containing a lead-like material

■ effectiveness of the design and construction of any equipment to limit the range of its emissions.

People working in the nuclear industry are particularly at risk because of the highly radioactive materials they work with. Doctors, dentists and radiographers are also at risk because they work close to radiation from X-ray machines.

Non-ionising radiation

Ultraviolet radiation from the Sun and some artificial sources can be harmful to the skin and eyes. Acute symptoms are sunburn and conjunctivitis of the eye. Chronic effects include premature skin ageing, skin cancer and eye cataracts. Ultraviolet light (UV light) is made up of three types of light from the Sun – UVA, UVB and UVC. The most dangerous type is UVC, followed by UVB. All types of ultraviolet light can, however, cause skin cancer from long-term exposure.

Sunshine and sun beds

Anyone who works outdoors can be exposed to UV light from the Sun over a considerable period of time and needs to protect their skin. People working with any kind of UV tanning equipment – such as sunlamps, sunbeds and tanning booths – and their clients may be exposed to UV radiation at levels that cause skin and eye damage.

Lasers

Lasers have wide occupational use including precision welding and cutting, eye surgery, entertainment and public display, compact disc players, barcode readers, office printers and surveying. The word *laser* is an acronym for Light Amplification by Stimulated Emission of Radiation. Lasers operate at various frequencies in the electromagnetic spectrum and there are, for example, infrared lasers and ultraviolet lasers. There are four classes of laser from Class 1 (inherently safe or safe by engineering design) up to Class 4 (most hazardous).

Eyes are the most vulnerable organs to laser exposure. The body's automatic blink reflex normally protects eyes from the Class 1 lasers used in everyday technology, such as barcode readers at supermarket checkouts. Higher classification lasers, such as those used in some entertainment light shows, can cause temporary or permanent blindness if they are beamed directly into the eye. Skin burns are also possible and there is also a risk of starting a fire.

Radio waves and microwaves

There is no evidence that radio waves or microwaves cause damage to humans, although there are some unexplained clusters of cases of cancer that have been claimed to be linked to microwave communications equipment. Microwaves used in ovens agitate the water molecules in food, creating the heat that cooks or warms the food. The radiation does *not* change the structure of the molecules in the food.

Controls

Ionising radiation

Authorisation

Employers whose work involves legally specified ionising radiation are referred to as **radiation employers**. They must gain prior legal authorisation to work with ionising radiation. Work needing prior authorisation includes industrial radiography, processing of products involving ionising radiation, research, the exposure of people for medical treatment and the use of accelerators (devices that use electric fields to propel electrically charged particles to high speeds).

Risk assessment

Radiation employers must carry out risk assessments and consider such issues as the:

- nature of the sources of ionising radiation to be used
- estimated radiation dose to which anyone could be exposed
- likelihood of contamination and its spread
- results of any previous **dosimetry** (the calculation of the absorbed dose in matter and tissue resulting from the exposure to ionising radiation)
- advice of manufacturers or suppliers of equipment about its safe use
- engineering control measures already in place or planned
- planned systems of work
- estimated levels of airborne and surface contamination likely to be encountered
- effectiveness and suitability of personal protective equipment
- extent of unrestricted access to working areas where dose rates or contamination levels are likely to be significant
- consequences of possible failures of the control measures.

Restricting exposure

Radiation employers must consider the possibility of using a substitute for the ionising radiation. If this is not possible, the radiation dose that employees or others could receive must be reduced to the lowest level possible. This can be achieved in a number of ways, including introducing and maintaining:

- engineering controls, such as shielding, enclosure, local containment and ventilation
- control devices, such as key-operated locks on exposure controls, door interlocks for enclosures and emergency exposure controls (off buttons)
- warning signals (visual or audible) that alert employees to their exposure level – for instance, where exposure limits can be reached in a short time
- restricted access areas where the exposure to radiation could be above a certain level and only designated personnel may enter the area
- safe systems of work – dealing with, for example, the number of people who are authorised to enter the area of exposure or to handle, store or transport the radiation source, the method of storage, handling and transport, and procedures when engineering systems have been disabled (when aligning X-ray optics equipment, for instance).

Where there is a significant risk of spreading contamination from a designated area, measures should be put in place to restrict that risk. For example, there should be washing and changing facilities for those entering and leaving the designated area. Eating or drinking in such an area must not be allowed. Employers can set up local rules which employees must follow in obtaining access to and working in these areas.

Personal radiation dose

The personal radiation dose to employees who go into designated areas must be monitored using specific equipment for the purpose. The equipment must be maintained

There are legal dose limitations for exposure to ionising radiation such as X-rays.

and calibrated regularly and records of the tests must be kept for at least two years. Special precautions must be adopted to restrict the exposure of young people and pregnant women.

There are legal dose limitations for the **effective dose** and **equivalent dose** to employees. The effective dose limits specify the maximum dose in a specified period for:

- employees aged 18 years and over

- trainees under 18 years

- pregnant women.

The equivalent dose limits for employees deal with exposure and the period of exposure of the:

- lens of the eye

- skin

- hands, forearms, feet and ankles.

Classified persons
If an employee is likely to receive an effective dose over the legal limit in any one year, he or she must be designated as a **classified person**. The employer must make an assessment of all the doses that the person receives and record them. Special monitoring arrangements must be made for these employees.

Medical surveillance
All classified persons and employees who have received exposure over the legally set level must be placed under medical surveillance by an appointed doctor or employment medical adviser. The surveillance should include an annual medical examination. Records of the examinations must be kept for at least 50 years.

Personal protective equipment
Where exposure to radiation cannot be controlled by any other measure, employers must provide suitable specialised personal protective equipment (PPE). It might include respiratory protective equipment (as part of pressurised suits that protect against exposure to radiation particles), footwear, eye protection and lead aprons and gloves.

Personal protective equipment must be examined thoroughly at suitable intervals and maintained properly. In the case of respiratory equipment a record of the examination must be kept for two years. Employers must provide appropriate storage for the PPE for when it is not being used.

Contingency plans
Employers must prepare a contingency plan covering all reasonably foreseeable accidents. The plan must restrict employees' and others' exposure to radiation in the event of an emergency.

Management of radiation protection

Employers must consult a radiation protection adviser – a specialist competent person who can give advice on the particular working conditions.

All employees working with ionising radiation must be given appropriate training in radiation protection and be provided with information and instruction suitable for them to know the risks to their health, the precautions to be taken and the importance of medical, technical and administrative requirements. Specific information about the risk to unborn children must be given to pregnant women in the workplace.

Arrangements for the control of radioactive substances, articles and equipment

All radiation sources must be kept in a sealed container, which must be able to prevent leaks. The container must be tested for leaks regularly and the records of such tests must be kept for two years. Employers must account for and keep records of the quantity and location of the ionising radiation and keep those records for two years.

Non-ionising radiation

Outdoor workers

It is not only on the beach that skin protection is needed. People working outdoors also need to protect themselves against overexposure to ultraviolet light from the Sun.

People who work outdoors, such as construction workers, police officers and grounds maintenance personnel, should follow a six point advice code to protect themselves from overexposure to ultraviolet (UV) light from the Sun (and to take general good care of themselves).

1 Cover up – especially around midday. Ordinary clothing made from close-woven fabric, such as a long-sleeved work shirt and jeans, will stop most UV.

2 Wear a hat – a wide-brimmed hat will shade the face and head. A safety helmet will provide some shade for the head. A neck protector (usually a flap of fabric or plastic) can protect the back of the neck.

3 Stay in the shade, whenever possible, especially at lunchtime.

4 Use a high factor sunscreen of at least SPF 15 on exposed skin. Apply as directed on the product.

5 Drink plenty of water to avoid dehydration.

6 Check skin regularly for unusual spots or moles. If they have changed shape, size or colour, or are itchy or bleeding, seek immediate medical advice.

Sunbeds and other cosmetic tanning

Employers who operate ultraviolet tanning equipment must assess the risks to both employees and customers from exposure to UV radiation and take effective measures to control the risks. Employees must be given suitable information and training to enable them to take all the necessary precautions to avoid unnecessary exposure to UV. They should protect clients from

Staff working with sunbeds and other skin tanning equipment need to know how to protect themselves and their clients from overexposure to ultraviolet radiation.

exposure by controlling the duration of each tanning session, the periods between each session and the total number of sessions per year. Employees should be able to give advice to clients about the risks involved in using UV tanning equipment, how the equipment works, how they can call for help in an emergency and how long they may use the equipment during each visit. It is good practice to record the date and length of each session for each client.

Lasers

The safety precautions for Class 1 lasers (see page 242) include:

- proper maintenance of the interlocks and the security of the panels
- use only by authorised staff
- the provision of warning labels
- adequate training and supervision.

Organisations using laser products in excess of Class 2 should appoint a competent person to advise on precautions that may be necessary. The controls might include:

- the prevention of continuous viewing of a direct beam
- not aiming the beam at people, especially at head height
- the provision of sufficient information to demonstrate that the equipment can be used safely
- minimising invisible and visible radiation
- rigidly mounting equipment
- supervision by a competent person
- controls against unauthorised use
- security of the laser control console
- provision of an emergency cut-off
- engineered features, such as beam enclosure and masking
- administrative controls including barriers, warning signs, key control of equipment and staff training.

Entertainment

Organisations using lasers in the entertainment, theatre and public exhibition sectors need to carry out a viewing safety assessment of employees and audiences. Beams must not deliberately scan audiences, roadways, occupied buildings or aviation airspace so far as is reasonably practicable. Precautions should be followed in setting up and aligning laser systems and functional checks should be made before public operation. Laser radiation exposure levels should be determined in advance at all appropriate positions where the laser may be directed.

Venue owners who have laser shows at their premises have a duty to co-operate with the installer so that they can complete the laser show safely. It is good practice for venue owners to ensure that the installer has adequately assessed the safety of the laser show at their premises.

Ravers blinded

Dozens of party-goers were partially blinded when a laser light show designed for outdoor use was used in a marquee. Heavy rain had prompted the organisers to erect massive tents for the all-night event near Moscow that had originally been planned for outdoors. Lasers that would normally be aimed into the sky were used without adequate adjustment so that some light refracted into dancers' eyes, causing permanent injury.

PPE

People who may be exposed to hazardous beams (especially during alignment and setting up procedures) need to be provided with suitable protective eyewear.

Specialist equipment

Specialist equipment that are common sources of ultraviolet radiation inside buildings include:

- UV reactors (for accelerating or inducing chemical reactions)

- germicidal lamps (for sterilising benches or flow cabinets)

- transilluminators (equipment that transmits light through tissues of the body).

All these lamps have shorter wavelengths than the UVA lamps used in most sunbeds, so harm from skin or eye exposure may occur after very short inadvertent exposure. Under no circumstances should any part of the body be exposed to the UVB and UVC radiation from them. Units containing germicidal lamps should be interlocked to prevent access while the lamp is on. Transilluminators must be used with gauntleted gloves and must be used with either the fitted Perspex UV shield in place or the operator should use a separate full face shield.

Legal requirements

The main legal requirements are covered by the Radiological Protection Act 1970 and The Ionising Radiations Regulations 1999. Employers who work with materials that contain small but significant amounts of naturally occurring radioactive substances are required to take action to restrict the radiation exposure of their employees and other people who may be affected by their work. European Directive 2008/46/EC on workers' exposure to physical agents (electromagnetic fields) was adopted in 2008 and is due to be implemented by 2012.

Noise at work

Sound is all around us. Some is pleasant, some is not and we often experience sound that we do *not want* to hear. This unwanted sound is normally described as *noise*. It is often associated with loud, unpleasant sounds that can either damage your hearing or create stress.

Around two million people a year are exposed to levels of noise at work that can be harmful. More than a million people have to rely on personal protective equipment, but many are not adequately protected and 500,000 have loss of hearing as a result of exposure to noise at work. Of these it is estimated that around 170,000 workers suffer deafness, tinnitus or other ear conditions. Workers in the manufacturing and construction industries are particularly at risk.

Key words and phrases

decibel – the unit for levels of sound that is abbreviated to dB.

exposure limit value – daily or weekly exposure of 87dB(A) or a peak sound pressure of 140dB(C).

hearing protection zones – any part of the workplace where an employee is likely to be exposed to high levels of noise and protection must be worn or exposure limited.

lower exposure action values – daily or weekly exposure of 80dB(A) or a peak sound pressure of 135dB(C).

noise – unwanted sound, or sound that can damage hearing.

occupational deafness – deafness caused by exposure to high levels of noise in the workplace over long periods.

permanent threshold shift – the prolonged exposure to loud sound that can permanently damage the ears' ability to detect soft sounds. This is often referred to as 'occupational deafness'.

personal protective equipment (PPE) – anything designed to be worn or held to protect against one or more workplace hazards.

temporary threshold shift – the exposure to high levels of noise for a short period that raises the ears' threshold of response so that the person cannot hear soft sounds for a while. Recovery takes a few hours to a couple of days.

tinnitus – a medical condition in which the sufferer experiences ringing in the ears.

upper exposure action values – daily or weekly exposure of 85dB(A) or a peak sound pressure of 137dB(C).

What is sound?

Hearing protection is needed when using a pneumatic drill because the noise is above levels that are considered safe.

Sound is produced by a vibrating source and transmitted as pressure waves through the air, other gases, liquids and solids.

It is measured electronically using a meter that converts sound received by a microphone into an electric current. The resulting reading is measured in **decibels** (often abbreviated to dB).

Sound at work is usually indicated by an 'A-weighting' scale, often abbreviated to dB(A), that measures average noise levels and takes into account the impact of sound upon the human ear. Every increase of 3dB *doubles* the noise level, so a seemingly small difference in numbers can be significant for hearing damage. Exposure to sound levels below 80dB(A) is generally considered safe, but prolonged exposure to sound above 80dB(A) can damage hearing.

A 'C-weighting', often abbreviated to dB(C), is used to express peak noise levels, impact or explosive noise.

Examples of approximate sound levels

What is noise?

Noise is generally thought of as *unwanted* sound, or sound that can damage hearing, but the regulations define it as any audible sound. Acceptable levels of noise at work are determined from research over a number of years and are specified by European Directives: in Britain they are covered by The Control of Noise at Work Regulations 2005. The standards are discussed later in this chapter.

Hazards

Exposure to loud sound can lead to hearing damage – loss of hearing ability and possibly ringing in the ears. Short exposure to loud sound can leave you temporarily deaf: you may have experienced this after being at a particularly loud concert. Your hearing returns to normal after a few hours or a couple of days. This is sometimes referred to as a **temporary threshold shift**.

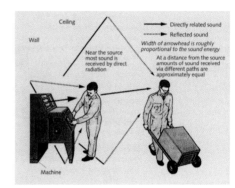

Long-term exposure to loud sound can cause permanent and irreversible damage to the hearing. This is sometimes called a **permanent threshold shift** or **occupational deafness**. In some cases, the damage to the hearing from exposure to loud continuous noise can result in a persistent ringing in the ears when the small hair-like cells in the inner ear cause an irritating echo inside the ear. This condition is referred to as **tinnitus**.

Some sources of workplace noise are more obvious than others. Construction workers, for example, are almost constantly exposed to noise from heavy machinery; ship-building workers are exposed to the noise of riveting; road maintenance workers are affected by noise from road drills and compressors; and people working with wood often have noisy circular saws nearby. In the leisure industry – for example, nightclubs, public houses and concert venues – music might be played at a volume that affects the hearing of disc jockeys, bar staff and, to a lesser degree, the customers. Even in offices there are sources of noise that need to be considered, including ventilation and heating systems, printers and telephones.

Risks

The level of the risk depends on the type of work being done, the work equipment being used and the length of exposure to noise.

The growth of call centres has raised concern about the possibility of hearing damage caused by wearing earphones and from the ambient sound levels because many people work close to each other. There is little evidence that this environment does cause hearing problems, but the repeated exposure to noise at any level can contribute to stress – see also page 221.

Loud noise can prevent effective communication between employees or can distract attention, so increasing the risk of an accident.

Controls

Employers must reduce the risk of damage to the hearing of their employees to the lowest level that is reasonably practicable.

Employers are required to:

- assess the risks to employees from noise at work
- take appropriate action to reduce the noise exposure that produces those risks
- provide employees with hearing protection if noise exposure cannot be reduced sufficiently by other means
- ensure that employees' work does not exceed the legal limits on noise exposure
- provide employees with information, instruction and training
- carry out health surveillance where there is a risk to health.

All or some of these responsibilities may be delegated to managers and supervisors. Safety representatives may be involved in risk assessments, monitoring and review.

Hierarchy of control

The provision of personal protective equipment is a last resort when other measures cannot provide adequate health and safety protection.

The hierarchy of noise control is first to eliminate the noise, if possible, then if this cannot be done, to reduce the noise at source. If this is not possible, the noise source should be enclosed. If enclosure is not possible, the room in which the noisy equipment is present should be noise-proofed. As a last resort, personal protective equipment (PPE) should be used.

Eliminate the noise source

The best control measure is to eliminate the noise source altogether by removing it from the workplace. For example, in many factories switching off the factory radio would often reduce noise below legal limits.

Reduce the noise at source

If the source of the noise, such as a machine, cannot be removed, the next best control measure is to *reduce* the noise at source. This can be done by replacing the machine with a quieter one or designing the process to be quieter.

Regular maintenance of the equipment will also assist in keeping the noise down – rattling machinery can be distracting and stressful. Some machines can be provided with anti-vibration mounts, or dampers, that reduce the noise that is amplified by the surface it is standing on.

Noise limiters can be fitted to some machines: they stop the machine from operating if the noise reaches certain levels. This is a common control in music and dance venues.

Silencers at an exhaust point can also reduce noise from a source, such as diesel generators or ventilation plants.

Using distance and enclosure

If the noise at source cannot be reduced, the distance between the source of the noise and the staff can be increased. Alternatively, an acoustic barrier can be placed between the noise source and the staff. An acoustic enclosure (or booth) could also be used to completely enclose the noise source. Pipes carrying hot fluids or steam that create noise can be lagged.

Limiting exposure

If the noise is still above the acceptable level (see 'Noise risk assessments' on page 253), limit the time that staff are exposed to the noise. This can be done by work rotation or by giving workers frequent breaks away from the noisy work area.

Personal protective equipment

The last resort is to isolate the workers from the noise source by organising their work within an acoustic refuge or by providing them with hearing protection. Ear defenders or ear plugs can be used for personal protection (see page 363). If they are needed, employers must provide them to all employees who are exposed to excessive noise and to those who ask for them. Employees who are exposed to excessive noise must use them. The **personal protective equipment** (PPE) must be maintained and repaired at the expense of the employer.

If the overall level of noise being heard by the ear needs to be reduced, then look for ear protection to deal with a wide range of frequencies. If one particular frequency is a problem, choose ear protection specifically designed to deal with that frequency. It may be as simple as matching the noise data from the machine's manufacturer to the EN rating on the PPE.

Ear protection should be a comfortable fit for the wearer and there should be a good seal between the protective equipment and the ear – the wearer needs to be happy with the type provided. The type of ear protection should also be capable of remaining hygienic, so the amount of airborne contamination in the work environment should be considered and staff should be instructed how to keep the equipment clean and to maintain it generally. Ear protection will only protect if worn all of the time while the wearer is exposed to noise.

Supervisors should check that ear protection is worn as the manufacturer intended. Ear plugs not being inserted fully or ear defenders being worn with personal music players can stop the PPE from doing the job it was designed to do. It is also important to ensure that the use of ear defenders does not lead to other hazards and risks – a refuse worker was hit by a car, for example, because he was wearing very effective ear defenders and did not hear the car coming.

There are a number of other disadvantages in using ear defenders and ear plugs:

- purchase costs
- availability
- discomfort for the wearer
- the difficulty of having a conversation
- difficulty of hearing warning signals, such as audio alarms, when they are worn
- cost of maintenance and replacement.

Other measures

Where there is general noise produced from a number of sources which cannot be controlled by the means already described, the design of the workplace can be important in limiting the level of noise in the workplace. This involves the use of soft furnishings, carpets, sound-absorbing materials, partitions and acoustic ceiling tiles.

Noise risk assessments

In some circumstances where noise levels in the workplace are complicated or high – at or above a level where the law requires employers to introduce protective measures for employees' hearing (see below) – employers may need specialist help to assess the problem. Where a specialist is required, employers should engage a competent noise consultant to carry out a noise risk assessment and give advice.

The assessment should provide managers, supervisors and safety representatives with enough appropriate information for making decisions about ways to reduce the noise exposure of staff.

Who is exposed and where

The risk assessment should identify all employees likely to be exposed to noise and the work areas where action levels of noise are likely to be exceeded (see below).

Exposure level and duration

The noise assessment needs to make a reasonable estimate of employees' exposure to noise that must be controlled. The assessment should compare the measured noise levels to the noise standards used in legislation. Measures for eliminating or reducing risks should be identified – according to the hierarchy of noise control (page 251 to 253). Finally the assessment needs to identify employees who should be included in a health surveillance programme (see page 134 to 139) and whether they are at particular risk.

The findings should be recorded and used to design an action plan to reduce the identified risks. The noise assessments should be kept until a new one is made. This must happen whenever you believe that the old one is no longer valid, or where there has been a significant change to the work involved, or where noise level monitoring shows that noise is reaching action levels.

Action levels

There are three legally designated levels of action to protect employees' hearing. They are designed to limit hearing damage caused by exposure to excessive noise at work.

If noise levels are exceeded, certain action must be taken by both employers and employees. The standards are referred to as:

- lower exposure action value

- upper exposure action value

- exposure limit value.

Lower exposure action value

The **lower exposure action value** is where the daily or weekly personal noise exposure reaches 80dB(A), or there is a peak sound pressure of 135dB(C). If the lower exposure action value is exceeded, employers must inform workers about the risks and provide ear protectors, if required, and take medical advice regarding potential hearing problems.

Upper exposure action value and exposure limit value

The **upper exposure action value** is where the daily or weekly personal noise exposure reaches 85dB(A), or there is a peak sound pressure of 137dB(C).

The **exposure limit value** is the maximum permissible daily or weekly personal noise exposure. It is 87dB(A) or a peak sound pressure of 140dB(C).

If the upper exposure action value or exposure limit value is exceeded, employers must reduce the noise exposure so far as is reasonably practicable, must provide hearing protection and ensure that employees wear the protection, and carry out health surveillance (see pages 134 to 139). **Hearing protection zones** must be designated and operate where the noise level is at 90dB(A) or above, or at a peak level of 140dB(C) or above. Anyone entering such areas must wear ear protectors.

It must be noted that noise measurements in the field are accurate to plus or minus 5dB, so, if your consultant reports that, for example, the lower exposure value is 79.9dB(A), an action plan may still need to be implemented.

Communication, information, instruction and training

Employees must be given adequate information, instruction and training about the risks to hearing. They should be informed about:

- the likely noise exposure and the risk to hearing the noise creates

- what managers and supervisors are doing to reduce the noise

- what they can do themselves to minimise hearing damage
- the procedure for obtaining ear protectors
- how to use ear protectors
- when and where ear protectors should be worn
- how to keep ear protectors clean and in good condition
- how to store ear protectors
- the procedure for reporting defects in hearing protection
- the employer's health surveillance system.

Managers and supervisors should discuss the risk assessment and action plan with safety representatives, including any proposal to average exposure over a week, selection of hearing protection, any hearing protection zones and the health surveillance system.

Supervisors should encourage staff to wear any ear protection provided and to report any defective equipment so it can either be withdrawn or repaired.

Health surveillance

If employees are regularly exposed to noise levels above the upper exposure action values, or are at risk for any other reason – they already suffer from hearing loss, for example – employers must provide hearing checks at regular intervals. Employees must be told the results of these checks, records must be kept and employees suffering hearing damage should be examined by a doctor. The surveillance system should be controlled by a competent occupational health professional, for example, a doctor or nurse with appropriate training and experience.

Legal requirements

The main legal provisions are covered by The Control of Noise at Work Regulations 2005. The regulations require workers' hearing to be protected from excessive noise at work that could temporarily damage their hearing or make them deaf.

Employers must assess the risk from exposure to noise, then eliminate or control it, using exposure limit values and action values. The legislation also covers the provision of personal protective equipment and health surveillance.

Vibration

Millions of people work with power tools and vehicles that cause vibration – rapid repeated movements back and forward or up and down. If their exposure to the shaking or jolting is not controlled, they may experience serious health problems.

Employers have legal duties to minimise the potentially harmful effects of vibration. Employees, safety representatives and supervisors all have a part to play in ensuring that people who are regularly exposed to vibration at work do not suffer ill effects.

Under The Control of Vibration at Work Regulations 2005 employers must assess the risk to employees from vibration and take steps to minimise the effects of exposure. Two types of vibration at work are identified in the legislation: hand-arm vibration and whole body vibration. They are discussed separately here.

Key words and phrases

carpal tunnel syndrome – pain and tingling in fingers caused by pressure of a nerve as it passes through the carpal tunnel in the wrist.

exposure action value (EAV) – the daily amount of vibration exposure above which employers are required to take action to control exposure.

exposure limit level (ELL) – the maximum level of vibration an employee may be exposed to on a single day

hand-arm vibration – mechanical vibration transmitted to hands and arms during work with hand-held powered equipment.

hand-arm vibration syndrome (HAVS) – a range of health problems in which there is damage to the blood flow, nerves, muscles, tendons and bones of the arm and hand as a result of using hand-held powered equipment at work.

hierarchy of control – a well tested system of graded health and safety controls. The sequence helps organisations to determine their most effective health and safety controls.

vibration – rapid repeated movements back and forward or up and down that might also be described as shaking, jolting or oscillating. Vibration at work is normally caused by mechanically operated and electrically operated power tools or by driving vehicles, such as tractors.

whole body vibration (WBV) – shaking or jolting of the body through a supporting surface. Vibration transmitted through the seat or feet.

Hand-arm vibration at work

Hand-arm vibration is mechanical vibration transmitted to hands and arms during work with hand-held powered equipment. If not controlled adequately, the vibration can cause physical damage to the arms and hands of people who use such tools regularly.

Work tools that vibrate include chainsaws, powered lawnmowers, hedge trimmers, strimmers/brush cutters, leaf blowers, road or concrete breakers, power hammers, jack hammers, jigsaws, impact wrenches, needle scalers, riveters, grinders, sanders and scabblers.

About five million workers are exposed to hand-arm vibration in the workplace in the UK. Two million of these workers are exposed to levels of vibration where there are clear risks of causing serious health problems.

If workers use vibrating equipment they may also be subject to risks from exposure to noise (see page 248 to 255).

Hazards

Uncontrolled exposure to vibration may lead to vibration white finger, a condition that involves numb fingers with pale skin.

Using power tools regularly without adequate controls on exposure to vibration can eventually result in a *range* of conditions known collectively as hand-arm vibration syndrome (HAVS), as well as to *specific* conditions such as carpal tunnel syndrome.

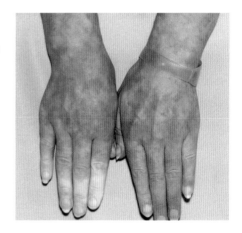

Hand-arm vibration syndrome (HAVS) is a group of health problems in which damage occurs to the blood flow, nerves, muscles, tendons and bones of the arm and hand. The commonest is *vibration white finger* in which there is numbness and whitening of the fingers.

Carpal tunnel syndrome is pain and tingling in fingers caused by pressure of a nerve as it passes through the carpal tunnel in the wrist.

The early symptoms

The symptoms include:

- tingling and numbness in the fingers

- loss of sensation in the hands – not being able to feel things properly

- loss of strength in the hands

- changes in the colour of fingers – going white (blanching), then becoming red and painful on recovery. This may be only in the finger tips at first and is likely to be particularly noticeable in cold and wet conditions.

Symptoms may appear after only a few months' exposure, but could take a few years to develop. They tend to get worse with continued exposure to vibration and can become permanent.

Impact of symptoms
The effects of the symptoms include:

- pain

- distress and anxiety

- disturbed sleep

- difficulty doing fiddly, or fine tasks, such as fastening buttons or assembling small components

- difficulty working outdoors, or in other cold or damp conditions

- reduced grip strength, which might affect the ability to do work safely.

These problems can severely limit the jobs that an affected person can do and can disrupt and damage everyday family and social activities.

Identifying the symptoms

It is important to identify symptoms as early as possible so that measures can be taken to prevent the symptoms becoming permanent conditions. This has implications for the information and training given to employees, supervisors and safety representatives and is discussed later in this chapter.

Risk

The regular maintenance and repair of vibrating tools, such as chainsaws, can help to reduce the harmful impact of vibration on the user – by replacing worn anti-vibration mounts, for example.

Occasional exposure to vibration is unlikely to cause ill health to most people. The greater the exposure level, the greater the risk.

The Health and Safety Executive identifies a wide range of industries with jobs requiring regular and frequent use of vibrating tools and equipment. They include:

- arboriculture and forestry

- building and maintenance of roads and railways

- construction

- foundries

- grounds, water course and estate management

People working in motor manufacturing and repair are among those at risk from vibration.

- heavy engineering

- manufacturing concrete products

- mines and quarries

- motor vehicle manufacture and repair

- public utilities and public services, such as electricity, gas, railways, telecommunications, water

- shipbuilding and repair.

Controls

Risk assessment

The Control of Vibration at Work Regulations 2005 require employers to assess the vibration risk to employees and set in place measures to control those risks.

The responsibility for carrying out these activities could be given to managers, supervisors or an outside contractor using specialist equipment. Whoever is involved needs to be a *competent person*. Training may need to be given.

Employees and safety representatives should be consulted. They could be involved in the steps required, provided they have had suitable training. If possible, agree a policy for managing vibration risks and for carrying out health surveillance if it is necessary (see pages 134 to 139).

The risk assessment involves:

- identifying where there may be risk of hand-arm vibration

- identifying the individuals who may be most at risk

- making a soundly based estimate of employees' exposures and comparing the estimate with action levels and exposure limits

- establishing the most suitable controls and ways to monitor them

- recording the assessment.

Which processes and equipment are involved?

The first step is to carry out a risk assessment of the processes where employees could be exposed to vibration. Ask staff about equipment they use that causes hand-arm vibration. Observe specific working practices and ascertain the total period they are in contact with the equipment over several days.

List all the equipment that can cause vibration. Collect information from the manufacturers' instructions or handbooks about model, power, vibration and its risks, and, if appropriate, specific warnings.

Who is at risk?

Make a list all the employees who use the identified powered equipment and record as accurately as possible how long the employees' hands are in contact with the equipment while it is vibrating in a typical day.

Ask employees whether they have experienced any of the symptoms listed above and whether there are any other problems with the equipment such as its weight or difficulty in holding it. Record all of this information.

Exposure action and limit values

Identify whether employees are exposed to levels of vibration above the exposure action level or the exposure limit value.

The **exposure action value (EAV)** is a daily amount of vibration above which employers are obliged to take action to control exposure to hand-arm vibration. The daily exposure action value is 2.5 m/s^2 A(8). The A(8) value shown here (and in the ELV below) is the daily vibration exposure in metres per second.

The **exposure limit value (ELV)** is the maximum amount of vibration an employee may be exposed to on any single day. The daily exposure limit value is 5 m/s^2 A(8).

Group the employees into three categories: high, medium and low risk. These rough groupings will allow you to do a basic risk assessment and decide whether employees are likely to exceed the EAV and ELV. You can then plan and prioritise control actions.

Those in the high risk group (above the ELV) are likely to be employees who regularly operate hammer-action tools for more than one hour a day or some rotary tools for more than four hours a day. Employees in the medium risk group (above the EAV) are likely to operate hammer-action tools for more than 15 minutes a day or rotary tools for more than one hour a day.

Controls should be focused on the high-risk group of employees.

Hierarchy of control

Use the **hierarchy of control** to decide on the most appropriate ways to eliminate vibration, or to deal with the risks that cannot be avoided. The hierarchy is:

- use alternative work methods that eliminate or reduce exposure
- select the best design of equipment for the task
- maintain equipment and replace it as soon as it becomes worn
- provide safe systems of work
- provide training, information and/or supervision
- issue personal protective equipment.

Alternative methods (substitution)

Consider using alternative work methods. This might involve using different equipment or mechanising or automating the work. Instead of using hand-held wall breakers for wall chasing, for example, specify built-in ducting in new buildings. In existing buildings, consider overcoating existing plaster and building-in the ducts. Where feasible, instruct tree surgeons to use a hand saw rather than a chainsaw.

Equipment selection
Select equipment that reduces the risk of vibration based on the power of the equipment and the vibration it produces. For example, to cut holes in brickwork use a diamond-tipped hole-cutting drill bit with a rotary action, rather than a tungsten-tipped one with hammer and rotary action.

Maintenance
Maintain equipment according to the manufacturer's instructions and any industry guidance to prevent avoidable increases in vibration. Blunt tools and worn anti-vibration mounts on a chainsaw increase vibration, for example.

Replace old equipment
When replacing old equipment look for the equipment with the lowest vibration and ensure that employees are trained in its use.

Safe work systems
Design a safe system of work, or use a permit to work system to control the hazards and risks. Limit the length of exposure by better job design, layout of the workstation, regular rest periods and work rotation (where staff switch tasks to avoid prolonged exposure).

Protective clothing
Ensure that staff have suitable protective clothing – to keep them warm and dry, for example – to help blood circulation and reduce the risk of white finger.

Monitoring

Check your controls regularly to see if the controls are suitable for existing risks and talk to employees about any new risks from vibration.

Health monitoring or surveillance

If despite the actions taken to control the risk, employees are likely to be regularly exposed above the exposure action value or are at risk for any other reason, a programme of heath surveillance must be introduced to identify anyone who may be at particular risk – such as people with Raynaud's disease (a blood circulation condition), or to identify anyone who is in the early stages of developing vibration-related circulation problems. Such a programme also helps to prevent disease progression, helps people stay in work and helps to check the effectiveness of the control measures.

Information and training

Employers must provide information for employees about:

- the health effects of vibration

- the sources of hand-arm vibration

- whether they are at risk and if they are above the ELV or the EAV

- the daily exposure duration
- the correct selection, use and maintenance of equipment
- ways to maintain good blood circulation, including the correct use of personal protective equipment (PPE)
- how to recognise and report symptoms
- health surveillance and its benefits
- the conclusions of consultation with employees and safety representatives.

Checklist for identifying whether the organisation has a problem with hand-arm vibration

- Do employees complain of tingling and numbness in their hands or fingers after using vibrating tools?
- Do employees hold work pieces, which vibrate while being processed by powered machinery such as pedestal grinders?
- Do employees regularly use hand-held or hand-guided power tools and machines such as:
  - concrete breakers, concrete pokers
  - sanders, grinders, disc cutters
  - hammer drills
  - chipping hammers
  - chainsaws, brush cutters, hedge trimmers
  - powered mowers
  - scabblers or needle guns.
- Do employees regularly operate:
  - hammer action tools for more than about 15 minutes per day
  - some rotary and other action tools for more than about one hour per day.

Chipping slag from foundry

A small foundry used a hand-operated pneumatic breaker to chip slag from the foundry's ladles, resulting in daily exposures well above the exposure limit value. The exposure was virtually eliminated by introducing a machine-mounted hydraulic breaker for most of this work.

Whole body vibration

Regular long-term exposure to whole body vibration (WBV) can lead to back pain. However, poor posture and heavy lifting can be contributory factors for those exposed – see also page 193 and 207 for information about handling loads.

Over five million working days are lost every year due to back pain and some of these lost days are due to back pain from WBV.

Hazards

Without suitable controls, whole body vibration can be caused by driving across bumpy surfaces or frequent travel by helicopter.

Whole body vibration (WBV) is the shaking or jolting of the human body transmitted through a supporting surface (usually the floor or a seat) or the feet. Examples include driving across an unmade road or uneven surface (like a field), or operating a machine that breaks up ground by impact hammering or drilling. Whole body vibration can be caused by operating machinery excavating holes or trenches, or loading materials onto lorries or other earth-moving vehicles, driving mobile machines (including some tractors,

fork-lift trucks and quarrying or earth-moving machinery). It can also be caused by the rotor blades of a helicopter, fast boats travelling across rough seas, trains and operating large compaction hammering or punching machines.

Risk

There is an increased risk of back pain associated with driving mobile machines that produce whole body vibration. Shocks and jolts may also exaggerate existing back pain, although the relative importance of whole body vibration is still not certain.

Contributing factors

Poor design of vehicle controls, poorly positioned seats that cannot be adjusted, sitting for long periods without changing position, poor driver posture, repeated manual handling, lifting loads and repeatedly climbing in and out of a high cab may aggravate an existing back problem or result in back pain.

Who is at risk?

Operators of machines in the construction, mining, quarrying, agricultural and forestry industries are often at risk of WBV and back pain. People with previous back or neck problems young people and pregnant women are the most likely to be at risk of back pain and at a higher risk from exposure to WBV.

Controls

Risk assessment

Risk assessments must be done on a similar basis to that for hand-arm vibration (above). Record the different types of machine used and driven by employees.

Exposure

Exposures may be high if, for example:

- machine or vehicle manufacturers warn about high levels of vibration in their handbooks

- such machines are driven or operated for several hours in a day or for long periods without a break and the driver/operator is continuously jolted or shaken

- driving is on unmade roads or roads with potholes

- machines or vehicles are used for unsuitable tasks

- operators have poor techniques, such as driving too fast.

Having done a basic risk assessment there normally is no need to measure the level of vibration exposure or to employ specialists to help with the risk assessment if controls can easily be put in place or if it is unlikely that the vibration levels will be anywhere near the action and limit values. If, however, the risk assessment suggests that the vibration needs to be measured it could be estimated using the HSE guidance and manufacturer's data. Once measured the values should be compared with those given below.

Exposure action and limit values

The exposure action value is the amount of daily exposure to whole body vibration above which employers must take action to reduce risk. It is $0.5m^2$ A(8).

The exposure limit value is the maximum amount of vibration an employee may be exposed to on any single day. It is $1.15m^2$ A(8). Exposure levels above this level significantly increase the risk of back pain.

But be careful in the risk assessment not to assume that the back pain is a result of the vibration alone, because it is possible that WBV is exacerbating back pain that has been caused by something else.

Even so, if it is found that vibration from machines or vehicles is causing WBV at a level above the EAV and ELV, then controls must be put in place.

Training and instruction for operators and drivers

Good techniques can help to prevent or alleviate problems. Drivers of large vehicles can do things such as:

- adjust the weight setting on their suspension belts where they are provided

- adjust the seat position and controls correctly, where they are adjustable, to provide good lines of sight, good support and ease of reach to the foot and hand controls

- vary the vehicle speed according to the ground conditions

- follow any site routes to avoid bumping and jolting on uneven or poor surfaces

- operate the steering wheel, brake, accelerator, gears and attached equipment as smoothly as possible.

Choose machinery suitable for the job

Select machinery and vehicles with the appropriate size, power and capacity for the work and ground conditions. Manufacturers' technical handbooks contain information on whole body vibration.

Maintenance of machinery, vehicles and roadways

Maintain site roadways in as smooth a condition as possible. Maintain vehicle suspension systems and replace solid tyres before they reach their wear limits. Obtain advice from manufacturers on seats when intending to replace them.

Work practices

Adopt work schedules that do not cause long periods of exposure and allow for regular breaks, particularly for people with back problems, young people and pregnant women.

Monitoring and health surveillance

Check regularly that your controls are working.

Introduce a simple health surveillance system. Establish a baseline of back conditions and measure improvements or worsening conditions over time.

Identify anyone who may be at particular risk – for example, people with previous back problems, young people and pregnant women. Periodically circulate a questionnaire to workers at risk, and refer people with back problems to an occupational health specialist.

Information

Provide employees with information on the health effects of whole body vibration, the sources of vibration and whether they are at risk from poor posture or manual handling of heavy objects. They should be aware of the levels of vibration and the daily exposure duration.

Make them aware of the various ways they can reduce risk by changing work practices; correct selection, use and maintenance of equipment; and the correct techniques for equipment use.

They also need to be aware of any health surveillance system and how to report back problems.

Legal requirements

The Control of Vibration at Work Regulations 2005 requires employers to assess the risk to employees from vibration and take steps to minimise the consequences of exposure.

Drugs, alcohol and passive smoking

In their leisure time many people like an alcoholic drink, some smoke tobacco and some take recreational drugs. However, it is essential to control the use of alcohol, smoking and drugs in the workplace to avoid potentially devastating consequences.

Key words and phrases

alcohol – the chemicals ethyl alcohol or ethanol, or the common term for alcoholic beverages in general.

alcohol abuse – excessive consumption of alcohol.

drug – a substance that has a physiological effect when in the body; a pharmaceutical product or ingredient prescribed as a medicinal treatment or used for illegal recreational purposes. Examples include narcotic, hallucinogenic or stimulant substances.

drug abuse – the illegal use of drugs and the misuse, whether deliberate or unintentional, of prescribed drugs or substances such as solvents.

passive smoking – breathing in the smoke from other people's cigarettes, cigars or pipes.

Hazards

A significant proportion of employers already consider **drug** and **alcohol** misuse to be a problem in the workplace. It has been reported that up to 14.8 million working days are lost each year due to excessive drinking. The Health and Safety Executive (HSE) estimates that approximately 25 per cent of all industrial accidents involve an employee who has been drinking alcohol. The ban on smoking at work and in enclosed public spaces acknowledges concern about the effects of smoking and of passive smoking.

Alcohol

Drinking alcohol in moderation is considered to be socially acceptable and may even have some beneficial health effects. Most people recover quickly from drinking a small quantity of alcohol, but if you drink excessively, or at the wrong time, it can lead to accidents and harm.

Large quantities of alcohol consumed over many years can seriously affect your health. When someone drinks alcohol, it is absorbed rapidly into the bloodstream. The concentration in the blood depends on the amount drunk, whether the person has eaten recently, their body size and weight and whether the drinker is male or female (women are affected more because their bodies are usually smaller). Consumed in excessive quantity, the alcohol level in the bloodstream may lead to alcohol poisoning and even death.

It takes about one hour for the body to remove one unit of alcohol from the bloodstream. One unit is equal to half a pint of ordinary strength beer or lager, a small glass of wine or a small measure of spirits. It is important to note that someone who drinks heavily the day or night before work may still be under the influence of alcohol when next reporting for work. Alcohol affects your physical co-ordination and reaction speeds. It changes your mood and thinking. You may feel more relaxed and less inhibited, but alcohol can also make you aggressive and this can lead to arguments and violence.

Drugs

Drugs used for recreation may have similar effects – for example, heroin can make you drowsy, while solvent abuse and barbiturates can lead to some of the same symptoms as drunkenness. However, there are other drugs that can increase the user's wakefulness, alertness, confidence and feeling of energy. These feelings can be just as risky as the effects of alcohol, and overconfidence and an excited attitude can easily lead to accidents.

Some prescribed medicinal drugs have side-effects – for example, impaired co-ordination and reaction speeds, or drowsiness. The user should have been warned about these side-effects when the drugs were prescribed, but not everyone is aware of the impact that medicines can have on their performance at work.

Alcohol and drug abuse

Typical signs of **alcohol and drug abuse** affecting performance in the workplace are:

- reduced work performance, possibly with poor judgement, poor concentration and low productivity
- increased absenteeism and poor time-keeping
- changes in mood, aggression and an increase in arguments with colleagues
- poor personal hygiene or the smell of alcohol on a person's breath
- borrowing money and even dishonesty.

Smoking

The health hazard from smoking and **passive smoking** is the smoke itself. Smoke contains a cocktail of chemicals, many of which are carcinogenic (cancer causing). Exposure to someone else's smoke can lead to irritation of the eyes, nose and throat; aggravation of asthma and hay fever; heart disease; and lung cancer. Pregnant women can be particularly sensitive to tobacco smoke: inhaling other people's smoke can lead to miscarriage, premature birth, stillbirth, neonatal death, low birth weight and birth defects. To protect employees from the health hazards of passive smoking, it is illegal to smoke at work and in enclosed public spaces.

Risks

People who take drugs or alcohol while at, or before, work have impaired judgement and physical co-ordination. Their attitude and mood can alter, so their sense of reality is weakened. This increases the likelihood that an accident will occur.

The degree of risk depends on the amount of the substance consumed, the type and concentration of the substance and the body's reaction. The task being carried out also has a bearing on the risk of an accident. For example, when driving a heavy goods vehicle, there is a much greater risk of an accident than when working in an office.

Passive smoking carries a smaller risk than smoking, but the risk is still significant. The World Health Organization has suggested that non-smokers who are exposed to what it calls 'second-hand smoke' are between 20 per cent and 30 per cent more likely to develop lung cancer, and potentially other cancers (including those of the stomach and liver), than people who are not exposed to second-hand smoke.

Controls

Employers have a responsibility to ensure, so far as is reasonably practicable, the health, safety and welfare of their employees. An employer who knowingly permits an employee to continue working while under the influence of drugs or alcohol may face prosecution.

Employees have a similar responsibility for their own safety and well-being and for that of their work colleagues and members of the general public who may be affected by their work activities.

Employees should not drink or take drugs before driving or working with machinery, electrical equipment or ladders. No one is allowed by law to work in a compressed air environment if under the influence of alcohol or drugs, and some railway workers are committing a criminal offence if they are unfit for work because of drink or drugs.

Managers and supervisors may need to find out if there is a hidden problem of people working under the influence of alcohol or drugs in their workplace. If you are involved in such work, you need to be sensitive to people's privacy.

You could talk to the employees and examine sickness and accident records to see if alcohol or drugs have been involved. It may be that the abuse of alcohol or drugs is related to problems of stress in the workplace, perhaps due to a heavy workload, or to unsocial hours or boring and repetitive work.

You should note if there are easy opportunities for employees to drink alcohol at work – for example, beer delivery workers and bar and club staff may have more temptations than many other employees. Managers could also find out whether there is poor supervision of employees so that alcohol and drug abuse continues unchecked.

A ban on smoking at work is believed to have saved many employees from problems caused by passive smoking.

Governments across the world have recognised the health effects of smoking at work and have banned smoking in the workplace. Some governments have used other control methods such as a combination of improved ventilation and designated smoking areas; separate rooms for smokers and non-smokers and a ban on smoking in shared areas; and employer-funded courses to help employees to give up smoking.

Alcohol and drugs policy

If you do find that there is a problem of alcohol or drugs misuse in the workplace, you can introduce a number of measures to deal with it. You should consult employees by setting up a working group of managers, supervisors and safety or employee representatives with the aim of introducing an alcohol and drugs policy to the workplace. The commitment of managers and the agreement of employees is essential for the introduction of such a policy.

A good alcohol and drugs policy applies to all staff, including managers, regardless of their work status. It should include a number of measures such as:

- rules that restrict drug taking and alcohol consumption at work

- a procedure to deal with employees with an alcohol or drugs problem

- an offer of help to staff who recognise and acknowledge that they have an alcohol or drug problem

- a policy of re-introducing rehabilitated employees into the workplace

- training for supervisors, safety representatives and managers about the company rules and procedures, the problems of alcohol abuse and how to recognise alcohol problems

- a promotional campaign about sensible drinking

- a condition of employment not to report for work if staff are under the influence of alcohol or drugs

- the monitoring of any action taken to see whether the policy has been effective and to ascertain whether new actions need to be taken.

The policy must make it clear why it is being introduced, who the policy applies to, and who is responsible for its implementation. The policy must also state the disciplinary procedure for dealing with employees who breach the rules on alcohol and drugs, and should contain details about the support available. Confidentiality is very important for those people who volunteer for help.

If help is needed in drawing up the policy, advice can be obtained from the local alcohol advisory service.

Screening

Testing or screening of the workforce could be introduced to find out the scope of the problem. This can be done:

- through the job selection process

- after any accident or near-miss

- when dealing with an individual who is suspected of working under the influence of alcohol or drugs.

Random testing could also be carried out, but this is a very sensitive and controversial issue and must be considered carefully before being introduced. There must be a high degree of certainty that there is a problem and the true extent of the problem cannot be found by other means. Screening should also be part of the contract of employment or an agreed modification to the contract.

Legal requirements

Under the Health and Safety at Work etc. Act 1974 and its equivalent in Northern Ireland employers have a responsibility to ensure, so far as is reasonably practicable, the health, safety and welfare of their employees.

Drugs and alcohol can increase the risk to employees' health and safety so must be controlled in the workplace. Employees have a responsibility for their own safety and well-being and for that of their work colleagues and members of the general public who may be affected by their work activities.

The Health Act 2006 in England makes premises that are open to the public and places of work smoke free. The Smoke-free (Premises and Enforcement) Regulations 2006 gives details of the premises covered and enforcement. Similar legislation is in force in Scotland, Wales and Northern Ireland.

Violence at work

The Health and Safety Executive defines violence at work as any incident in which a person is abused, threatened or assaulted in circumstances relating to his or her work. The type of behaviour covered in this definition includes verbal insults and threats and, on rare occasions, physical attacks. Despite a steady reduction in violence against workers since 1995, there are over 600,000 annual incidents of violence at work.

Key words and phrases

violence at work – a physical assault on, or abusive or threatening behaviour toward, an employee at work or in connection with work.

Hazards

The results of physical violence at work can be highly visible, but violence can also affect people in less obvious ways such as demotivation, anxiety, stress, fear, phobias and difficulty in sleeping.

Who is at risk?

People working in many different jobs are at risk of violence at work. They include those whose work activities involve:

- handling cash or valuables – for example, in banks, building societies or petrol garages

- working alone – for example, cleaners, social workers and other home visitors, farm and forestry workers, and taxi drivers

- working at night – for example, security guards on night shift, hospital reception staff and off-licence staff

- inspection and control and the use of authority to carry out certain statutory duties – for example, police, traffic wardens, security guards, prison officers, health and safety inspectors, fire officers and environmental health officers

- handling customer complaints or enquiries – for example, reception and customer services staff

- close contact with clients – for example, nurses, doctors and social workers.

Employees are also particularly at risk in poorly managed organisations where mistakes or delays may prompt client aggression – for instance, where money or social or welfare services are provided.

A comprehensive risk assessment should establish which employees are at risk. It should also identify many categories of people who might be violent.

Controls

Supervisors and safety representatives have a crucial role in identifying whether violence at work is a problem in the workplace because they are close to the 'frontline'. They are able to report to managers and to recommend changes in procedures for the protection of the employees.

If you suspect there is a problem of violence in the workplace, or employees are subject in their work activities to violent behaviour outside the workplace, you need to find out the extent of the problem. You could have informal discussions with employees or carry out a survey to find out whether staff have ever been verbally abused, threatened, or attacked by other employees or clients or customers. Where there seems to be a regular or severe problem of violence to employees follow these steps:

- set up a recording system for all violent incidents, detailing what happened, the victim's name, the attacker or abuser's name, if known, and any witness contact details or witness statements

- carry out a risk assessment of all activities that could involve violence – identify the hazards and identify who might be harmed
- assess the risks
- introduce preventive measures, where necessary.

Good practice

A hospital and the local police worked together to reduce violence to staff in a hospital's accident and emergency department. Among other things, they:

- arranged a greater police presence in the hospital
- provided training for accident and emergency staff in violence-related issues

- installed closed-circuit television
- revised the hospital's policy on aggression against staff
- set up meetings every two months to discuss safety and security.

There has been a steady decrease in violent crime in the accident and emergency department and also an improvement in staff morale.

Work environment

The preventive measures that can be taken include making the work environment secure and discouraging people from being violent. You can do this by, for example:

- introducing video surveillance systems, building alarms, personal alarms, and coded security doors through which only staff members can go
- providing comfortable seating, fixed furniture, pleasant decoration and subtle lighting.

Safe systems of work

Safe systems of work can help to reduce the risk of violence. Take, for example, where cash is handled. Think about accepting credit cards or cheques, or even consider setting up a token system for security reasons – it may also improve business. In a cash business, make sure that money is banked regularly and that the route to the bank and the time of banking are changed frequently.

If employees work on a site away from the normal workplace, make arrangements for them to keep in touch with their base – for instance, by telephoning at regular pre-arranged intervals.

There is more information about safe systems of work on pages 121 to 126.

Lone working

Try to avoid systems where people have to work on their own. These employees are usually described as *lone workers*. Where there is a high risk of violence, another person should also be employed to work alongside the lone worker.

Anyone who must unavoidably work alone should be medically fit and suitable to work alone. During recruitment care should be taken to appoint people who are confident and can be trained to deal with difficult clients diplomatically and to cope with difficult situations.

Emergency procedures

There should be special procedures in place to deal with emergencies where there is a threat of violence that might be averted. For example, a system of alerting security staff where an employee is concerned that he or she may be subject to violent behaviour, either before meeting the potentially violent person, or during an interview.

Safe way home for late-night workers

In some cases, employers should make sure that staff can get home safely – for instance, bar staff in a night club may need special arrangements for travelling home late at night or early in the morning. This may involve arranging for a taxi or making sure that staff have access to secure car-parking spaces. As well as improving personal safety, this will also probably improve staff morale.

Special safety clothing

In extreme cases, special personal protective clothing may need to be provided for employees who are at a high risk of experiencing violence. They might include police officers as well as security guards who collect and deliver money to premises, hospital security personnel or night security guards.

Staff training and information

Train employees to recognise the signs of aggression and know how to deal with them. Give staff information about other precautions that have been taken to protect them. If you know who is likely to be violent, then tell the employees.

Client advice

Give clients or customers information about delays where appropriate – for instance, that queues might form. People are less likely to be angry or to become aggressive if they are kept informed about what is going on and how long delays will last.

Keeping an eye on things

As with many other health and safety issues, you need to monitor the level of violence in the workplace. This involves recording all incidents and analysing them regularly. Supervisors need to discuss incidents with the victims and to work closely with safety representatives to find out if there are any new measures that could reduce the incidence of violence in the workplace.

Procedures after an incident

Working with supervisors and safety representatives, managers need to establish procedures to help an employee immediately after an incident and in the longer term. Effective help after an incident can often minimise harm, such as stress, to the employee later on.

Make sure that the victim is not left alone after the incident. Some people might want time alone, but arrangements should be made to ensure that the employee has the option of support throughout the recovery period. This could include the offer of counselling, if appropriate. Managers should consider allowing the person time off work if he or she wants it, and offering the help of legal advisers if appropriate.

Investigation

There should be procedures for investigating the incident thoroughly. This might be carried out by managers, supervisors, safety representatives or specially trained employees. If there is a safety committee, the findings should be reported to the committee for comment. Once the findings have been assessed, review the risk assessment and safe systems of work and introduce any new measures that would decrease the chance of a violent incident happening again.

Legal requirements

Under the Health and Safety at Work etc. Act 1974 employers have a legal duty to ensure, so far as is reasonably practicable, the health, safety and welfare at work of their employees. The Management of Health and Safety at Work Regulations 1999 also state that employers must consider the risks to employees, which include the risk of reasonably foreseeable violence. They must also decide how significant these risks are and what to do to prevent or control the risks and implement those controls.

Feature

Bullying and harassment – invisible violence

It is not only *physical* violence that can affect people at work. Bullying and harassment can make people's lives miserable. Some employees worry about going to work. Others become irritable, anxious or depressed. Others still experience panic attacks or loss of self-confidence and self-esteem. Some turn to alcohol and tobacco consumption.

It affects the quality of work, the quality of life and the amount of time taken off work for stress-related problems. It can also impact on other areas of life including personal relationships and family life.

Research shows that bullying does not just affect the people who experience it first hand: it also affects the people who witness it, lowering general morale, damaging team work and, in some cases, leading to time off work by the colleagues of the person who is being bullied.

Bullying costs employers 80 million lost working days and up to £2 billion in lost revenue every year.

Bullying and harassment can be described as offensive, intimidating, malicious or insulting behaviour. It is an abuse or misuse of power involving behaviour intended to undermine, humiliate, denigrate or injure the recipient.

Bullying and harassment may be by an individual against an individual (perhaps by someone in a position of authority such as a manager or supervisor, even if it is inadvertent) or involve groups of people.

It can take many different forms. ACAS, the Advisory, Conciliation and Arbitration Service, includes spreading malicious rumours; insulting someone by word or behaviour; copying e-mails that are critical about someone to others who do not need to know; picking on someone or setting them up to fail; excluding or victimising someone; overbearing supervision or other misuse of power or position; unwelcome sexual advances – touching, standing too close, the display of offensive materials; making threats or comments about job security without foundation; deliberately undermining a competent worker by overloading them with work and constant criticism; and preventing individuals progressing by intentionally blocking promotion or training opportunities.

Bullying can also involve comments about age, race, sex, disability, sexual orientation, religion or belief. It might be carried out through the of tone of voice and body language, not just through the words used.

An authoritarian style of management can often create a culture where bullying and harassment thrive, so employers need to set a good example.

Employers can tackle bullying in the workplace through a written formal policy, making it clear that bullying and harassment will not be tolerated. It should set out the steps to be taken to prevent bullying happening and clarify the responsibilities of supervisors and managers.

Complaints of bullying and harassment can usually be dealt with through grievance and disciplinary procedures. They need to set standards of behaviour. Written guidance and training sessions can help to promote awareness of what behaviour is acceptable and the damaging effects of bullying and harassment.

Managers and supervisors need to maintain fair policies for dealing promptly with complaints from employees. Employees need to be sure that they will get a sympathetic response if they make a complaint. Finally, employers need to be supportive.

The workplace
The work environment

We spend about one quarter of our lives at work, so our working conditions can have a significant effect on our health and may be more important to our general safety than our own homes. There are usually more people in the workplace than in domestic premises. There is often activity, more machines, a greater variety of materials being handled and, possibly, more dangerous substances in use.

Although work environments vary considerably, every workplace has a number of common factors, or characteristics. In this chapter we look at the main typical workplace hazards, risks and controls under the headings of ventilation, temperature, lighting, cleanliness, workspace organisation, workstations, seating, floor conditions and traffic routes.

Information about the basic workplace facilities needed for employees' well-being and comfort at work is given on pages 294 to 295.

Key words and phrases

cleaning schedule – a list that includes the work areas to be cleaned, the frequency of cleaning and the type of cleaning material to be used.

local exhaust ventilation – a ventilation system that captures and removes air contaminants at the point they are being produced before they escape into a workroom.

work environment – the surroundings in which work is carried out, including buildings, rooms, sites, working areas, the air, temperature and lighting.

workplace – any place, or places, where employees are likely to work or where they have to go in the course of their employment or incidentally to it.

(work) premises – any building or space, including outdoors, where work takes place.

workstation – an assembly comprising a work surface, such as a desk, and all the necessary equipment needed to carry out the assigned tasks. A workstation also includes the immediate surrounding area affected by the work activity at the workstation.

Hazards

Typical hazards in the work environment are:

- air pollutants
- hot and cold temperatures
- poor lighting (dim or bright)
- accumulation of rubbish, spilled liquids and contamination
- cramped working space
- badly organised workstations
- poor layout.

Slips, trips and falls are one of the main problems in the workplace and account for a large proportion of work-related accidents (see pages 161 to 167).

Ventilation

Poor ventilation in work premises leads to poor quality air. Harmful gases, fumes, vapours and dust can accumulate in the air if there is poor air movement. Poor ventilation can also lead to headaches, allergic reactions and nasal problems. Too much, or poorly designed, ventilation can cause draughts which can lead to uncomfortable working conditions and musculoskeletal disorders. In addition to problems caused by insufficient clean, fresh air, there may also be airborne problems caused by specific work activities or the use of particular materials or equipment. These might include:

- the products of combustion from liquefied petroleum gas (LPG), used, for example, in a portable heater
- the products of gas combustion – for example, from a cooker or hob
- vapour – for example, from the use of strong adhesives
- fumes – for example, from welding
- aerosols – for example, from paint spraying
- unpleasant odours – for example, from toilets.

Temperature

Some workplaces need to be cold or hot because of the nature of the business. For instance, a frozen food distributor needs walk-in freezers to store food in the best possible condition, but people, who are usually more comfortable at warmer temperatures, have to work in them. The air in an indoor swimming pool needs to be warm so that swimmers feel comfortable when they get out of the water, but lifeguards and other pool-side staff may find the air temperature too warm for their comfort because they are usually wearing more clothes than the swimmers. Many hospitals and nursing homes also need to be warm because patients and residents need more warmth than those working there.

Organisations need to find the best balance between the nature of the work and the health and safety and comfort of staff, customers and clients.

Cold working environments can make workers' fingers numb and they suffer hypothermia – when the body temperature falls below normal – and frostbite. Hot work environments may be very uncomfortable, causing staff to perspire and feel weary and generally uncomfortable. This can lead to irritability, impatience, outbursts of bad temper, dizziness and fainting – all of which can contribute to accidents.

Lighting

Low lighting levels may be appropriate while staff watch a short video presentation, but would be inappropriate for stairways.

Poor light levels, either natural or artificial, can lead to eye strain, headaches, fatigue and stress, and can create hazards that would otherwise not occur – for example, difficulty in going down steps because shadows are cast over the treads. Too much light can also cause problems – for example, the headlights of a fork-lift truck could dazzle a pedestrian who then trips over, or the glare from sunlight on a computer screen placed next to a window with no blinds could make working at the computer difficult and stressful.

Sparks from loose connections could cause a fire and someone working on the lighting could get an electric shock. If light switches are poorly positioned, staff may need to negotiate their way across a dark room to switch on the light: on the way they could trip over desk or table legs, boxes or anything on the floor.

Cleanliness

As workplaces vary, cleanliness is a relative term. You would not, for example, expect the floor of a cow shed to be clean to the same standard as the work surface of a restaurant kitchen, nor would you expect the walls and floors of a vehicle repair garage to be as clean as those of a hospital operating theatre. Cleanliness is important in all workplaces to prevent slips, trips and falls and to protect against disease, but may be paramount in work environments such as food premises, hospitals and tattoo or body piercing salons to prevent contamination that leads to poisoning or infection.

Each workplace has its own hazards associated with cleanliness. The main ones include:

- contamination of the floor or ground – by liquids and rubbish, for example – that leads to slipping and tripping hazards

- the accumulation of dirt, leading to offensive smells and slipping hazards

- the creation of conditions that encourage the multiplication of pathogens (disease-causing organisms), such as bacteria in broken or overflowing drains

- dust inhalation, leading to conditions such as asbestosis

- the concentration of dust, leading to explosion – for example, flour or wood dust in the air can ignite easily and may explode.

Workspace organisation

Everyone needs sufficient space to work – both for physical and mental well-being. Lack of space could make it easy for staff to slip, trip or knock into objects, fittings (such as lights) or other people. It could also increase exposure to noise from machines, such as photocopiers or printers, and even from other workers. Employees could suffer from physical discomfort in cramped conditions, and any of these conditions could make it hard for staff to concentrate and could even lead to stress.

Workstations

A **workstation** is an assembly made up of a work surface, such as a desk, and all the necessary equipment needed to carry out the assigned tasks. A workstation also includes the immediate surrounding area affected by the work activity at the workstation.

Computer workstations often include a desk (workbench or other work surface) and chair; display screen equipment; any optional accessories such as a modem, printer and document holder; and a telephone.

The layout of a workstation can help to prevent injuries and ill health caused by repetitive work, particularly at computers, supermarket checkouts and conveyor belts. These hazards include those which could result in musculoskeletal disorders (see pages 178 to 192).

If the workstation is too small or restricted, staff may cause themselves injury – for example, when they try to manoeuvre a long piece of wood on a workbench that has restricted space around it. Eye problems may occur when using computers for long periods, if they are not set up correctly (see pages 187 to 188).

Seating

Poor or unstable seating can cause back pain, tiredness and discomfort, or could break or topple over, causing injury. Seats can contribute to musculoskeletal disorders if they are not adjustable to the employees' physical characteristics such as height and leg length.

Floor/ground conditions and vehicle routes

Holes, slopes, obstructions and uneven or slippery surfaces can cause slipping and tripping hazards. A worker could easily trip on a hole in a floor and, if he or she is carrying something, could drop the load, possibly causing injury to people and damage to the premises. Someone driving a vehicle that hits a hole could lose control of the vehicle or the load being carried. Slopes make it difficult for employees to push and pull roller cages or to carry goods up and down them. Fork-lift trucks and other workplace transport that have to negotiate slopes in a workplace might have difficulty balancing the load, which could lead to an accident.

Wet floor surfaces and trailing hoses create a risk of slipping or tripping in this brewery.

Obstructions to vehicle and pedestrian routes restrict access and movement and increase the likelihood of collision. It is easy to slip on a wet floor, and people can trip up steps or fall when walking down them.

Badly damaged and maintained floors could mean that a floor eventually collapses, possibly dropping people and machines down below. Floors may also collapse if they are overloaded by, for example, a heavy machine or materials that are too heavy for the weight-bearing capacity of the floor.

If vehicles such as fork-lift trucks are used in an area where people move about, there is always the risk that pedestrians will be knocked over or crushed. (See pages 208 to 216 for more information about workplace transport.)

Risks

The risks from the work environment are relatively low, but they increase with a number of factors:

- ventilation – risk increases with exposure time and increased concentration of an air pollutant

- temperature – risk increases as the temperature reaches extremes of heat or cold

- lighting – risk increases in poor light (dimness or brightness)

- cleanliness – risk increases with the time that a work environment is left uncleaned and as a result of the accumulation of dirt and other contamination

- space – risk increases in restricted spaces

- workstation – risk increases over time for the person using the workstation if it is badly positioned

- floors and traffic routes – risk increases if maintenance is poor and the condition of the floor deteriorates

- doors and windows – risk increases when doors are translucent or openable windows are cleaned.

Ventilation

If workplace ventilation is insufficient to remove harmful substances, the pollutants remain in the air for longer, so increasing workers' exposure to the harmful substances. The greater the concentration of pollutants in the air, the greater the risk to workers. For example, poor ventilation in a flour mill may allow flour dust to reach a concentration at which an explosion could occur if there was a source of ignition close by. Even so, better rates of air exchange can cause draughts and contribute to an increased risk of musculoskeletal disorders.

Temperature

Extreme heat or cold can reduce employees' comfort and concentration, making them more likely to make mistakes that lead to injuries.

Employees working at extreme temperatures – for example, in cold stores or near baking ovens or furnaces – are at high risk. Hot dry air can lead to throat and eye irritation. As the temperature increases, people may suffer heat stroke. Heat and humidity can cause tiredness and irritability that, in turn, may lead to accidents.

If employees' fingers are numb from the cold, there is an increased risk of an accident involving manual handling and other tasks where you need to keep a firm grip on an object. Cold conditions at outdoor workstations increase the possibility of slipping on ice or even of developing hypothermia in extreme circumstances.

Lighting

There is a high risk of accidents because of dim lighting or glare – for example, because lights are badly positioned or windows and reflective surfaces are unshaded. Poor lighting near a machine or steps, and glare and dazzle increase the likelihood of accidents and injury. If staff have to walk through an unlit room because there is only one light switch on the other side of the room, slips or trips are likely to occur.

When moving from bright light to a dark area, the eyes have difficulty in adjusting immediately: during the short period of adjustment, an accident could happen.

Cleaning

There is considerably increased risk of slipping if spills are not cleared up immediately. The process of cleaning can cause other, more widespread, problems.

Brushing a dusty floor with a broom can, for instance, make the air very dusty, while using a damp mop will create less airborne dust. In food premises, airborne dust could cause widespread food contamination. In a hospital, surgical equipment could be contaminated.

The type of dirt or dust is significant in assessing the level of risk – for example, grease on floors increases the risk of slipping. Garden soil in food premises increases the risk of contamination leading to a food-borne illness. If asbestos is damaged so that asbestos fibres are released into the air, there is a serious risk that workers will inhale the asbestos fibres and may develop mesothelioma (a lung cancer) at a later date.

In extreme circumstances, if a workplace is contaminated with sewage, there is a serious risk of general infection.

Space to work

A small and cramped workspace increases the risk of accidents and stress occurring. This is particularly likely where the restricted space is around a machine or where large articles are being moved around. If an employee is forced by space restrictions to work near to a noisy machine, he or she may eventually develop hearing problems, while in the short term, he or she may experience symptoms of stress.

Workstation

Long periods spent working at a poorly designed workstation may lead to a musculoskeletal disorder such as repetitive strain injury. Where the workstation is for a computer, the level of risk often depends upon the height of the keyboard and the relative position of the operator's back, legs, feet, arms and hands.

If a workstation is outdoors, such as a woodworking machine on a building site, the weather can increase the likelihood of bad ground conditions which may result in slipping on wet mud, ice or snow. Employees working outdoors may also be exposed to high and low temperatures that drain their energy and concentration, increasing the risk that they will drop tools and materials, cut themselves or fall.

Floors and traffic routes

The greater the degree of damage to floors, the greater the likelihood of accidents. This also applies to the gradient of the floor, its smoothness and unevenness. Lack of maintenance and inspection of floors can lead to an unsafe, rotten, wooden floor going unnoticed.

Where very heavy weights are being placed on wooden floors, the risk of collapse increases with the weight. If a floor is obstructed and the obstruction reduces the space to walk – for example, on stairs – accidents are more likely to happen. If there is a large area of wet floor and no warning sign, it is more probable that someone will slip. Staircases without handrails, steep staircases and worn or damaged treads create a greater risk of slips, trips or falls.

Where vehicles and pedestrians have to use the same routes, or where their respective routes cross in the workplace, there is more chance that pedestrians will be crushed or knocked over.

Similar risks occur from the ground conditions when employees work outdoors.

Doors, walls and windows

Many doors, walls and windows are made of translucent materials that are sometimes difficult to see – for example, ordinary glass – and increase the chances that someone will walk into them or cut themselves. Openable windows present a high risk of a fall if they are not secured properly during cleaning. Windows positioned low down create a risk that a child will fall through them.

Controls

Each aspect of the work environment needs to be controlled. The general rules for indoor work environments are:

- keep the work environment in an efficient state, good working order and good repair
- carry out effective repairs as soon as possible
- remedy dangerous defects immediately
- inspect and clean regularly
- keep records of dangerous defects and maintenance.

The main principles are as follows.

- Ventilation – the air movement must be controllable, the means of ventilation must be adjustable and cleanable, and mechanical ventilation systems must be cleaned and maintained as appropriate.
- Temperature – use heaters, cooling equipment and clothing to regulate temperatures.
- Lighting – there should be natural, artificial and emergency lighting.
- Cleaning – this must be frequent, depending on the degree and type of activity, and all spills must be cleaned up immediately.
- Workspace – there must be a minimum space for working of $11m^3$ (11 cubic metres) per person. This is a legal requirement for indoor working.
- Workstations – should be designed to be adjustable to the shape and comfort of the individual operator, and there should be adequate breaks away from the workstation.
- Floors and traffic routes – should be inspected and maintained regularly and kept free of obstruction. The surface should be of a non-slip material, there must be handrails on staircases and all routes should be well signposted.
- Doors and windows – should be suitably constructed and fitted with safety devices to keep them closed when required.

Ventilation

The plants in these nursery polytunnels and the people working in them both benefit from a good supply of clean air.

Every workplace must have effective and suitable ventilation for every enclosed workspace. The ventilation system must provide a sufficient quantity of fresh and purified air and should also ensure that unpleasant smells are minimised.

Windows that can be opened are the most common way to provide sufficient fresh air. It must be possible to open the windows, skylights and ventilators without risk to the health and safety of the person who is opening them.

286 Health and safety for managers, supervisors and safety representative

There are many workplaces where the ventilation needs to be mechanical. Such systems need to be cleaned, tested and maintained regularly and kept free from airborne contaminants.

Ventilation systems should be designed so that the air to be recirculated is filtered to take out impurities and so that the output of air does not cause draughts near employees and their workstations. Audible or visual warnings are needed to warn of any failure of ventilation equipment.

Where employees have to work with harmful substances close by, a particular type of ventilation – usually referred to as local exhaust ventilation (LEV) – is used to take away the harmful substance before it gets to the air that they breathe. Local exhaust ventilation is a system that captures and removes air contaminants at the point they are being produced before they escape into the workroom. Examples of this type of system are an enclosure in a school chemistry laboratory or a ducting inlet above a fixed wood-sanding machine.

Special ventilation is needed for asbestos, lead, radiation and situations where legionnaires' disease may be a problem. It is also required in confined spaces to take out the products of combustion or any other gas or vapour that may lead to an explosion or suffocation risk – for example, in underground work or metal tank construction.

The supply rate of fresh air should not fall below 5 to 8 litres per second per occupant, but for heavily contaminated buildings it could need to be up to 36 litres per second per person. These are recommended standards. Advice from a ventilation engineer is needed to ensure that this standard is being provided and maintained. Workers should be allowed regular breaks from places with high levels of air movement, which are usually draughty.

Temperature

There must be a means to measure the temperature in the workplace. As a general rule, organisations should maintain a comfortable working temperature. A temperature of 16°C in indoor premises is recommended in the *Approved Code of Practice to the Workplace (Health, Safety and Welfare) Regulations 1992*. If employees are involved in considerable physical effort, as in a slaughterhouse or warehouse, for example, the workplace temperature can be 13°C. The legal temperature that should be maintained depends upon the use of the room, but organisations should take measures to reduce the need for such low temperature.

The temperature of premises can be affected by the construction of the building and its facilities. However, hot pipes could be insulated, windows shaded and workstations placed away from direct sunlight. However, a workplace must be adequately thermally insulated where it is necessary, having regard to the type of work being carried out and the physical activity of the people carrying out the work.

Where the temperature of the workplace has to be very warm or very cold – for example, in a Turkish bath or a cold store – a system of work could also be introduced to reduce the effect of the extreme temperatures on workers. This might mean that staff rotate tasks and take regular breaks.

Other measures might include the use of fans or air conditioning; duckboards on cold floors; or self-closing doors. Provide adequate, appropriate, warm personal protective clothing.

Lighting

Suitable and sufficient light, preferably natural light, is required in the workplace. This includes emergency lighting.

All artificial lighting should be cleaned regularly and repaired and replaced whenever necessary. All windows and skylights need to be cleaned regularly.

You should position workstations to take full advantage of natural light. To prevent eyestrain there should be no shadows, dazzling lights or glare affecting the workstation. You can use specially designed light fittings to avoid causing problems.

Light switches should be positioned so they can be found quickly and used easily. Do not let lights be obscured by stacked goods or other obstructions.

Stairs and staircases must be well lit and the lighting should be arranged so that there are no shadows obscuring the treads.

Cleaning

Cleaning should be well organised. The standard of cleanliness depends on the activity in the workplace. Generally, floors and traffic routes should be cleaned once a week and waste removed daily at least. If the activity produces a lot of waste or dirt, then the frequency of cleaning needs to increase.

Ensure that everyone follows a clean-as-you-go system, under which staff clean up spills immediately. Make certain that areas where there is unexpected dirt or waste are also cleaned as soon as possible.

Cleaning systems should be designed to avoid danger to other people – for example, warning signs should indicate the spread of spillage. Where cleaning may create dust, the amount of airborne dust should be reduced by sprinkling water or using a damp mop or other moistened cleaning utensil. In certain workplaces – such as food factories, restaurants and hospitals – the walls, floors and ceilings should be constructed so as to minimise areas where dust or germs can accumulate, especially where the control of contamination and infection are essential.

Space to work

Staff need enough space to do their work and to get to and from their workstation or work area with ease. Adequate floor space, ceiling height and unoccupied space are necessary in all workplaces. The approved code of practice recommends a general minimum workspace of $11m^3$ per person when the workroom is empty. As furniture, fittings and equipment need to be included within the recommended workspace, rooms may need to be larger than $11m^3$ per person, or have fewer people allowed to work in them.

Workstation

Workstations must be suitable for any employee who is likely to work at the workstation. The workstation should be designed so that the task can be carried out safely and comfortably at a suitable height in relation to the work surface. This is important for all staff and is particularly important for workers with physical disabilities.

Seats must be provided for each person whose work can or must be done sitting down. The seats should support the lower back. A footrest should be provided if the person cannot put his or her feet flat on the floor.

Everyone at work needs adequate freedom of movement and the space to be able to stand upright. If staff feel cramped, they may need to relieve the physical discomfort and work only for short periods, taking regular breaks.

At workstations outdoors, there needs to be protection from the weather. The workstation design must allow for swift and easy exit, and the area must allow work to be carried out so that the worker is unlikely to slip or fall.

Floors and traffic routes

Non-slip surfaces are need for some floors and stairs.

Floors and traffic routes must be constructed so that they are suitable for their purpose. There must be no holes in the floor and no slopes without handrails. The surface must not be uneven and floors must not be slippery. Open sides of staircases should be fenced off and handrails provided on one side at least.

Floor surfaces that are likely to get wet or where spills occur frequently need to be constructed of slip-resistant materials. Where liquids are likely to be spilt or there are large quantities of water or other liquid present – in laundries, breweries and food processing factories, for example – arrange a method for catching liquid or draining it away.

Slip-resistant footwear should be provided for employees where slipping is a high risk, even if other precautions have been taken. Busy fast food restaurants present a particularly high risk because they tend to use frying oil which can get onto the floor, there are often a lot of spills in the kitchens and in the customer areas, and the staff tend to be young and inexperienced.

Floors and traffic routes need to be kept free from obstruction and any article or substance that could make someone slip, trip or fall. Car parks and paths surrounding the workplace should be protected against the hazards of snow or ice.

Doors and windows

In most cases, workplace doors should swing both ways. Conventionally hinged doors should have a transparent viewing panel. Power-operated doors should have safety features such as an emergency stop button or switch, and flaps to protect fingers that become trapped as the door closes.

Windows designed to open should open and shut properly without posing any risk during everyday use or cleaning. To prevent cuts, translucent windows and walls should be made from material, like toughened glass, that shatters into many pieces when broken, rather than into sharp shards. All translucent surfaces in walls and walkways should be made easy to see with in-built visual devices or stickers.

Poor work conditions – sick building syndrome

Sick building syndrome is the popular name given to a workplace where a significant number of employees complain about a range of 'flu-like or cold-like symptoms. Symptoms include skin problems, sore throats, persistent coughs, blocked noses and sinusitis, stiff shoulders, back ache, tiredness, headaches and digestion problems. Office buildings are more prone to being affected than other types of buildings. Sickness records are a good source of information in identifying whether a building is 'sick'.

The causes of sick building syndrome are really not known but they are likely to include a combination of poor ventilation or poor air conditioning systems; indoor pollutants such as ozone from photocopiers or solvents; poor maintenance and cleaning; noise; poor office and workstation layouts; and poor lighting and temperature control.

The controls that need to be introduced to deal with sick building syndrome are those that can be used to control the likely cause. For example:

■ ensure air conditioning and ventilation is maintained at regular intervals

■ replace fluorescent lighting with low-flicker lighting

■ increase levels of cleaning

■ replace old photocopying machines because they may produce more ozone than newer models

■ increase the amount of working space for each employee

■ reduce noise levels in the workplace.

It is important when dealing with sick building syndrome to consider the whole building before deciding which control measures to introduce. It is also important to ask the employees about the conditions in which they work and raise awareness of sick building syndrome so that all potential problems can be identified.

Working outdoors

Working outdoors presents a special set of hazards that must be controlled. The general rules for outdoor working are:

■ protect against hot and cold temperatures and from ultraviolet (UV) light

■ ensure that there is adequate lighting in the hours of darkness

■ design workstations to be adjustable to the individual operator

■ arrange adequate breaks away from the workstation

■ maintain ground conditions and traffic routes to keep them free of obstruction and as tidy as possible.

Legal requirements

According to the Workplace (Health, Safety and Welfare) Regulations 1992 employers must comply with certain standards in the workplace covering:

- ventilation of enclosed workplaces

- indoor temperature and the provision of thermometers

- lighting (including emergency lighting)

- cleanliness of the workplace, furniture, furnishings and fittings; the ability to clean the surface of floors, walls and ceilings; and the accumulation of waste materials

- room dimensions and unoccupied space

- the suitability of workstations (including workstations outdoors) and the provision of suitable seats

- the condition of floors and the arrangement of routes for pedestrians or vehicles

- the material or protection of windows and other transparent or translucent walls, doors or gates so that they are apparent

- the way in which windows, skylights or ventilators are opened and the position they are left in when open

- the ability to clean windows and skylights

- the construction of doors and gates

- escalators and moving walkways

- the provision of suitable sanitary conveniences, washing facilities, supply of drinking water and cups or other drinking vessels

- the provision of suitable facilities for clothing, changing clothing and for rest and eating meals.

Feature

Confined spaces

Two men were overcome by fumes from bituminous paint while cleaning and painting the inside of a tank compartment on a barge. Their work area was a 'confined space' and the accident could have been avoided if they had been trained, informed and supervised to a far higher standard so that they knew how to avoid danger.

A confined space is any enclosed area where there is a risk of serious injury or death due to hazardous substances and dangerous conditions. Storm drains (as shown above), sewers, storage tanks, silos, vats, ventilation ducting, process vessels in the chemical industry, large industrial boilers or even unventilated rooms are all confined spaces.

Toxic atmospheres can occur where a hazardous substance is present – for example, the remains of a stored substance in a tank which is being cleaned or removed.

Gas or fumes can be introduced from a space near to the work area – for example, in a sewer, tunnel or culvert. A gas can build up from a work process – for example, the flame-cutting of metal or a fire could

produce carbon monoxide, making the atmosphere toxic. Lack of oxygen is caused by, for example, the displacement of the available oxygen by the gases from rotting vegetable matter, rusting metal or burning. Oxygen enrichment occurs when more oxygen than normal is present in the atmosphere. This increases the risk of fire or explosion – for example, an oxygen cylinder could leak during flame-cutting.

Flammable or explosive atmospheres can arise where flammable or explosive substances are present, such as oil or petrol in a tank, flour in storage silos or wood dust in a bag filter.

Liquid or solids entering a confined space can increase the risk of harm. Water coming into a sewer, for instance, increases the risk of drowning. The unexpected loading of grain into a silo increases the risk that someone will be trapped in the silo or be asphyxiated.

Excessive heat can increase the risk of heat stroke or heat stress due to lack of ventilation or the wearing of personal protective equipment.

The Confined Spaces Regulations 1997 require employers to identify confined spaces and carry out a risk assessment to identify measures necessary to avoid work within a confined space – the work might, for instance, be done from outside the confined space by using specialist tools.

Where entry to the confined space cannot be avoided, employers must create a safe system of work or a permit to work system (see pages 121 to 126). They should consider providing ventilation, breathing apparatus or a rescue harness, and test the air. There should be good communications between workers and supervisors during the operation.

Effective training must be provided and emergency arrangements must be in place before work starts. The arrangements should include the provision of rescue and resuscitation equipment, the availability of experienced rescuers and access to a telephone to contact the emergency services.

Welfare at work

It is compulsory to provide basic workplace facilities for employees' well-being and comfort at work. Such facilities include those for personal hygiene, resting and, where appropriate, changing and eating and drinking.

The general well-being of employees is in the interests of employers because a healthy and contented workforce works well. Many employers do more than required by law because they know it helps to create a culture of co-operation and high morale. In turn, these can help to maintain health and prevent accidents.

Where it is necessary, doors, passageways, lifts and stairs, showers, washbasins, toilets and workstations used by people with disabilities at work must be organised to take account of their needs. Rest rooms must also have suitable seating adequate for the number of people with disabilities.

Key words and phrases

welfare – in the context of health and safety, the promotion of employee well-being and comfort by the provision of facilities such as those for personal hygiene, eating and resting.

Hazards and risks

Toilets, washing facilities and clothes storage

Welfare facilities at work include changing areas, clothes lockers and toilets.

The availability of toilets and washing facilities is fundamental to good hygiene. Without adequate facilities, there is a serious risk that an infectious disease will spread between employees, causing illness and time off work. The facilities need to be kept clean and employees should be encouraged to use them.

Personal hygiene is also essential to prevent contamination by dangerous substances used during work activities. There is a serious risk of illness from chemical poisoning if there are no washing facilities for workers. Lesser risks occur if there is no provision made for storing personal outdoor clothing: if a worker's work clothes are contaminated – by, for example, lead or asbestos – those hazardous materials could be transferred to personal clothing and contaminate the employee's own home and family.

Everyone needs to be able to perform their bodily functions with privacy, otherwise there may be discontentment and stress may ensue.

Resting, eating and drinking

Drinking water is essential to maintain bodily fluids and energy, especially in warm conditions. Without drinking water, people become fatigued, irritable and, in some cases, dehydrated. Concentration can decrease and this increases the likelihood of an accident, particularly in work activities such as manual handling.

Without rest breaks people often become fatigued and irritable and may not be able to maintain their concentration. This increases the risk of an accident. Rest and eating facilities help employees to recuperate, eat and generally 'recharge their batteries'. In temporary workplaces, such as construction sites, rest and eating facilities also provide shelter and warmth from inclement weather. In outdoor work, such as agriculture, arboriculture and horticulture, even the provision of suitably equipped vehicles can help to provide some shelter, comfort and a place to rest and eat.

Controls

There is a statutory requirement to provide employees with basic **welfare** facilities at work. These include toilets, washing facilities, the means to dispose of women's sanitary products, the provision of drinking water and places to change, rest and eat.

Toilets and washing facilities

Toilets and washing facilities must be available for all employees. They need to be in easily accessible places. They must be kept clean, properly lit and ventilated. Separate rooms with toilets and washing facilities must be provided for men and women, except where the room can be locked from the inside. They must be provided with a supply of toilet paper and, for female employees, a means of disposing of personal sanitary products.

All washing facilities must have hot and cold running water, soap and hand-drying facilities, such as towels or air-dryers. The number of facilities depends on the number of employees in the workplace and according to the guidance in the *Approved Code of Practice to The Workplace (Health, Safety and Welfare) Regulations 1992*.

Where the work is dirty or strenuous, or where there is the possibility of contaminating the skin with harmful materials, showers or baths with hot and cold water and a thermostatic mixer should be provided.

If staff work in remote workplaces without suitable plumbing and a water supply, chemical toilets and water containers may need to be provided. In temporary worksites portable toilets and washing facilities will have to be provided.

Resting, eating and drinking

Drinking water must be available, with cups or another drinking method provided.

Facilities for staff rest periods, particularly for pregnant women and nursing mothers, must be made available. Rest rooms must have tables and enough seats with backs for the number of people likely to use them at any one time.

Where workers regularly eat meals at work, facilities should be provided, including facilities for making a hot drink, so they can do so comfortably. Where hot food cannot be obtained close to the workplace, many employers choose to provide a means for heating employee's own food – for example, by providing a microwave oven.

Clothes storage

Storage for clothing is necessary, particularly for special items worn at work but not taken home, and for storing outdoor clothing that must not be taken into workplaces such as surgeries or food preparation rooms. The storage area needs to be secure. Where appropriate, there must be somewhere to allow clothes to dry. Changing facilities are also necessary in some situations, particularly if special clothing is worn for work. There should be enough privacy for workers to change clothes, particularly where there are both men and women workers.

Legal requirements

The Workplace (Health, Safety and Welfare) Regulations 1992 place many requirements on employers. Among other things, these relate to the temperature indoors; cleanliness of the workplace, furniture, furnishings and fittings; the accumulation of waste materials; room dimensions and unoccupied space; the condition of floors; the construction of doors and gates, escalators and moving walkways; the provision of suitable sanitary conveniences; the provision of suitable washing facilities; the provision of a supply of drinking water and of cups or other drinking vessels; the provision of suitable accommodation for clothing, facilities for changing clothing and suitable facilities for resting and eating meals.

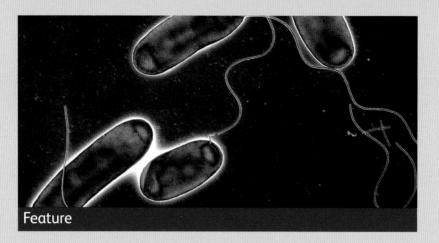

Feature

Legionnaires' disease

Legionnaires' disease is a serious respiratory illness caused by *Legionella pneumophilia*, a type of bacterium that thrives in warm undisturbed water and can be distributed in tiny water droplets.

Anyone can become infected, but the people most at risk are the elderly, smokers, alcoholics, people with weakened immune systems such as those suffering from cancer, diabetes, chronic respiratory or kidney disease.

The illness was first identified in 1976 when 29 people died after a meeting of the American Legion in Philadelphia.

Legionella bacteria can be found in any water system, and are typically in cooling towers, spa and whirlpool baths, hydrotherapy pools, misting machines, showers and air conditioning units. The bacteria thrive at temperatures between 20°C and 45°C but can survive at much lower temperatures. However, they can be killed by temperatures hotter than 45°C, and this is the way they are usually controlled in domestic water systems.

To discourage the growth and multiplication of the bacteria, water systems should be designed with pipework that is as short and as direct as possible. Hot water pipes and tanks should be well insulated to keep the water at above 45°C and the tanks should be covered. In addition, various types of disinfectant can be used, including biocides (chemicals that kill living organisms), chlorine dioxide, ozone, ultraviolet light and thermal treatment.

In hot water systems, the water should be stored at 60°C or above and distributed at above 50°C. (When water at a temperature above 44°C is used for washing or bathing, there is a risk of scalding. Residential care homes, hospitals and so on should fit thermostats to ensure that the temperature of the bathing water is below 44°C.)

Regular and thorough checking, cleaning and disinfection routines are essential. There should also be an annual check of all the water systems in the workplace including a visual inspection of all the components of the system. The system should be drained, if necessary, to determine whether there is any debris in the system that needs to be removed.

Employers must register cooling towers and evaporative condensers with the enforcing authority (usually the local authority) where the device is situated.

Electricity and electrical equipment

About 5 people die at work every year from electrocution or electric burns. In addition, about 100 people are injured in electrical accidents. These figures cover only the *reported* accidents and there are many other incidents in which people receive an electric shock but do not suffer any lasting injury.

Key words and phrases

arcing – a highly visible discharge of electricity through the air between two conductors.

circuit-breaker – an automatic device that breaks the flow of electricity through a circuit to protect it from damage caused by overload. A standard circuit breaker performs a similar function to a fuse by breaking the circuit if the current is excessive. It offers no protection from electric shock. See also residual current device (below).

competent person – a person with the appropriate qualifications, knowledge and experience to identify the risks arising from a situation and the measures needed to control them.

dead – in the context of electricity, a description of a system, equipment or wire that has been isolated from all sources of electricity.

earth – in the context of electricity, a connection between an electrical system or equipment and the ground for safety purposes.

electrical installation – the electrical cables and fittings in a building.

electric shock – a shock when a person touches live parts of an electrical circuit.

electrocution – death caused by an electric shock.

fuse – in the context of electricity, a safety device that breaks the flow of electricity through a circuit to protect equipment from damage caused by overload. It offers no protection from electric shock. It consists of a short piece of wire that melts ('blows') and stops electricity flowing to the appliance if the electric current reaches an unsafe level.

insulation – a high-resistance material surrounding anything electrical that contains the electric current safely.

live – in the context of electricity, a description of a system, equipment or wire that is connected to a source of electricity.

permit to work – a formal document that specifies the work to be done and the precautions to be taken.

portable equipment – in the context of electricity, movable equipment with a lead and a plug.

residual current device (RCD) or residual current circuit-breaker (RCCB) – a safety device fitted to an electrical circuit to offer a degree of protection against electric shock. It disconnects the supply if there is an abnormal current flowing to earth – for example, when someone touches a live conductor.

risk assessment – a systematic process for identifying workplace hazards and assessing the risks involved from those hazards.

Hazards

The main hazards associated with electricity are:

- electric shock or electrocution from contact with live parts

- arcing

- fire

- explosion.

Electric shocks are the most common danger from electricity. They occur when someone touches live parts of an electrical circuit. The body acts as a conductor and the electric current passes through the body, prompting violent muscle spasms that can directly affect the heart and the ability to breathe. The victim may suffer cardiac arrest, and may fall or be thrown against other objects. Often the victim cannot let go of the live conductor.

Electrocution is death from contact with live parts of an electrical circuit when the path of the electricity passes through the heart and stops it.

Electrical **arcing** is where an electric current passes through the air between two conductors. The intense yellow flash – at a temperature over 3,000°C – can damage the eyes, burn the skin (if the route to earth is a person) and ignite flammable materials nearby.

Electrical faults can also produce sparks that can lead to a fire, or, where flammable vapours or dusts are involved, to an explosion.

When electrical circuits become overloaded – for example, when too many plugs are in an adapter – the adaptor or socket can overheat and start a fire.

Risks

The risks involved in working with electricity and electrical equipment can be outlined under two headings:

- fixed electrical systems

- sockets, plugs, switches, cables and equipment.

Fixed electrical systems

Many situations can increase the risk of an accident involving electrical systems or equipment. Here are just a few.

- Where electrical equipment is poorly designed, constructed, installed or maintained.

- If the person working with the equipment is not trained or experienced in the use of that equipment.

- If the worker is working **live** and the live parts are not insulated.

- If people are working near high-voltage overhead power lines, using ladders or vehicles that make contact with the lines.

- If the equipment is used in an unsuitable environment – for example:

- domestic cable is used outdoors where vehicles can run over it, causing damage
- an unsuitable electric cable is used in wet conditions
- equipment designed for domestic use is used in an industrial situation.

■ If the working environment contains a flammable gas or flammable concentration of dust, there is an increased risk of fire and explosion.

■ Where a system is provided with unsuitable or insufficient protective systems, such as fuses, earthing or earth bonding, **circuit-breakers** or **residual current devices**.

■ If the **fuse** rating is too high for the equipment or system being protected, the fuses may not 'blow' when needed so that overheating and fire might result.

■ Where unauthorised do-it-yourself repairs have been made, there is a greater chance that equipment will overheat or catch fire – for example, where silver paper or a nail has been used to replace a fuse, the appliance might melt before the silver paper or nail does so.

■ Where higher voltages are involved, the risk of electrocution and electric shock are greater, but voltages as low as 50 volts can be fatal in some circumstances. Even with very low voltages, there is a risk from heating effects and arcing when high currents are available – for example, if you were to short-circuit a car battery.

Sockets, plugs, switches, cables and equipment

There are a number of common faults that increase the risk of injury and damage.

■ Sockets are wired incorrectly or the connections become loose.

■ The cord grips in plugs do not hold the cord securely, so they strain the wiring connection in the plug, increasing the likelihood of a short circuit, electric shock, electrocution or fire.

■ Plugs are wired with the wrong fuse – a 13 amp fuse in a plug where a 5 amp is more appropriate.

■ Switches develop poor connections through regular use and some arcing or sparking can occur.

■ Where insulation is damaged or burnt, the conductors can be exposed. This often happens when using extension leads. The bending and constant wear and tear causes the insulation to break or split.

■ Two cables are connected by makeshift plastic connectors and tape that allow the connection to loosen or break. This type of repair should not be permitted.

■ Extension leads are used while coiled, generating heat that could lead to a fire.

■ Some parts of electrical systems and equipment, such as plugs, sockets, motors and switches, can become hot if faults occur. This is normally because of loose connections. In any system or equipment, loose connections can result in an electric shock, electrocution or fire. Charring is an indication of the problem, as is a distinctive smell from the hot insulation material.

■ Systems are overloaded by connecting several plugs to one socket via three-way adapters. This increases the risk of a bad connection, with resulting overheating and sparks.

- Equipment is used without protective circuit breakers. Using electrical equipment outdoors, without this sort of protection, considerably increases the risk of electrical injury.

- Portable electrical equipment can be seriously misused and abused. It is moved frequently and used in environments where there are other hazards, such as explosive atmospheres or flammable materials. For example, vacuum cleaners and electric drills used on construction sites can be thrown about and the casings damaged, plugs can be crushed and leads twisted – so accelerating the deterioration of the equipment and increasing the level of risk, particularly if the equipment is not inspected before use and examined thoroughly at regular intervals by a competent person.

Controls

Simple electrical systems and equipment

The first form of control covers the day-to-day electrical equipment and systems we all come across and can generally work with safely. Simple procedures can be set up for dealing with small faults and carrying out regular safety checks. This can be done by someone with a reasonable knowledge of the way electricity works and the dangers it presents.

There are a number of basic controls and safety rules that should be adopted for your workplace. You can, for example, set up a system of testing and maintenance for the electrical systems and all electrical equipment. All but the very basic checks, maintenance and repair of systems and equipment (for example, changing a plug or tightening connections) should be done by a **competent person**, preferably a qualified electrician or electrical engineer. (See also below.)

Installation, testing and maintenance

Existing electrical wiring and equipment must be sound and be properly installed to the standards in the current edition of the Institution of Electrical Engineers' *Regulations for Electrical Installations*. This is the accepted standard for all electrical systems and equipment in the UK.

Employers must make sure that systems and equipment are inspected and tested, where appropriate, regularly.

Fixed wiring should be tested and inspected periodically – the interval depends on the use of the system. Heavily used systems should be inspected every 12 to 18 months. Otherwise, they should be inspected every five years. Fuse boards, wall sockets and portable equipment should be inspected every week. Circuit breakers should be tested every three months. Electrical installations should be inspected by a competent person.

Portable Appliance Testing (PAT) is the regular inspection and testing of all electrical equipment used at work. This includes tools, office equipment, and appliances such as kettles, vacuum cleaners, and office fans. The frequency of testing and inspection depends on a risk assessment, but some of the factors to be taken into account include the:

- type of equipment

- manufacturer's recommendations

- age of the equipment

- workplace environment

- frequency of use

- likely abuse of the equipment

- records of maintenance, inspection and testing.

For example, in the construction industry, equipment may need to be inspected every three months, while industrial cleaning equipment may need to be inspected every 12 months and computers up to every five years.

Competent persons

When using contractors to do electrical work, make sure that they are registered with an organisation that checks the work of its members, such as the National Inspection Council for Electrical Installation Contracting. You also need to ensure that the workers you employ are competent to do the work you require. It is no good employing a TV repair engineer if you want someone to rewire business premises.

Safety rules and precautions

Supervisors and managers need to ensure that employees and others are following basic safety rules when working with electrical equipment and electrical installations. Here are some simple rules when working with electricity.

Plugs and sockets

Check that sockets and plugs are wired correctly and that socket connections are secure. You can use a socket tester to do this. It is useful to known the colour coding for electrical wires. Brown is live, blue is neutral, and green and yellow stripes is earth. There was a much earlier system of colours (with red for live, black for neutral and green for earth). If you have these old colours in the wiring in your workplace, have the wiring checked and preferably replaced.

The cord grips in plugs should secure the supply cable. Plugs should be provided with the appropriate fuse. If a plug, socket or switch feels hot, have it checked.

Cables

Where insulation is damaged or burnt, the whole cable should be replaced. Ensure that employees never use any electrical equipment with a worn cable or a damaged casing.

If there is no alternative but to join two cables, make sure that a plug and socket joint is used, rather than plastic connectors and tape. Charred plugs and sockets and other parts of the electrical system should be replaced. Any loose connections should be tightened.

Avoid the use of extension cables and three-plug adapters. If they are needed for a long period, then arrange for permanent wiring and more wall sockets. If there is no alternative but to use extension cables for a short period, avoid kinking them and keep oil, grease and water well away from them. Ensure that staff place the cable in a position where people will not trip over it.

Never permit staff to connect several extension cables together, and ensure that they always unwind coiled leads to their full length before use.

Earth

Anything capable of conducting electricity, such as metal pipework, metal benches or casing to electrical appliances, should be connected to earth.

Disconnecting
If anyone is to maintain or repair the system or equipment, make certain that they
disconnect the system or equipment first.

Maintenance, repair and test records
To ensure that appliances are tested regularly, create an inventory of electrical equipment
and keep it up to date. Keep a record of the test, maintenance and repairs to the electrical
installation, including dates, names of the contractors used and any alterations carried
out. Label each appliance, stating the last test date, and make sure that whoever does the
test signs the label.

Portable electrical equipment

Portable electric equipment is very common and is used in hazardous conditions in
factories, construction sites, homes and gardens. About a quarter of all reportable
electrical accidents involve portable equipment.

A major problem is failure to maintain the equipment. It is important to train employees to
make a visual inspection before using an appliance, including cables, plugs and casings.
Damaged or faulty equipment should be removed immediately so that it can be repaired
or replaced.

Ideally, no personal mains-connected equipment, such as kettles or radios, should be allowed
at work, but if they are permitted, the equipment should be tested before use. All employees
should be trained in the basic safety checks to make. These are referred to as *user checks*.

All portable electrical equipment should be included in **risk assessments** and maintained
properly. Designate an employee to oversee the maintenance. Formal visual inspection
and testing should be carried out at frequent intervals. Defective equipment should be
taken out of use. Repaired equipment should be checked before being used.

Make sure that the system of checks, maintenance and repair is reviewed regularly, so that
follow-up action is always taken where there are problems. Consider creating a separate
inventory of portable electrical equipment.

Where feasible in high-risk situations, particularly for work outdoors, reduce the voltage (by
using a voltage reduction transformer) or use battery-powered equipment.

Supervising electricians and electrical contractors

Many areas of electrical work need specialist attention, but supervisors (and supervising
managers) should know what to look for when working with electricians or electrical
contractors.

Risk assessment of work procedures
Make sure that contractors have carried out a full risk assessment before any work is
undertaken on an electrical system, particularly where the system is high voltage.

When planning work on an electrical system, contractors should consider the work to be
done, the hazards of the system and equipment to be worked on, the people doing the
work, the level of supervision necessary, any precautions to be taken and, if necessary, a
safe system of work to be used. For example, written procedures and safety rules should be
designed for fault finding.

Any work on an electrical system or electrical equipment should be planned well in advance and carried out by competent people. There should be adequate information about the system and the equipment to allow the work to be done safely – for example, drawings of the system and records of any work done on it.

Anyone supervising a contractor doing a job should have good knowledge of electrical safety and should discuss the job with the workers assigned to do it before any work starts.

The electricians must be aware of any precautions they need to take to keep risk to a minimum. There must be good communication between the electricians and their supervisor or manager during the job and there must be a clear emergency procedure should anything go wrong.

The supervising contractor should make arrangements for regular checks to be made on the work, whether it is in progress or not (for instance, because work has stopped for rain or while awaiting components). The workplace supervisor should find out whether these precautions have been taken by the contractors. If they have not been taken, insist that the contractors' workers follow good health and safety practice.

Design of electrical systems

It is the responsibility of the employer to ensure that the systems installed are designed so that all parts of the system can be isolated. Control panels need to be designed with insulated conductors to allow the worker to carry out testing and fault-finding with a low risk of shock and electrocution. Separate power systems and control systems can be installed to reduce the need to work near high-voltage cables. All systems should be designed so that there is sufficient space and lighting to work safely.

If managers or supervisors suspect that an installation is not up to this standard, they should bring it to the employer's attention.

Safe procedures

First of all, the cable, system or equipment to be worked on must be identified. Secondly, the equipment should be disconnected from all sources of power. Thirdly, the equipment or system should remain isolated while work is going on – it should not be possible, for instance, to reconnect a plug during the work without the knowledge of the person carrying out the work.

If you are managing or supervising electrical work, make everyone aware that the work is going on, including posting notices. The parts being worked on should be checked, using voltage indicators, to ensure that they are dead. All conductors should be earthed.

In more complex situations it may be necessary to control maintenance work by issuing a **permit to work**. A permit to work is a formal document that specifies work to be done and the precautions to be taken. It is issued, signed and dated by a competent person who is authorised by the employer to issue such permits relating to the specific equipment or systems. It usually states:

■ the name of the person being given the permit

■ the precise equipment that has been isolated

- where it has been isolated and where the conductors have been earthed
- where warning notices have been placed
- the nature of the work being done
- whether there is any other hazard nearby
- other precautions to be taken during the work.

Working on live equipment should only be permitted in the following situations:

- where it is unreasonable for the work to be done while the power is dead – for example, if a number of other supplies need to be temporarily cut off while the work is done
- where it is reasonable for the work to be carried out in the particular circumstances while the cables are live. In such cases, danger may be present but injury must be prevented
- where proper precautions have been taken to prevent injury. This can include using competent staff and planning the job properly.

Street light shock stopped worker breathing

A council employee was in a coma for two days after an electric shock from a street light threw him from his ladder, knocked him unconscious and stopped him breathing. His colleague, who had been holding the bottom of the ladder, also suffered an electric shock but recovered in time to give life-saving first aid.

Normal procedure when servicing a street light was to switch it off, using the isolator switch at the base of the light column, before starting work. Neither of the two men assigned to the task had been trained to do this or instructed in how to carry out a proper risk assessment. Unknown to the men, there was a wiring fault in the street light. They received electric shocks when the first man tried to change the bulb.

The council had failed to provide proper training to employees working on electrical equipment and had not explained the need for a thorough risk assessment.

Legal requirements

The Electricity at Work Regulations 1989 set the health and safety requirements for electricity at work. They cover the construction and maintenance of electrical systems and electrical equipment; the carrying out of electrical work; the provision of protective equipment, insulation and joints of electrical systems; and other specific and general requirements when working with electricity, electrical systems and equipment.

Under The Electrical Equipment (Safety) Regulations 1994 electrical equipment must be designed and constructed to protect against hazards from electricity.

The Provision and Use of Work Equipment Regulations 1998 require employers to select suitable work equipment and ensure that it is maintained in safe working order and in good repair.

Gas supply and equipment

Although explosions involving gas are rare, many people can lose their lives when an explosion does occur. Where there are no fatalities, there are still devastating consequences for the people living or working in the buildings affected and in those nearby. Poorly maintained gas systems can also cause death through carbon monoxide poisoning.

Key words and phrases

competent person – someone with the appropriate qualifications, knowledge and experience to identify the risks arising from a situation and the measures needed to control them. In the context of gas safety, a person who is required by law to be approved by the Health and Safety Executive, such as a CORGI-registered gas engineer/technician.

Gas Safe registered – someone who is recognised as competent in the Gas Safe Register, which is the examining and control organisation for gas fitters.

gas – an air-like substance that expands freely to fill any space available, irrespective of its quantity.

gas system – all gas installation pipework, fittings and appliances including ventilation and flues.

installer – in the context of gas supply and installation, a person who carries out work on a gas system or a gas storage vessel.

Hazards

Gas normally burns in air to produce heat, carbon dioxide (CO_2) and water vapour (the products of combustion). For anything to burn, it must have oxygen which is freely available in air. Air consists of mainly nitrogen (about 80 per cent) and oxygen (20 per cent) with minute amounts of carbon dioxide and other gases.

In normal circumstances, the oxygen in the air combines with gas in the presence of an ignition source, such as a pilot light or sparking device, and burns normally. However, if the supply of oxygen is restricted by a lack of air supply to the gas, then soot and carbon monoxide are produced (instead of carbon dioxide). This is called incomplete combustion.

The main hazards associated with gas systems and appliances are therefore:

- explosions – when gas has leaked from a system or an appliance and the gas is ignited
- fire, which usually follows an explosion
- carbon monoxide poisoning
- suffocation – if gas leaks into the air where people are working
- flammable substances in gas cylinders.

Carbon monoxide

The use of some poorly installed or poorly maintained systems and appliances can result in incomplete gas combustion when gas is not burned properly and carbon monoxide is produced.

Carbon monoxide (CO) is a poisonous gas that can kill. You cannot smell it, taste it or see it. The early symptoms of carbon monoxide poisoning are tiredness, drowsiness, headache, stomach aches and chest pains. Carbon monoxide poisoning is a particular hazard where there is insufficient oxygen available for the occupants in the room and for the appliance (see below).

Similar hazards occur where products of combustion are not removed safely from the room where the appliance is placed.

Risks

High-risk situations in the use of gas can be grouped into four categories:

- incomplete gas combustion
- failure to remove the products of combustion safely
- insufficient available oxygen
- gas leaks.

Incomplete gas combustion

There are three main causes of incomplete gas combustion:

- inadequate ventilation – for instance, because windows are not opened often enough

- defective ventilation system – for instance, ventilation apertures in a room containing a gas appliance are blocked, either accidentally or deliberately
- defective fan supplying the air to the gas appliance.

Failure to remove the products of combustion

Where the products of combustion are not removed safely, there is a serious risk that the products will remain in areas where people are working. This can occur if a flue or chimney is:

- damaged
- not big enough to remove the products of combustion from the workspace
- blocked by soot or debris.

The ventilation for a gas appliance may also be affected by other ventilation requirements such as extractor fans in the same room. This may prevent the products of combustion being removed from the room properly.

Insufficient oxygen

An inadequate supply of oxygen can occur where there are insufficient or obstructed ventilation openings, such as windows that can be opened and ventilation apertures in a room. The problem usually involves appliances without a flue, appliances with an open flue or other types of appliance that draw combustion air from the room containing the appliance. Where a new appliance with greater gas burning capacity is installed in a room and no account is taken of the increased oxygen requirement, there is a likelihood that the ventilation openings in the room will be insufficient.

The evidence as to whether or not there are safe levels of oxygen in a room with a gas appliance can be established by:

- air tests for oxygen
- air tests for carbon monoxide
- medical conclusions from the symptoms of staff working in the relevant room.

Gas leaks

Leaks can happen where there has been bad workmanship, the materials used are not satisfactory or the appliance or gas system has not been maintained properly. It has been known for garden hoses to be used instead of proper flexible gas connections and some pipes have been left open when they should have been sealed off.

Other problems

Problems involving gas may also occur when:

- appliances are fitted too close to combustible material
- safety devices have been damaged by accident or disabled on purpose.

Council fined for school carbon monoxide levels

A primary school class had to be evacuated after being overcome by carbon monoxide fumes. An investigation by the Health and Safety Executive found that the gas was coming from an inadequately maintained boiler and leaking into the classroom. The local council pleaded guilty to breaches of health and safety legislation and was fined and ordered to pay costs. The inspector said that several factors were to blame, but the council's failure to operate an effective gas safety management system was the most significant matter.

Controls

The most important control in dealing with gas and gas fittings and appliances is to ensure that any work is carried out by a **competent person**. Employers must ensure that such people are registered with Gas Safe or are employed by a person who is Gas Safe registered. A competent person must be trained and experienced in the specific type of appliance or specific work being done. All gas consumers are advised to have their gas appliances inspected and serviced at least every 12 months by a Gas Safe installer.

Any person who installs a gas fitting has to make sure that the fitting is suitable for the purpose for which it is to be used. There are specific requirements for the type of fittings to be used in the installation and use of gas systems and appliances – for example, no lead pipes or fittings can be used and there are strict controls on the use of non-metallic fittings. Gas fitters or installers are bound by strict work procedures and equipment standards in carrying out any work on a gas system or appliance, particularly in preventing the release of gas, in sealing gas pipes and in testing to ensure that there is no escape of gas, however slight, when work has been completed.

The standards for ventilation, flues, installation tubing and appliances, and the training of gas installers are contained in many British Standards and approved codes of practice. Some of the most important procedures and standards are outlined below.

Safety procedures and standards

The use of ignition sources, such as naked flames, and the creation of sparks is banned where there is a risk of explosion. The procedures for work on gas systems and appliances require the systems and appliances to be connected to earth by electric cables. This is to prevent an electrical discharge igniting any leak of gas.

Pipework should be installed in a safe position, taking into account any other installations that might affect safety, such as other pipes, drains, electrical cables and appliances. Installers should inform the occupier of a building in which a meter has been installed that electrical equipotential bonding (pipework connected to earth) is required. Gas fittings have to be protected from damage including corrosion and blockage.

Alterations to buildings must not be done where the alteration would breach gas safety regulations. Any installation pipework must not affect the structure and fire resistance of the building.

There are specific requirements for the protection of pipes that pass through walls and floors, including the adequate ventilation of ducts and voids that have pipework in them. Where pipework is accessible for inspection, it should be marked in some way to identify it as carrying gas.

Gas appliances must be installed in a position that allows them to be easily accessible for inspection, maintenance and operation. The manufacturer's instructions must be left for the occupier of the premises.

Gas meters need to be installed so that they allow easy inspection, maintenance, testing and the purging of meters. The housing of meters must allow easy gas dispersal and contain no combustible materials.

Certain gas appliances, such as gas fires, gas water heaters and space heaters, must not be installed unless they are room-sealed. This means that their combustion systems must be sealed from the room in which the appliance is located. They obtain oxygen for combustion from the open air outside the building or from a ventilated, uninhabited space inside the premises. The appliances vent the products of combustion directly to the open air outside the premises.

Emergency notices must be provided to describe the action to be taken if there is a gas escape.

People who carry out work on gas systems and appliances are required by law to report any appliance they suspect of being dangerous to the person who is responsible for the premises – this might be the supervisor or manager. They also have the authority to ban the use of an unsafe appliance.

Where gas other than natural gas escapes (for example, carbon monoxide), specific action needs to be taken, such as to turn off appliances, ventilate the room or building to disperse the carbon monoxide and not to use the suspected appliance again until it has been checked by a competent gas installer. If it is suspected persons have been exposed to carbon monoxide poisoning, urgent medical advice must be obtained.

In domestic premises, the installation of CO alarms is a useful back-up precaution, although they must not be regarded as a substitute for proper installation and maintenance.

There are special requirements for liquefied petroleum gas (LPG) installations, including the maintenance of gas pressure from storage tanks or cylinders. Unauthorised persons should not tamper with regulators used in these systems.

Employers must ensure that gas appliances, flues and pipework are maintained in a safe condition. (Landlords who let domestic premises must ensure that gas appliances, flues and pipework are inspected every 12 months. Records of these inspections must be kept and issued to tenants.)

Legal requirements

The Gas Safety (Installation and Use) Regulations 1998 set the standards for the installation and use of gas systems and gas appliances. They cover the qualification and supervision of the workers involved; the standards of materials and workmanship; the general safety precautions; emergency controls; standards of meters, pipework and appliances; and the maintenance requirements for employers, self-employed persons and landlords.

Feature

Safety signs

There is a unified system of visual safety signs throughout the European Union. The signs convey their health or safety message through a combination of shape, colour and symbols or pictures.

 A circle with a blue background is used to indicate that an action is mandatory. In other words, it *must* be carried out.

 A circle with a red outline and a red line from the top left to the bottom right indicates that an action is *prohibited*.

 A rectangle with a green background is *advisory*. The sign shown here indicates an emergency route.

 A triangle with a black outline provides a *warning*. The sign shown here warns that something is flammable.

Employers must provide safety signs where a hazard cannot be avoided or the risk has not been controlled by other means. Signs must be kept clean, easy to see and undamaged, and unfamiliar signs must be explained to employees and visitors.

Employers may also need to consider providing other types of warning, such as acoustic signals to warn that a vehicle is reversing or that doors are closing, announcements over a public address system, recorded warning messages or brightly coloured tape to mark off a hazardous area or to mark pipework containing dangerous substances.

Warnings and safety information may also need to have text – for example, fire procedure signs, first aid notices and construction site notices (as above).

A recent initiative by the United Nations aims to have a worldwide system for classifying and labelling *chemicals* according to the health, physical and environmental hazards they create.

The Globally Harmonized System of Classification and Labelling of Chemicals (GHS) has introduced new warning symbols that you will gradually start to see.

Current symbol	New symbol	Current symbol	New symbol
Danger/ Very toxic	Danger Fatal if swallowed	Category 1 carcinogen	Danger May cause cancer

Current symbol	New symbol	Current symbol	New symbol
Danger/ Corrosive substance	Danger Causes severe skin burns and eye damage	Irritant	Warning Causes skin irritation

Fire safety

Fire prevention is one of the most well developed health and safety controls in the workplace. Even so, about five people are killed at work each year, about 60 suffer major injuries and about 220 are off work for more than three days because of a fire-related injury. Fire can also devastate a business because of the time and cost involved in repairing property damage and rebuilding customer loyalty.

Key words and phrases

competent person – a person with the appropriate qualifications, knowledge and experience to identify the risks arising from a situation and the measures needed to control them.

emergency plan – the actions to be taken in a particular workplace in the event of a fire or other emergency.

safe system of work – a set of procedures for carrying out tasks safely.

Hazards

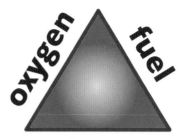

Fire is a chemical reaction producing heat, light and flame when three components come together:

- oxygen
- ignition or heat
- fuel.

If the three come together in certain conditions, a fire is highly likely to start. This is why the identification of fire hazards focuses on these three components.

Oxygen is present in the air. It can also be found in oxygen cylinders in, for example, hospitals, residential care homes and welding operations. Ignition and heat sources include electrical equipment, heating appliances, cigarettes, naked flames and sources of static electricity, such as nylon. Anything that burns is a fuel, and fuels come in three forms:

- flammable gases – such as liquefied petroleum gas (LPG) and acetylene
- flammable liquids – such as paints, thinners and adhesives
- flammable solids – such as wood, paper, card and plastic.

The dangers from fires include burns and the harmful effects of inhaling smoke and toxic gases – the products of combustion.

Risks

Fires happen if care is not taken to control the three components of a fire. Oxygen-enriched atmospheres (used in medical procedures and welding, for example) or high concentrations of oxygen (where oxygen cylinders are stored, for instance) create a high risk of fire. Risk is increased in any situation where the oxygen supply to a fire is difficult to control – outdoors, in automatic ventilation systems and where doors and windows are open. Risk is also increased if there are sparks, naked flames (from electrical equipment, blowtorches or Bunsen burners, for example) hot surfaces or hot materials.

The presence of a fuel – such as flammable material including paper, cardboard, plastic, wood, packaging, clothing, furnishings, paint, thinners and gases – increases the likelihood of a fire.

People are more at risk from fires indoors than from fires outdoors. This is mainly due to the difficulty of getting out of a building if there are poor fire precautions and emergency provision.

Poor management and supervision

Many problems stem from poor organisation of the workplace. Examples include:

- poor housekeeping and waste control – for example, accumulated rubbish or poor storage of combustible materials

- poor control of cigarette-smoking outside the workplace
- inadequate control of flammable substances – for example, unsuitable or careless storage, or careless use, of flammable materials
- lack of care when using heat-producing equipment – for example, when using portable heaters – or obstruction of ventilation for heaters, machinery or electrical appliances
- lack of fire precautions and electrical maintenance
- electrical equipment left switched on when not in use.

Controls

To prevent a fire from starting, you must stop the three components coming together, particularly the fuel and ignition source. To put a fire out, you have to control the oxygen supply to the fire, take the fuel away or cool the ignition source. The following pages outline the precautions for avoiding a fire and what to do if one does occur – including how to get people out of the workplace and deal with the fire.

Fire risk assessment

The first step in this process is to carry out a fire **risk assessment**. This duty may fall to managers or supervisors and could involve the assistance of safety representatives and employees.

The fire hazards in the workplace should be identified as well as the people who might be in danger. Consider the dangers to employees, visitors and members of the public who might be in the workplace when a fire breaks out, and consider the problems they could encounter when trying to escape.

Next, assess the risks associated with the hazards and decide whether the existing fire precautions are adequate and, if not, how to eliminate the hazard or reduce the risks. Record the findings and the actions you take to deal with the findings.

A review of the assessment should be done every so often and kept up to date. There should be a review if the work activity or the arrangements in the workplace change significantly, or there is reason to believe that the assessment is no longer valid. The assessment should indicate the measures an organisation needs to take. They might include improving:

- control of the components that create fire
- fire detection and alarm measures
- the means of escape from the workplace
- the fire-fighting equipment provided.

Preventing fire

To prevent a fire from starting, you should try to control the source of oxygen and reduce the sources of ignition and fuel. Limiting any one of these components will reduce the risk of fire.

Reducing the sources of oxygen

You could limit the amount of oxygen in a room by keeping doors and windows closed, but this needs to be balanced against employee comfort. The design of the workplace through compartmentation (dividing the building into separate protected sections or units) can restrict the oxygen available to a fire. If ventilation systems are not being used, they should be closed off. If there are any oxygen-rich atmospheres in the workplace, they should be strictly controlled.

Reducing the sources of ignition or heat

Unnecessary heat sources should be removed from the workplace or replaced with safer alternatives – for example, central heating radiators could replace infrared heaters. Naked flames should be avoided and ignition sources should be positioned safely. There must be a **safe system of work** for hot processes that minimises the chance of ignition – for example, refuelling petrol-driven equipment should take place outdoors.

Cigarette smoking remains a source of ignition despite the ban on smoking in the workplace. Employees and others still smoke outside workplaces, so that a smouldering butt discarded near flammable materials could start a fire.

Work equipment, electrical equipment and installations, including ventilation systems, should be maintained to minimise their potential as a source of ignition.

Reducing sources of fuel

Flammable substances should be removed, reduced or substituted in the workplace. Make sure that flammable materials are handled, transported, stored and used safely – see also pages 323 to 327.

Refuse and waste should be removed promptly and regularly. Flammable waste should be stored until disposal in fire-resistant containers.

Fire detection and warning

All organisations need a system that warns of danger as soon as possible after a fire starts. This gives the best chance of escape. In small workplaces, verbal alerts may be enough – just shout, 'fire'. Larger workplaces need an electrical detection and alarm system. Automatic detection systems include heat, smoke and flammable gas detectors.

Everyone in the workplace should know how to contact the emergency services. Such a procedure should be in the organisation's emergency plan (see page 318 to 320).

Means of escape

If a fire does occur, people need to get out of the building as quickly as possible, without the risk of injury or having to fight through smoke. In larger workplaces several escape routes may need to be provided.

Where the means of escape has been approved under building regulations the arrangements made in order to obtain the approval should be adequate.

Two principles should be followed in designing the means of escape – increase the time available for a person to escape from the fire and reduce the time taken by people to reach a place of safety.

The methods for increasing the time available are compartmentation, fire doors, smoke vents, smoke curtains and sprinkler systems.

Reducing the time to get to safety can be done by creating minimum travel distances, protected means of escape, early detection and warning systems, fire extinguishers to fight small fires, adequate fire escapes with outward opening doors, training staff, practice fire drills, assistance to leave the building for disabled people, clear signs to indicate the route of escape and emergency lighting.

Means of fire fighting

Once a fire has started, there should be enough portable fire-fighting equipment available to extinguish the fire in its early stages. It is most important to note, however, that this equipment is not provided for employees to fight a fire that has been burning for some time. It is a matter of judgement whether employees should fight a fire with this equipment. The equipment has limits. Ask the advice of a fire officer on this.

In small workplaces one or two extinguishers may be all that is needed, but in larger workplaces more fire extinguishers will be needed in appropriate positions.

Other types of fire-fighting equipment can be provided, for example, fire hoses connected to the mains water supply. Another example is the provision of fire blankets for use on small fires involving clothing, cooking oil or fat. Some modern buildings may have automatic fire-fighting systems such as sprinkler systems.

Fire extinguishers
Since 1997 all new fire extinguishers must have a red body and a colour-coded label showing their contents. Before 1997 the extinguishers themselves were colour-coded. These may continue to be used until they fail their annual inspection: at this point they must be replaced with the newer type extinguishers.

There are five types of portable fire extinguisher. They are as follows.

- Water – red label
  This cools the fire by controlling the heat and the ignition source.

- Foam – cream label
  This smothers the fire by controlling the oxygen supply.

- Powder – blue label
  This works in the same way as foam.

- Carbon dioxide – black label
  This starves the fire of oxygen by replacing the oxygen with carbon dioxide in the vicinity of the fire.

- Wet chemical – yellow label
  This puts a non-combustible layer of
  soapy chemical between the fuel and
  the oxygen.

Fires are classified as class A, B, C, D or F.
The class of fire determines the type of fire
extinguisher that should be used.

Class A Fires involve solid materials, such
as wood or paper, that form
glowing embers. Use water, foam
or powder to put these fires out.

Class B Fires involve flammable liquids
such as paints, oils or fats. Use
foam, carbon dioxide or powder to deal with these fires.

Class C Fires involve flammable gases, such as methane and butane, and should be put
out using powder.

Class D Fires involve combustible metals, such as sodium, titanium or magnesium, and
should not be dealt with using any of these fire extinguishers. Only the fire service
should deal with this sort of fire.

Class F Fires involve cooking fats and oils. Only specially trained people using special wet
chemical extinguishers should tackle such fires.

Where electrical equipment is involved in a fire, use powder or carbon dioxide.

Maintenance and testing

All fire safety measures and equipment, including fire doors, escape routes, fire detection
and alarm systems, emergency lighting and fire-fighting equipment, need to be kept in
good working order. Managers and supervisors should ensure that there are regular checks
of the fire doors and the routes and means of escape to make sure, for example, that the
fire doors are closed and the escape routes are not obstructed. The fire detection system,
alarm system and emergency lights should be tested weekly and serviced regularly, and at
least once a year. Fire-fighting equipment should be checked for damage and apparent
working order every week and a **competent person** must check and test the equipment for
efficient working order every 12 months. Any defects should be repaired immediately.

Information, instruction and training

All employees should know what to do in the event of a fire. The most basic information
should include:

- the location of escape routes from their workplace
- where the fire alarm system is
- how to use the fire alarm system.

'Fire action' notices help to give clear information about the fire precautions in the workplace. For example, instructions on what to do in the event of a fire and a warning that lifts, escalators and revolving doors are unsafe during a fire and must not be used as a means of escape. These notices should also indicate where people should gather together outside the workplace when it has been evacuated.

Employee training should take account of the fire risk assessment and it should outline the contents and procedures in the emergency plan. Training should include:

- identifying the sources of fuel and ignition and their control
- general fire precautions
- detecting fires and raising the alarm
- what to do in the event of a fire
- the location and routes of the means of escape from the particular workplace
- the location and use of fire-fighting equipment
- where flammable substances are stored or used, and the precautions to be taken
- how to evacuate members of the public
- the arrangements for assisting people with limited mobility or impaired vision or hearing.

Supervisors and safety representatives should receive additional training, including the details of the fire risk assessment and the emergency plan.

Fire drills can be used to test everyone's understanding of the emergency plan. A drill should be arranged at least once a year.

Competent persons

Employers must appoint **competent persons** to help with fire precautions and emergencies. If you are the manager, give responsibility to some employees to carry out various duties in the event of a fire, for instance, to supervise an assembly point and make sure that no one returns to the building until the official all-clear is given. Such employees must be given an appropriate level of training.

The servicing and maintenance of fire detection and alarm systems and fire-fighting equipment should be done by competent persons such as fire alarm installers and insurance consultants. Advice on means of escape can be obtained from fire protection officers and building control officers. Fire protection officers can be contacted at your local fire service and building control officers at your local council.

Emergency plans

An **emergency plan** contains the actions that managers, supervisors, employees and others need to take in the event of a fire. The intention of the plan is to ensure that everyone knows what to do in the event of a fire and can escape safely. The emergency plan can be used to respond to other emergencies such as:

- environmental/natural disasters – for example, floods or chemical spills or leaks

- explosions

- medical emergency – for example, a serious injury or fatality, epidemic, pandemic or poisoning

- major violence – for example, murder, suicide, kidnapping, hostage-taking, school shooting, bomb threat

- large assemblies – for example, strikes, riots and demonstrations.

The rest of this section uses fire as the reason for evacuation but the plan could be used for evacuation caused by any other emergency.

If there are more than five people in the workplace, there must be an emergency plan. The fire risk assessment is most important in drawing up the emergency plan. It identifies particular hazards and the risks that will need to be taken into account when drawing up the emergency plan.

Scope

An emergency plan can range from a simple fire notice in a small workplace, to a much more detailed plan in large workplaces. The plan should include clear information about the following topics:

- action to be taken in the event of a fire

- information on the alarm system

- details of the means of escape

- assembly points outside the workplace

- availability and position in the building of fire-fighting equipment

- duties and responsibilities of appointed employees in the event of a fire

- how the emergency services are to be contacted and who will do it

- procedures for dealing with the emergency services, once they arrive at the workplace

- details of the hazards and risks in the workplace that might affect the emergency service personnel in performing their duties, such as the presence of flammable substances, gas cylinders and so on

- training arrangements for employees

- the arrangements for people with additional needs, such as those with impaired vision, limited mobility or learning difficulties

- in large workplaces, drawings of the fire precaution systems may be helpful – for example, the location of the main electrical supply switch and mains gas shut-off valve, the escape routes, the position of fire detection and alarm systems, emergency lighting systems and fire-fighting equipment.

Evacuating disabled people

Some disabled people are at greater risk from fire if they cannot hear or see warning systems or are unable to leave premises quickly. Their needs must be considered in all emergency plans and special provision may be particularly appropriate in workplaces where there is residential accommodation, such as hotels, guesthouses, residential homes and conference facilities. All staff should be made aware of special evacuation procedures and these should be rehearsed during fire drills.

Information in Braille may need to be made available to people with visual impairment about the location of fire exits and evacuation procedures. Procedures should be arranged for alerting people with hearing impairments if alarm systems are audio only. There are a number of options that could be considered including flashing lights on smoke detectors and/or specialist alarms installed in rooms made available to people with hearing impairment.

Auxiliary aids could also be available for emergencies, such as wheelchairs. Where there are steps and ramps they should have appropriately situated handrails.

Fire checklist

Regular checks should be made throughout the workplace to make sure that all precautions are being taken and equipment provided can be used without risk to the people using them. This work is most likely to involve supervisors, safety representatives and specially trained staff.

Workplace
Are flammable substances stored, including gas cylinders?
Are there arrangements for the storage and disposal of flammable waste?
Are there suitable arrangements for the disposal of smoking materials, if allowed anywhere outside the building?
Are the fire instructions clear and easily seen?
Is electrical equipment maintained in ways that help to prevent fire sources?
Are there adequate controls on the use of heating appliances?

Fire drills
Carried out once every six months?
Do they take into account the number and different groups of people using the building?
Records kept?

Fire detectors
Is the fire detection and alarm system checked regularly?
Does it allow people to escape to a safe place in time?
Is the electrical system provided with a back-up power supply?

Fire alarms
Tested once a week?
Can everyone in the workplace hear it? Is it also visual?
Maintenance and testing records kept?

Smoke detectors
Tested once a week?
Maintenance and signed records kept?

Fire-fighting equipment
Have you trained staff in the use of fire-fighting equipment?
Checked monthly and tested by a competent person once a year?
Maintenance records kept?

Fire escape routes
Are there enough fire exits for the number of people in the workplace?
Fire doors, escape routes, emergency lighting and signs checked regularly?
Emergency lighting tested weekly, with servicing every year?
Maintenance records kept?
Clear of obstructions?

Fire doors and exits
Clearly marked?
Easily opened in an emergency?
Kept closed?

Training
Are employees given information, instruction and training about:
- fire risks and precautions?
- what to do in the event of a fire?
- raising the alarm?
- contacting the emergency services?
- evacuation procedures?
- escape routes and assembly areas?
- helping people with special needs?

Information for visitors
Are all visitors provided with information about what to do in the event of a fire?
Is there information in Braille available on request?
Is information translated into suitable other languages?

Checks before leaving the workplace unoccupied
Are doors and windows closed?
Is all electrical equipment switched off or unplugged?
Are all naked flames put out?
Are all flammable substances stored away safely?
Are smokers' materials safely put out?

Fire records

You need to keep a range of records, for example:

- a copy of the fire risk assessment

- a copy of the emergency plan

- plans of the fire detection and alarm system

- plans of escape routes

- plans of the fire-fighting equipment including automatic fire-fighting systems and fire extinguisher locations

- maintenance and testing records for the fire detection and alarm system, emergency lighting, automatic fire-fighting equipment and fire extinguishers.

Legal requirements

The Management of Health and Safety at Work Regulations 1999, The Regulatory Reform (Fire Safety) Order 2005 and the Fire (Scotland) Act 2005 require employers to carry out a fire risk assessment; identify the significant findings of the risk assessment; provide and maintain fire precautions to safeguard those who use the workplace; and provide information, instruction and training to employees about the fire precautions in the workplace.

Employers must also nominate people to undertake special roles required under the emergency plan; consult employees about the nomination of people to carry out those roles and about proposals for improving the fire precautions; inform other employers who also have workplaces in the building and establish a suitable means of contacting the emergency services. Some workplaces might need to apply for a licence or other form of approval before using the workplace.

Fire precautions legislation deals with general fire precautions including the means of detection and giving warning in case of fire; the provision of means of escape; means of fighting fire; and the training of staff in fire safety.

See also page 327 for legal requirements about flammable substances.

Flammable and explosive substances

A fire burnt for several days after massive explosions at the Buncefield Oil Storage Depot, Hertfordshire, that were heard as far away as France and Holland. Homes and businesses were destroyed and 40 people were injured. Tall plumes of smoke pumped into the atmosphere and at one point covered most of south-east England.

A flammable substance is any natural or artificial substance, in the form of a solid, liquid, gas or vapour, that is liable to catch fire. Examples include petrol, heating oil and wood or flour dust.

An explosive substance is any kind of dust that can explode when airborne (an explosive atmosphere).

Flammable and explosive substances can be found in most workplaces. Some are stored and used in large quantities, such as in petrol filling stations, and others are required only in small amounts, such as flour in a small bakery or cans of petrol and oil in a gardener's machine store.

Precautions are needed in all workplaces to prevent the risk of a fire or an explosion.

Key words and phrases

explosive atmosphere – airborne substances that can explode when ignited.

explosive substance – is any kind of dust that can explode when airborne.

flammable substance – any natural or artificial substance in the form of a solid, liquid, gas or vapour that is liable to catch fire.

hierarchy of control – a well tested system of graded health and safety controls. The sequence helps organisations to determine their most effective health and safety controls.

ignition source – something that can light a flammable substance, causing a fire or explosion.

Hazards

Flammable substances, when mixed with air in the presence of an **ignition source**, can catch fire or create an explosion. Burns and blast injuries can be minor, very serious or result in death. Cylinders containing flammable gas present extra hazards. The hazards include the blast from an exploding cylinder, impact from flying parts of the cylinder or from falling cylinders, and contact with the gas which may be particularly cold.

Risks

The factors that increase the risk of explosions and harm are:

■ lack of ventilation

■ the presence of ignition sources

■ lack of control over storage conditions and proximity to other hazards

■ lack of knowledge of the properties of flammable substances

■ lack of training.

Poor ventilation allows a flammable gas to accumulate in the work environment so that the concentration in the air reaches a level at which it could catch fire or explode. The presence of ignition sources, such as naked flames, lighted cigarettes, sparks from welding operations or electrical equipment, static electricity or even hot surfaces, can increase the risk of an explosion or fire.

If flammable substances are spilt or allowed to leak into the work environment, risk is greatly increased. Other hazards in the workplace can also lead to a greater chance of fire or explosion – for instance, a workplace vehicle could crash into containers, causing a leak.

Flammable liquids can flow for some distance and then ignite. The liquid and its vapour can catch fire and find its way back to the source and ignite the bulk of the liquid, often causing an explosion.

Dust in the air, such as that from wood, flour, wheat and magnesium, can ignite under certain conditions and explode, causing damage and harm.

Flammable substances that get onto workers' clothes create a serious risk to personal safety – employees could become a human torch. Inadequate disposal of contaminated materials can also increase the risk of a fire.

Another physical hazard involves gas cylinders which, if not secured properly, can fall over, causing a leg or foot injury.

Controls

Employers must carry out a risk assessment of any work activities involving dangerous substances and provide measures to eliminate or reduce risks as far as is reasonably practicable.

They must also provide information and training to employees on the risks and controls for relevant flammable substances.

A **hierarchy of control** should be followed when deciding controls for flammable substances. The first consideration should be whether a non-flammable substance could be used. If it cannot be replaced, adopt a number of other controls to reduce the risk.

The basic hierarchy of control is to:

- substitute the substance for one that eliminates or reduces the risk
- control ventilation
- control ignition sources
- control storage containers
- make sure flammable substances and their storage containers are kept well away from other processes and storage areas.

The ventilation of a work environment where there are flammable substances must be sufficient to disperse flammable gases and vapours, so that an ignitable concentration does not form. Ignition sources, such as naked flames, lighted cigarettes, sparks from welding operations or electrical equipment, static electricity or even hot surfaces, should be strictly controlled. It is best to prohibit them in the areas of high risk.

Employers must classify places where explosive atmospheres may occur into zones and mark the zones where necessary.

Workrooms where flammable substances are handled should be separated from other parts of the workplace by fire-resistant partitions.

Storage containers should be designed to avoid spillage, the release of vapour and the effects of fire. They must be strong and resist wear and tear during normal use. They must be constructed of a material that will resist any corrosion by the substance they contain and not be susceptible to a build-up of static electricity, which could spark and cause a fire or explosion.

Emergency procedures

There must be emergency procedures in place to deal with the consequences of an accident if, despite all the precautions, something does go wrong. Staff must be instructed in these procedures, particularly in what to do in the event of a leak or spill, and any first aid procedures to be followed.

Specific controls

Flammable substances come in various forms and there are some specific precautions needed to reduce the risk of an accident that involves them.

Flammable gases

Gases, such as liquefied petroleum gas (LPG), are often stored at high pressure inside a cylinder. Their uncontrolled release can lead quickly to an explosion.

LPG is stored in cylinders that need to be secured against a wall or static structure. Their valves and fittings need to be protected against accidental damage. Hoses and the pipes between the cylinder and the heater or equipment also need protection against damage. They should be inspected regularly and any damaged or worn hoses should be replaced immediately.

Many of the controls that apply to pressure vessels (see page 351 to 356) also apply to gas cylinders – for example, training, examination by a competent person and marking them to show that they have been inspected by a competent person. However, some additional controls are necessary.

When filling cylinders, workers should wear personal protective clothing, such as safety shoes, protective gloves, hearing protection and goggles.

The cylinder valves and regulators must be checked to make sure that they are fitted correctly, are in good working condition and are not leaking. Valve protection caps should be used, particularly for transporting. Cylinders should be stored securely in the open air or in a well ventilated part of a building, away from heat sources.

Flammable liquids
These liquids can give off vapours which can then ignite violently.

The containers in which flammable liquids are stored must be secure and lids must fit tightly. The containers should ideally be kept in a special storage area, separate from other goods and equipment used in the workplace. If this is not possible, they should be stored in a purpose-made bin or cupboard. They should be allocated for use in an area with good ventilation and no sources of ignition. Containers should be kept closed when not in use.

Trays or buckets should be provided to catch spills and there should be materials available to absorb spills immediately. Materials used to mop up spills should be stored in metal bins before disposal. Contaminated materials must be disposed of carefully, possibly by calling in disposal experts.

Avoid spills on clothing as they can be a serious risk if ignited.

Flammable dusts
Ensure that the work environment is reasonably free from dust by setting up a regular cleaning schedule. Any accumulation of dust should be cleaned up immediately. Good ventilation should be maintained and local exhaust ventilation should be used in wood-working premises to control the level of wood dust.

Flammable solids
Some solid materials are flammable and must be stored well away from sources of ignition, such as hot surfaces or electrical equipment with hot parts. The workplace must be kept tidy and free from discarded flammable solids, such as packaging materials, textiles and plastic foam.

Chemicals

Some chemicals can explode if they are exposed to air, water or other reactive chemicals. For example, sodium reacts violently with water, and chlorine-based disinfectants release toxic and explosive chlorine gas when in contact with acid or oxidising detergents. Disinfectants containing peracetic acid form explosive mixtures with cleaning materials containing acids or alkalis.

It is important to know the properties of these chemicals, so check labels and safety data sheets to ensure that the hazards are understood and make certain that staff use the chemicals correctly.

Staff need training and supervision to make sure they know enough to prevent the mixing of incompatible chemicals.

Oxygen

If the workplace has an oxygen-rich atmosphere, such as in some parts of hospitals, there is an increased risk of flammable substances igniting or exploding. Precautions include never using oxygen instead of compressed air, never using oxygen to 'sweeten' air in a work area or confined space and never using grease or oil on equipment containing oxygen.

Emergencies

There need to be special procedures to deal with a leak or spill of a flammable substance and staff should be instructed in these emergency procedures. If special first aid facilities are needed, then staff need to be trained how to use them.

Legal requirements

According to the Dangerous Substances and Explosive Atmospheres Regulations 2002 – usually known as DSEAR – employers must carry out a risk assessment of any work activities involving dangerous substances.

Some of the dangerous substances included in the regulations are petrol, liquefied petroleum gas (LPG), paints, varnishes, solvents, and dusts, which when mixed with air, could cause an explosive atmosphere.

Employers must provide measures to eliminate or reduce risks as far as is reasonably practicable (in particular ventilation, ignition source control,

separation of the substance from ignition source and fire resistance of the workplace). They must also provide equipment and procedures to deal with accidents and emergencies; provide information and training to employees; and classify places where explosive atmospheres may occur into zones and mark the zones where necessary.

The Equipment and Protective Systems for Use in Potentially Explosive Atmospheres Regulations 1996 specify requirements for equipment intended for use in potentially explosive atmospheres.

Work activities and equipment
Work equipment

Work equipment includes many familiar items – such as a washing machine, refrigerator or a paper stapler – as well as less familiar ones requiring specialist training, such as a piling machine for building foundations, a computer or laboratory equipment. As the meaning of work equipment is very wide, it is important to understand the variety involved.

Key words and phrases

CE mark – the official European Union safety marking required for certain types of equipment.

competent person – someone with the appropriate qualifications, knowledge or experience to identify the risks arising from a situation and the measures needed to control them.

danger zone – an area where employees are exposed to dangerous machine parts.

fail to safety or **fail-safe** – a design that enables a machine to come to rest in a safe state if it stops working for any reason.

hierarchy of control – a well tested system of graded health and safety controls.

hierarchy of protection – levels of protection for safeguarding employees from dangerous parts of machinery.

inspection of equipment – visual checks by a competent person on items of equipment to verify that they can be operated, adjusted and maintained safely.

inspection of the health and safety system – the assessment of the health and safety performance of a workplace, to enable any remedial measures to be taken.

in-running nip – points between a pair of moving parts, or moving and fixed parts, that can create traps into which clothing or parts of the body can be drawn.

permit to work – a formal document that specifies the work to be done and the precautions to be taken.

PUWER – a common abbreviation of The Provision and Use of Work Equipment Regulations 1998.

safe system of work – a set of procedures for carrying out a task safely.

use – in relation to work equipment, starting, stopping, programming, setting, transporting, repairing, modifying, maintaining, servicing and cleaning.

work equipment – apparatus used at work including machines, appliances, tools, installations, ladders, hoists and lifting equipment.

What is work equipment?

The legal requirements for work equipment cover everything from hand tools to manufacturing plant.

Legislation describes **work equipment** as any machinery, appliance, apparatus, tool or installation for use at work. This covers virtually all equipment provided for work.

Machines include lathes, printers, diggers, circular saws, power presses and overhead cranes, while *appliances* include computers, televisions, videos, refrigerators, washing machines and laboratory apparatus. Under the heading of *tools* are included saws, hammers, knives and screwdrivers. The term *installation* is used to describe a collection of machines connected together for making an end-product. Such machines include beer-bottling and food-canning equipment. In addition, there are *work aids* such as ladders, portable cleaning machines, hoists, fork-lift trucks and mobile devices such as motor vehicles that are not normally used on public roads.

Typical hazards

There are several typical types of safety hazard associated with mechanical work equipment. They are:

- contact of parts of the body with moving parts of the equipment
- trapping (of fingers or other parts of the body)
- entanglement (of clothing or hair)
- ejection of parts or materials
- catching fire or overheating
- explosion involving the work equipment itself or the material being processed
- impact – crushing of parts of the body by moving parts or the material being processed.

There are also other hazards, such as noise and vibration, that are discussed in separate chapters.

Machines

Contact
Accidental physical contact with many machines can cause serious injury. The motion of a machine generally indicates the type of hazard a machine presents.

One type of hazard is the moving parts of the machine, such as the rotating shaft of a drill, the blade of a fan, the cutting blade of a meat slicer or the drive-shaft of an engine. Another type of hazard is contact with the material being processed, such as hot metal rods, newly baked bread, wood or metal being turned on a lathe or chemicals being mixed in a vat.

Guards must be in position before starting

Some machines, such as car engines and air conditioning units, have hot parts. Others are used to process hot materials. Contact with such equipment or materials could result in burns or scalds.

There are also machines that operate at low temperatures and contact with them can lead to frost burn or severe skin damage. An escape of gas, dust, liquid or vapour may occur in machines where pipes or hoses become holed or leak and the substance inside can cause heat, cold or chemical burns.

Trapping and entanglement

Hands, clothing, hair and materials can be caught and dragged into machinery, causing cuts, abrasions and the loss of fingers or limbs. Some workers lose their lives in such accidents. People and their clothing can become trapped between the moving parts of machinery, trapped between moving parts and a fixed structure or entangled with the material being processed.

Do not oil or clean machine whilst in motion

Cutting or grinding machines, rollers and abrasive wheels are typical examples of equipment where such hazards exist. Newspaper printing machines and dough-making machines have rollers running in opposite directions, these are in-running nips which may also include a rotating part next to a fixed part. These situations create a severe hazard because an employee who entangles clothing or traps part of a hand could get drawn further into the machine and lose a finger, hand or even an arm. Similar severe hazards also occur in machines with moving parts that slide past one another or past a fixed part.

The material being processed can also present hazards. For example, a rotating bar on a lathe could draw clothes into contact with the dangerous parts of the machine. If the worker tries to release the entangled material, he or she may then be dragged into the machine itself – farm workers have lost their lives by trying to release jammed wheat or other harvested material when a machine is still running. Material entangled in machinery can cause the machine to stop or parts to break.

The cleaning and maintenance of some pieces of equipment are particularly hazardous operations. Many serious accidents have happened when operators have tried to clean or maintain a machine while it is in motion. Workers have lost fingers, hands or arms by trying to clean food-slicing machines or machines with in-running nips or with rollers.

Ejection of material

Some machines process materials that can be ejected and hit someone. For example, a lathe shaving a metal bar could throw off pieces of metal. If the machine itself breaks down completely or has broken parts, it may produce debris that can be thrown off at speed, hitting people or causing damage to other equipment or the building. Abrasive wheels, if not constructed correctly or operated within their recommended speed, can disintegrate – a

process often described as *bursting*. Another example is where molten metal from a die-casting machine can be spattered around the workplace.

Fire and explosion

Some machines are used in confined spaces where an air-borne suspension of combustible dust, vapours, fumes and gases can lead to a flammable atmosphere. If the flammable atmosphere ignites, it can then explode.

Impact

Severe injuries can occur when the body, or part of it, is crushed by work equipment or the material being processed. For example, the driver of a grass-cutting machine could be crushed if the machine overturned. Similarly, a worker directing a small crane being used to unload roof trusses from a parked lorry could be crushed if the load swings unexpectedly. One employee's head was crushed in a vacuum-forming machine because his employer had failed to put in place a proper system of inspection and maintenance necessary to prevent accidents and had failed to provide proper machine guards.

Appliances

The hazards from appliances such as televisions, refrigeration units and gas boilers include electric shock, electrocution and an explosion in the compressor of refrigerators and gas boilers.

Apparatus

There is a wide range of hazards associated with apparatus. For example, Bunsen burners may cause skin burns, while hot substances, such as molten metal from a ladle, can result in severe burns or even death.

Skin contact with substances such as acids and alkalis can cause chemical burns (skin injuries), while explosions can happen when pressure builds up in a heating apparatus or large boiler, or when gas leaks from hoses.

Tools

Saws, hammers, knives and screwdrivers all have the potential to harm the person who is using them and other people nearby. Saws and knives can cause serious cuts to skin and even bone. In the most severe cases, amputation of fingers or limbs can occur. Screwdrivers can also cause cuts to a user. Hammers can cause crushing, while a loose item, such as a hammer head, if not secure, could come off and hit someone.

Installations

The hazards presented by installations are similar to those mentioned under the heading of machines (above). These include moving bottles and cans, powered conveyors, powered capping equipment and pressurised filling points.

Work aids

Ladders, hoists and lifting equipment

Whenever anything is being lifted with the help of equipment, such as a hoist, and whenever someone is working at a height on ladders or scaffolding, personal injury and severe physical damage can result.

With some lifting equipment, the hazard lies in the construction and operation of the equipment itself. An electric, overhead travelling crane or its load could strike a maintenance worker at ground level or someone else who is engaged in other ground-level activities and is unaware that the crane is in operation.

Mobile work equipment

Under this heading is any work equipment that operates while it is travelling, or which travels between the locations where it is used. Examples are mechanical diggers, dumper trucks, mobile elevating work platforms and fork-lift trucks. Typical problems with mobile work equipment include:

- falls – because people come off the moving equipment accidentally

- impact – when people get crushed because the equipment rolls over or they are knocked over by material being carried by the equipment

- trapping – when people get caught in wheels, tracks or forks

- harmful fumes – for instance, when carbon monoxide is given off from a combustion engine in an enclosed space

- contact and entanglement – especially involving hot or moving parts during maintenance tasks.

Risks

The risks from the use of work equipment depend on factors which can be grouped into several categories:

- construction and use

- installation

Safe systems of work are needed for road construction and repair. Employees need to be protected from hot materials, while other road users need to be directed away from the work area and newly laid surfaces.

- work procedure
- conditions in which equipment is being used
- maintenance and cleaning
- guarding
- training and supervision of employees
- type of equipment
- type of material being processed or moved by the equipment
- personal protective equipment.

Construction and use

Risk depends on how the equipment is constructed. Parts of poorly constructed equipment could fail, increasing the risk of injury or damage. Poorly designed controls could mean that equipment cannot be turned off quickly and safely or that it starts accidentally. Risk also increases if equipment is used for purposes for which it was not designed.

Installation

If equipment is installed properly and is inspected regularly after installation and during use, risk is reduced.

Work procedure

Employees working close to material being processed risk trapping their hands – for example, between the fixed die and the press of a die-casting press. Using hand-held tools as well as a machine, such as a lathe, increases risk considerably. There is a high chance that the tool will come into contact with moving parts and either be trapped between the fixed and moving parts, or be thrown off the machine.

A particularly high-risk, illegal activity is to use a fork-lift truck to raise someone who is standing on the forks rather than standing in a properly designed cage.

Conditions in which equipment is being used

Certain types of equipment are intrinsically more dangerous than others. For example, a chainsaw creates a higher risk of injury than a pair of scissors, although both are used for cutting.

The work environment also affects the level of risk of injury. There is, for example, a higher level of risk when a competent tree surgeon uses the correct type of chainsaw for work in a tree than when carrying out groundwork with the correct equipment, such as cutting up logs. If a fork-lift truck is being used on flat dry ground there is a relatively low risk that it will tip over, but if it is used on a severe slope in wet conditions there is a higher risk that it will topple.

Where mobile work equipment is used there is also an increased risk in unsuitable conditions, for example:

- on uneven or slippery surfaces
- on steep gradients
- if the operator is speeding
- if the tyre pressures are not suitable for the work being done
- if there are sharp changes in direction in the workplace
- if the material being carried is itself unstable or hazardous.

Maintenance and cleaning

If work equipment is not maintained properly at reasonable intervals, there is an increased risk of wear and tear of the parts which, in turn, could lead to an accident or failure of the machinery. If any work equipment is not maintained properly by a **competent person**, who is trained to maintain that type of equipment, there is a greatly increased risk of injury or damage.

The cleaning and maintenance of equipment while it is running is a very high-risk activity. It may be that there is no alternative to carrying out work when the equipment is still powered up, but strict controls and procedures are necessary for this activity to take place safely – for example, the issuing of permits to work (see pages 125 to 126).

Guarding

There is a high risk of injury or damage if equipment is operated without proper guarding of the moving parts, or if the material being processed is not contained within the machine. This could come about when the equipment is not provided with guarding, the guard has not been maintained or has been disabled in some way.

Training and supervision of employees

If employees are not given proper training, instruction or information about how to operate particular equipment safely, the risk of injury is high. For example, if a chainsaw operator has not been trained in its use and the dangers it presents, there is a much greater risk of injury than if it is used by a trained worker. Operators of some equipment may need a 'certificate of competence' before they use the equipment so they can be adequately insured against any damage they cause accidentally.

The right equipment is essential for doing a job safely and to a high standard. It needs to be maintained to a high standard that will not lead to accidents and injury.

Type of equipment

Risk is relatively low if equipment is not powered – a combine harvester, for example, is much more dangerous than a hay rake. There is a high risk of burns from high and low temperature equipment, such as irons, foundry equipment, gas cookers, cold stores and steam pipes. Using the wrong equipment for the job also increases risk, for example, using a ladder instead of an access tower.

Type of material associated with the machine

There is a high risk of injury if the material being processed by the equipment is corrosive, loose or hot.

Mobile work equipment

There are other risks involved with mobile work equipment such as:

- allowing machinery to be started by unauthorised people
- operating the equipment with poor facilities for braking, stopping or lighting
- using the equipment when the operator's vision is restricted
- not providing fire extinguishing equipment
- operating equipment (such as quad bikes) without roll-over protection or seat belts.

Personal protective equipment

If personal protective equipment is not provided for use with certain machines, such as chainsaws or angle grinders, there is an increased risk of injury to the operator. Using PPE which is not suitable for the job also increases risk – for example, higher specification ear defenders are needed to protect against the noise from a wood chipper than for a chainsaw, as the level of noise from each piece of equipment is different.

Controls

Risk assessment

A risk assessment of the activity should be made before the equipment to be used is chosen. This risk assessment will help in choosing the most suitable equipment for the task.

Think about the work to be done by the equipment during normal use, setting up, maintenance, repair, breakdowns and the removal of blockages. Think about the people who will use the equipment – for example, inexperienced workers, young people, or workers with languages difficulties. Think about the guards and whether they are well designed or not and particularly whether they can easily be disabled.

The principles of preventing injuries and damage apply to work equipment as well as to any other hazard at work, so a **hierarchy of control** can be used to eliminate hazards and reduce risks:

- substitute, if possible
- control risks at source (such as by guarding) or use the equipment to current standards
- carry out safe working procedures
- provide suitable and sufficient training, instruction and/or supervision
- provide personal protective equipment (PPE).

First of all, remove the hazard, if possible. This can be done by using another, safer machine or by redesigning the task. Secondly, try to prevent access to the dangerous parts of the machine by enclosing them (guarding) and by ensuring that the workplace environment allows operators to work with the equipment without being distracted.

Thirdly, ensure that the machine's operating controls are easy to see and to operate, especially in an emergency. The design should enable the machine to stop working and come to rest in a safe state if something goes wrong: this is described as **fail to safety** or **fail-safe**.

Fourthly, always consider health and safety issues when selecting equipment to buy. If the equipment has a **CE mark**, then it has been designed and produced to European standards of design and manufacture and complies with the essential requirements of the relevant European legislation dealing with safety, health, the environment and consumer protection. Generally, the conformity to the relevant Directives is done through self-declaration (where the manufacturer states it has made the equipment to EU standards). Make sure that all the operational and safety instructions have been provided with the equipment.

Other practical control measures that can be used to protect employees from hazards and the risks from work equipment are described below.

Suitability of work equipment

Work equipment must be constructed, or adapted to be suitable, for the purpose for which it is provided and must comply with The Provision and Use of Work Equipment Regulations 1998 (often abbreviated to **PUWER**).

Choose the right equipment for the job. If the use of a machine in any circumstances appears to compromise the operator's health and safety, then it may not be suitable for that purpose. For example, in some supermarkets knives commonly supplied for carpet cutting and do-it-yourself jobs may be used to open cardboard boxes, but safety knives or case cutters can do the same job much more safely.

Maintenance

Work equipment must be maintained in efficient working order and in good repair. There should be a maintenance log for each piece or type of equipment, which should be kept up to date. All machinery should be maintained frequently – the interval depends on:

- how often the equipment is used
- where it is used
- whether it is doing the same operation all the time or different operations.

The maintenance of certain dangerous work equipment (this is determined by risk assessment), such as large ovens in a bread factory or industrial paper shredders, should be carried out when it is shut down or not being used. However, where equipment cannot be shut down, safe systems of work (see page 339) can be designed so that the maintenance is done with minimal risk to the employee carrying out the work.

When cleaning or maintenance procedures are carried out it is essential to ensure that general safety procedures are observed, as well as any particular safety measures appropriate to the equipment.

General safety measures are those that:

- switch off the equipment and disconnect the power supply
- support any parts that could fall
- secure mobile work equipment so that it cannot move
- remove or isolate any hazardous substances
- depressurise pressurised equipment
- follow the manufacturer's and workplace instructions for safe working
- work in a manner that does not put others at risk.

Inspection

The purpose of an **inspection** is to identify whether the work equipment is safe to operate and maintain, to ensure that any wear and tear can be detected and to carry out any repairs before the risk of injury increases to an unacceptable level.

All inspections should be recorded in a log. Work equipment should be inspected:

- before its first use
- after it has been installed
- if it is moved to a new site
- at reasonable intervals, with the frequency determined by its use and the conditions in which it operates, the manufacturer's instructions and any appropriate legislation and codes of practice
- whenever there is a change in procedure or materials being used
- if there is an accident or incident.

Inspection should include visual checks, function checks and checks that safety devices are in operation. It can also include simple testing.

Guarding

There are four levels of protection for safeguarding workers from dangerous parts of machinery, which are known collectively as the **hierarchy of protection**. It is important to ensure that the measures are considered and adopted in sequence.

1) Install fixed guards – for example, one enclosing a high-speed belt on a newspaper-folding machine or perimeter fencing around a machine with a large movable arm. The guard should be sufficiently robust to withstand the conditions and process in which it operates. It must be fixed in such a way that workers need a special tool to remove it. A key-locking device would be appropriate.

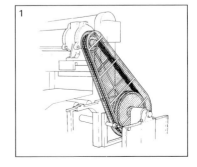

2) Restrict access to dangerous parts by minimising the number of staff with permission to work or walk near the machine or dangerous part, or by erecting barriers or walls that prevent unauthorised access to such areas. The area protected is often referred to as the **danger zone**. This arrangement is sometimes known as a *distance guard*.

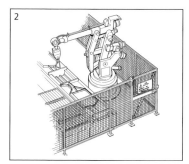

3) Install interlocking guards that stop the machine operating unless the guards are in the correct position. They also stop the guards from being opened while the machine is operating until the dangerous parts of the machine have come to rest. These guards are commonly used where materials tend to get jammed in the work equipment, or where the material needs to be handled frequently. They can be mechanical, electrical, hydraulic, pneumatic or any combination.

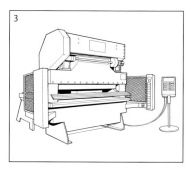

Trip guards and devices automatically stop or reverse the machine before an operator reaches a point of danger. Examples include light beams, touch-sensitive contact surfaces, trip barriers and pressure-sensitive mats – for example, for use in thermoform, fill and seal (TFFS) machines in the packaging industry.

Automatic guards are moved into position by the machine and are designed to isolate an operator, or his or her hands, before trapping can occur. These types of guards are suitable only if there is adequate time for them to operate, so the machine must be slow moving, such as power presses and drop hammers.

Self-adjusting automatic guards are triggered by the movement of the work piece and return to a closed position when the job is complete.

All the guards must be suitable for their use, of good construction, maintained in good condition and kept in good working order. They must be designed so that they cannot be easily by-passed.

4) Provide protection devices – implements that prevent contact with dangerous parts, such as jigs (devices that hold materials and guide the tools safely), holders and push-sticks (used with circular saws, for instance).

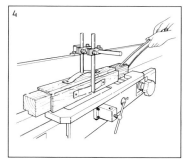

Other controls include systems where a machine will not run unless the operator has both hands on the control points.

Employers must also provide adequate and suitable information, instruction and training, and ensure that there is appropriate supervision.

Safe systems of work

A **safe system of work** is a procedure designed to ensure that work is done safely. It is normally necessary to implement a safe system of work where hazards and risks cannot be adequately controlled by other means. The hazards should be identified and the work planned in detail. All employees involved in the work should be informed about the procedure.

The work should be implemented in the way that the procedure states and it should be monitored and supervised. All work equipment should be operated according to the manufacturer's instructions and within the limits stated. (See also 'Safe systems of work' on pages 121 to 126.)

Equipment controls

There must be various mechanical and electrical control devices on equipment so that machinery can be started and stopped manually, as required, and to enable the operator to change speed or pressure, as appropriate. Controls must be easy to see and identify and must be situated in a safe position for operation.

A machine must not be able to restart automatically, and control devices may be needed for resetting a machine before it is restarted. There may also need to be emergency stop controls which should be used only in exceptional circumstances, not in normal operation.

It must be possible to isolate work equipment from all its sources of energy – for example, a residual current device would cut off the electricity to a floor cleaning machine that was being used in wet conditions.

Stability

Work equipment must be stabilised where necessary – for example, by clamping, bolting or some other suitable means. Ladders, for instance, should be set at the correct angle (that is not too steep) to the structure they are leaning on. They should be secured at the top, or, if this is impossible, at the base. Mobile stepladders with wheels should be fitted with brakes.

Workplace environment

Look at the workplace environment in which work equipment is being used. There must be suitable and sufficient lighting. If gas, dust, vapour and so on are emitted from the work equipment, then ventilation controls are necessary.

It is also important to keep the area around the equipment clean and tidy, and to ensure that the area is not cramped. If the activity is outdoors, consider safety in relation to the weather, the ground conditions or the gradient in which the work equipment is being operated.

Personal protective equipment

If the hazards cannot be eliminated or the controls cannot reduce the risk to an acceptable level, personal protective equipment (PPE) should be provided – see pages 357 to 365.

Competent people

Make sure that all work equipment is maintained and inspected by a **competent person** who has the relevant knowledge and experience. The principle is to ensure that anyone doing a task has sufficient information, instruction and training to do the job safely and to ensure that the equipment is left in a condition that is safe for others. It is good practice to restrict the number of people using, repairing or maintaining the equipment. This reduces the risk of harm to someone who is not a competent person.

Training, information and instruction

All staff, whether workers, supervisors or managers, must be provided with adequate information, instruction and training in the use, repair and maintenance of equipment that they need to use in their jobs.

The information provided should include the hazards and the risks involved and the precautions to be taken. There should be general safety training in the use of equipment and specific training for certain types of equipment, such as mobile work equipment and dangerous equipment including chainsaws.

It is also important to display any safety markings and warnings on or near work equipment. Some work equipment must be marked with maximum operating limits – for example, the safe weight of a load carried on a hoist, or the maximum rotation speed of an abrasive wheel.

Mobile work equipment

Where mobile work equipment with a combustion engine is used inside buildings, it must be possible to introduce sufficient clean air and to vent the contaminated air.

No one must be permitted to travel on mobile work equipment, unless it is suitable for carrying people and has facilities that minimise the risk that they will fall from the equipment. Roll-over protection is needed, where appropriate, including stabilisers, operator-restraining systems, roll-over cages and counterbalance weights (for example, with tractors or fork-lift trucks).

There should be devices that prevent unauthorised people from starting the equipment, as well as brakes, lighting and fire-fighting equipment, as necessary.

Fork-lift truck operators should be selected carefully and given appropriate training and authorisation before they are allowed to drive the trucks. The training must be carried out by a qualified instructor. Both the employee and employer should keep records of the training, including refresher training.

When using hired equipment, ensure that it is safe to use at the point of hire. Enquiries should be made about how it is to be used and advice provided on how it should be used. The safe use of equipment is the responsibility of the person who hires it.

Equipment records

The things to include in the records of workplace equipment can include:

- type and model of equipment
- identification mark or number
- normal location
- date of inspection
- inspector's name
- faults noted
- action taken
- who the faults were reported to
- date of repairs carried out.

Legal requirements

All work equipment must comply with the European Union Directives concerning the design and construction of work equipment and the safety of products.

The Provision and Use of Work Equipment Regulations 1998 require employers to ensure that equipment provided for use at work is suitable for its intended use; is safe for use, maintained in a safe condition and regularly inspected to keep it safe for use; is used only by people who have received adequate information, instruction and training; and is accompanied by suitable safety measures such as protective devices, markings and warnings.

Specialised work equipment may be covered by other legislation, such as The Pressure Equipment Regulations 1999.

Mechanical lifting equipment and operations

People and goods have to be lifted in many workplaces using specialised equipment. Injuries are relatively uncommon, but there are more than one thousand dangerous occurrences every year involving the failure, collapse or overturning of lifting equipment.

Key words and phrases

carrier – in relation to lifting equipment, any device, such as a passenger lift car or the cage of a construction site hoist, used to support people being lowered or lifted. In rope-based systems, such as climbing, the harness is the carrier.

competent person – someone with the appropriate qualifications, knowledge or experience to identify the risks arising from a situation and the measures needed to control them.

examinations – in the context of lifting equipment, an organised or formal evaluation involving measurements and tests.

inspection – in the context of lifting equipment, visual checks and functional tests only.

lifting equipment – work equipment for the lifting or lowering of loads, including the attachments for anchoring, fixing or supporting the equipment.

lifting operation – an activity involving the lifting or lowering of a load using lifting equipment.

load – any movable object, including a person or animal.

safe working load (SWL) – the maximum load that equipment may lift safely.

scheme of examination – written details of the formal examination and inspection of lifting equipment or a pressure system.

work equipment – apparatus used at work including machines, appliances, tools, installations, ladders, hoists and lifting equipment.

Lifting equipment

Lifting equipment includes any device used at work for lifting or lowering **loads**, whether they are goods or people. Examples of lifting equipment include:

- passenger lifts in department stores
- cranes on construction/demolition sites and docks
- electric overhead travelling cranes in the steel stockholding industry
- vehicle inspection hoists in garages
- patient hoists in hospitals or residential care homes
- people hoists in swimming pools
- fork-lift trucks
- vehicle tail-lifts
- ropes and mobile elevating work platforms used by tree surgeons.

Lifting equipment also includes the attachments used for anchoring, fixing or supporting it.

Lifting operations include such activities as a crane lifting steel beams on a building site, a fork-lift truck lifting a pallet of fruit from a lorry to a storage rack in a warehouse and a patient being lifted into a bath with a hoist in a hospital or nursing home.

Manual handling is *not* the same as a lifting operation because lifting operations involve lifting *equipment* and tend to involve loads that could not be lifted manually.

Hazards

The hazards involved with lifting equipment and lifting operations normally involve someone being crushed, trapped or struck by the load being lifted or the **carrier**. The carrier is the device used to support people being lowered or lifted – for example, a passenger lift car and the cage of a construction site hoist. It may also be possible to fall out of a carrier.

The lifting equipment itself can strike someone – for example, a fork-lift truck can run someone over. There have also been many cases of foot injuries when a fork-lift truck has run over a person's feet. People could also get caught on the forks and carried along.

If lifting equipment fails, the results can be devastating. For instance, cranes have collapsed, lifts have broken down and the carrier has been damaged, and slings have been overloaded when they have been stretched and deformed because the safe working load – the maximum load that the equipment may lift safely – was exceeded. Chains or ropes have snapped, causing the load to fall to the ground. In such cases, the load may hit someone or something, or the force of the load when it hits the ground could send debris flying.

It is also possible for lifting equipment to overturn if the equipment and the lifting operation are mismatched with the load. If two or more pieces of lifting equipment are being used in a single lifting operation, there may be a collision between the two.

Hazards near to where lifting equipment is being used need to be considered. Overhead power lines, low bridges, warehouse racking and underground services, such as sewers or drains, might not always pose a significant risk in other circumstances, but they could create a high risk during lifting operations.

Risks

The factors that need to be considered when using lifting equipment include the:

- environment in which the equipment or operation will take place

- size and nature of the load

- condition of the equipment

- way in which the lifting operation is carried out.

The environment

Lifting equipment must be made stable before it is used.

It is important to ensure that the ground on which the lifting equipment is placed is stable and does not slope too much. Weather conditions are also important. Excessive wind speed, poor visibility – in mist, fog, lightning, hail storms and heavy rain, for example – all influence the risk involved in using lifting equipment and carrying out lifting operations.

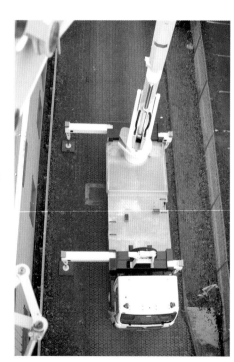

If the load is being lifted inside a building, the combined load of the equipment and the material being lifted is important because the floor must be able to support the combined weight. Indoor air pollution may also have an influence on risk as the operator should be able to see the load and the path through which it moves – for example, in a foundry the smoke or gases from the process may obscure the driver's vision. Similar risks arise where the work environment is noisy and communication is affected.

The size and nature of the load

The risk increases with the weight of the load, and the shape of the load influences the precautions to be taken to reduce the risk. If the load is greater than the safe working load, or if unsuitable equipment is used, the equipment might collapse. In the case of fork-lift trucks, the size of the load could affect the driver's view of where he or she is going, creating a high risk of injury or damage, or both.

The condition of the equipment

If the equipment is not maintained, repaired, inspected and examined, the risk increases greatly. This is certainly the case where there is corrosion to vital parts of the equipment or there is excessive wear to, or failure of, moving parts – for example, cracked or deformed chain links or broken wires in wire ropes.

The way the lifting operation is carried out

Lifting must be carried out only after proper planning and where there is a **competent person** to control the lift. If an inexperienced person with little knowledge of lifting equipment and lifting operations plans or supervises a lifting operation, the risk of an accident is much greater. Risk is also much greater if carriers are open or are not provided with suitable guards or barriers when people are working under the load being lifted.

There are also similar risks if care is not taken to set up the lifting equipment correctly before the lift takes place – for example, if the ropes attached to the load are not placed securely on the hook of the lifting equipment.

Controls

Lifting equipment should be regarded as **work equipment** and the general controls that apply to work equipment also apply to lifting equipment. (See also 'Work equipment' on pages 328 to 341).

In general, the controls that apply to work equipment focus on regular inspection and maintenance, while the controls that apply to lifting equipment and operations concentrate on safe procedure.

There are similarities between the controls suitable for lifting equipment and for pressure systems, particularly the thorough examination and written scheme of examination. Both need thorough examination at predetermined intervals, both need to be inspected by a competent person and both can be examined according to a written scheme of examination.

The controls used for lifting equipment are intended to ensure that the equipment is strong and stable enough for the job to be done safely, and that it is positioned and installed to minimise risks. The controls also help to ensure that the equipment is in a condition for safe use.

Strength and stability

All lifting equipment must be of adequate strength and stability to lift each load, taking into account the mounting or fixing point of the equipment – for example, using an anchorage system, counterbalance weights, ballast, outriggers or stabilisers. The mounting or fixing points are the points where the weight of the equipment and the load transfer to the surface on which the equipment is standing. This surface must be able to support both the lifting equipment and the load together. When planning a lifting operation also consider the weight of any accessories used, such as lifting magnets, clamps and shackles.

Lifting people

Where lifting equipment is used for lifting people, it should be designed so that the passengers and others are prevented from being crushed, trapped or struck by the carrier. Precautions must also be taken to prevent anyone falling from the carrier: so, a lift car must be fully enclosed when in use, for example. In passenger lifts, the doors must be fitted with a device to prevent the lift-car doors from striking passengers when entering or leaving the lift car and the car must not move if the doors are open.

Mobile platforms – for example, on a construction site hoist – should have edge protection in the form of a 2m high enclosure.

The equipment must have a suitable device to prevent the carrier falling. This can be in the form of multiple ropes, chains or hydraulic pipes.

Passenger lifts are covered by lifting legislation and must be thoroughly inspected every six months.

If someone is trapped in the carrier, he or she must not be exposed to danger and it must be possible to free him or her easily. This means that if people are trapped, they can summon help – by, for example, a telephone in a lift or a whistle in a construction hoist. There must be a way to lower the carrier in an emergency, or there should be a rope ladder, or similar device, provided.

The equipment must be able to lift at least twice the maximum safe working load marked on it (see page 347).

Lifting equipment must not be used to lift people if it is designed to lift only goods.

Positioning and installation

Loads must be lifted or lowered in a way that prevents them from falling or hitting anything.

Lifting equipment must be positioned (mobile equipment) or installed (fixed position) in a way that minimises the risk that the load will strike someone, drift, fall or be released unintentionally. The aim is to keep the load under control and prevent trapping points being created. For example, a passenger lift is guided along its path enclosed in a lift shaft which gives no access to ordinary lift users.

Free-hanging loads, like a steel beam suspended from a crane on a building site, need measures to prevent them coming loose or falling. Control methods for such operations normally involve multiple ropes,

check valves for hydraulic systems or safety nets for palletised loads. Specially designed hooks can prevent free-hanging loads being detached from the hook. These hooks should have safety catches fitted or be shaped to prevent accidental displacement of the sling.

Pneumatic, hydraulic, vacuum or magnetic equipment should have braking systems to ensure that a load does not fall in the event of a power failure or the unintentional release of the load.

There needs to be some way to prevent people falling down a lift shaft. Automatic interlocked gates are usually provided for this purpose. The gates cannot be opened, except when the lifting equipment is stationary at the landing. Carriers must not be able to move away from the landing unless the gates are closed. If these measures are not possible, other suitable methods should be used. If enclosure and gates are used, they must be at least 2m high.

Marking lifting equipment with safe working loads

Safe working loads (SWL) must be clearly marked on the lifting equipment – for example, 'SWL 500kg'. Accessories used in the lifting operation must also have their own SWL marked on them. Accessories include such things as slings, shackles, swivel or eye bolts, karabiners, lifting magnets and lifting beams.

A safe working load is a load value based on the strength or stability, or both, of the equipment when lifting – in other words, the maximum load that the equipment can lift safely. The SWL refers to the whole range of operation of the particular piece of lifting equipment – for instance, where a lift truck has a telescopic jib. With the jib in its shortest position the SWL is at its maximum, but if the jib is fully extended, the SWL becomes much lower because the centre of gravity changes so that the whole truck can become unstable. This sort of equipment must be clearly marked with information about how the SWL is affected in different types of operation.

Carriers must be clearly marked with the SWL *and* the maximum number of persons they are safe to carry.

Organisation of lifting operations

Lifting operations involving the use of lifting equipment must be properly planned by a competent person. They must also be carried out safely and supervised appropriately.

It is essential to plan, organise and co-ordinate every lifting operation. Good communication is essential to avoid accidents.

A risk assessment is normally necessary to identify the hazards, assess the risks and secure the resources necessary to carry out the operation safely. A plan of the lifting operation itself is necessary. Consider the load being lifted:

- its weight

- its shape

- its centre of gravity

- the availability of lifting points

- where the load is at present

- where it will be lifted to.

Also consider:

- how often the lifting equipment will be used to carry out the task

- the knowledge, training and experience of the workers involved in the operation

- whether people have to work under the load when it is being lifted

- whether the operator of the lifting equipment can see the load clearly throughout the time that the load is being lifted

- which, if any, attachments are used to lift the load and secure it

- what type of environment the load will be lifted in, particularly if it is in the open air

- which measures are in place to prevent the equipment from overturning

- whether there are any nearby hazards, such as overhead power lines or warehouse storage racking.

For routine lifts, such as those of a vehicle tail-lift or a patient hoist, the plan needs to be drawn up only once, but if the lift operation is complex, then the plan needs to be done before every lifting operation.

Thorough examination and inspection

Lifting equipment must be examined thoroughly after installation or assembly (in the case of lifting equipment fixed in a building) to ensure that it is installed properly and safe to use. In the case of lifting equipment used outside buildings, it must be examined thoroughly before first use. Equipment then must also be examined thoroughly:

- every six months if it carries people

- every 12 months for every other piece of lifting equipment.

All lifting equipment must have a formal inspection every six months if it carries people and otherwise every 12 months.

A **scheme of examination** should be drawn up by a competent person to ensure that the lifting equipment is examined thoroughly at appropriate intervals.

An examination scheme identifies and specifies the parts of the equipment that must be examined, states the intervals for the examination and specifies the parts that need to be tested.

If the lifting equipment has deteriorated or has been damaged so that the safety of the lifting equipment is affected, a further examination must take place. The examination should be in accordance with an examination scheme and carried out by a competent person.

Arrangements must be made for the lifting equipment to be inspected by a competent person between the dates set for the thorough examination. An **inspection** includes visual checks and functional tests only (compared to an examination which is an organised or formal evaluation involving measurements and tests). The frequency of the inspections depends on the risk from the lifting equipment: it could even be daily before use.

The requirement to inspect regularly helps to maintain health and safety conditions by detecting any deterioration and making sure that unsafe equipment is not used and defects are fixed or equipment replaced.

Employers must not allow lifting equipment to leave their control, unless it is accompanied by physical evidence that the thorough examination has taken place. This is normally a copy of the last examination report.

Lifting equipment examination reports – contents

- Name and address of the employer for whom the thorough examination has been made.

- Address of the premises where the thorough examination was made.

- Sufficient information to identify the equipment, including, if known, the date of manufacture.

- The date of the last thorough examination.

- The safe working load of the lifting equipment.

- Whether it is the first thorough examination.

- Whether the equipment is installed correctly and safe to operate.

- For subsequent examinations, whether it is within 6 months (if lifting people) or 12 months (for goods), or in accordance with an examination scheme, together with a statement that the lifting equipment is safe to operate.

- Identification and description of any part found to have a defect that could become a danger to people.

- Information about any repairs, renewal or alteration required to remedy a defect and a period for the remedy to be completed.

- The latest date by which the next thorough examination has to be done.

- If a test is done, details of the test.

- The date of the thorough examination.

- The name, address and qualifications of the person making the report, if he or she is self-employed, or, if an employee, the name and address of the employer.

- Date of the report.

Competent person

The person carrying out the thorough examination must have appropriate practical and theoretical knowledge and experience of the lifting equipment to be examined so that defects or weaknesses can be detected.

Reports and defects

Defects which could become a danger to people must be reported to the employer immediately. Reports of the thorough examination, signed by the competent person, must be given to the employer and to any person who hires or leases the equipment.

If the competent person thinks that there is an imminent risk of serious personal injury, a copy of the report must be sent to the relevant enforcing authority as soon as possible. If a person making an inspection finds defects, he or she must notify the employer (and any person hiring out the equipment) and make a written report as soon as is practicable. The equipment concerned must not be used before any defect is fixed.

Keeping information

The report of the first thorough examination must be kept for the time that the lifting equipment is in operation. Subsequent examination reports must be kept until the next thorough examination or for two years, whichever is the later. These reports should be readily available for inspection by the enforcing authority, should they want to see them.

Legal requirements

Under The Lifting Operations and Lifting Equipment Regulations 1998 employers must ensure that lifting equipment is strong and stable enough for safe use and is marked with a safe working load. It must be positioned and installed to minimise risks. Employers must also ensure that lifting equipment is examined and inspected by competent people at regular intervals. Lifting operations must be planned, organised and performed by competent people. There are special requirements for lifting equipment for lifting people.

Pressure systems

A pressure system consists of a pressure vessel or a pipeline containing a liquid or gas under pressure, together with associated pipework and protective devices. Examples of pressure systems include boilers, pressure cookers, autoclaves and compressed air systems such as tyre pressure equipment and compressed air-powered drills. Systems can be fixed or mobile.

Key words and phrases

competent person – someone with the appropriate qualifications, knowledge or experience to identify the risks arising from a situation and the measures needed to control them.

owner – in the context of pressure systems, the employer or self-employed person who owns a mobile pressure system.

pressure system – a system of one or more pressure vessels, associated pipework and protective devices.

safe operating limits – the operating limits (incorporating a suitable margin of safety) beyond which system failure is liable to occur.

scheme of examination – written details of the formal examination and inspection of a pressure system or lifting equipment.

user – in the context of pressure systems, the employer or self-employed person who has control of the operation of an installed pressure system.

Hazards

About 150 **pressure systems** fail each year and some lead to serious injuries or death. The causes of failure are usually poor maintenance, unsafe systems of work, poor training or inadequate repairs or modifications.

The main hazard from pressure systems is the liquid or gas stored under great pressure. If the system fails, the compressed liquid or gas is forced out, causing an explosion that can propel the contents and parts of the pressure system on to people and equipment nearby. If the escaping liquid or gas is flammable, a fire could follow.

Risks

The level of risk from pressure systems depends on factors including:

- the amount of pressure in the system
- the type of liquid or gas in the system
- the age and condition of the equipment
- how suitable the equipment and pipework are for the type of system
- how simple it is to operate
- the environmental conditions in which it is operated
- the skills and knowledge of the people who design, manufacture, install, maintain, test and operate the system.

Pressure systems must be maintained and tested by a competent person at regular intervals.

The higher the pressure in the system, the higher the risk of explosion. If the system contains steam, there is a greater risk of scalds. If the system contains compressed air, then there is no risk of scalding, but there is a moderately high risk of being struck by flying debris, particularly if the system is not operated correctly.

All equipment must be properly designed and constructed from suitable materials. It must also be installed properly. If it is not, there is an increased risk of failure and injury – for example, if a plastic hose is used when a steel pipe is specified by the manufacturer.

Poor maintenance, inadequate repairs and clumsy modifications can all badly affect the condition and useful life of the system.

Lack of training and supervision can lead operators to adopt unsafe systems of work, such as going in to a pressure vessel (like a large boiler) without letting anyone else know or not following the correct safety procedures during operation.

Controls

Owners and **users** need to maintain the system and make sure that a written scheme of examination (see page 354) is drawn up and followed at all times. Proper records of maintenance, repair and modification must be kept, all operators must be adequately trained in the operation of the system and maintenance engineers must be adequately trained in the maintenance of the system.

Design, construction and installation

Designers, manufacturers, importers and suppliers of pressure systems have a responsibility to ensure that the system is designed properly and constructed from suitable materials. The system must also be designed and constructed so that necessary examinations can be carried out: if access is needed to the interior of the system – for cleaning the inside of a boiler, for example – staff should be able to get in and out with minimal risk.

The system must also have protective devices – for example, pressure gauges or pressure release valves – that warn of imminent danger. Alternatively, the system should be designed to release the contents of the system safely if the pressure rises above the safe operating level. The installer must make sure that the vessel is installed in such a way that the operation of the protection devices or inspection facilities is not impaired.

Information and marking

The designer or supplier must provide sufficient written information about the design, construction, examination, operation and maintenance of the system. If there is any modification of the system, information about it must be provided by whoever does the modification. The information that should be marked on the vessel includes the:

- manufacturer's name
- serial number to identify the vessel
- date of manufacture
- standard to which the pressure system was built
- maximum and minimum allowable pressure
- design temperature (the temperature at which the system has been designed to operate safely).

Safe operating limits

Safe operating limits are the operating limits (incorporating a suitable margin of safety) beyond which system failure is liable to occur. The user of a system must not operate it unless safe operating limits have been established. The owner of a mobile system must provide the user with written information about the safe operating limits, and the system must be clearly marked with those limits.

Written scheme of examination

Pressure systems must not be used unless a **scheme of examination** – written details of the formal examination and inspection of the pressure system – has been issued. The scheme of examination must be carried out and issued by a **competent person**. It should cover the vessels, protective devices and pipework. It should also include:

■ the nature and frequency of the examination

■ any special measures necessary for safe examination

■ details of any repairs or modifications necessary to prevent danger or to ensure that the protective devices are working effectively

■ the date by which these repairs or modifications need to be done

■ the date by which the next examination should be done.

The examination should be carried out at regular intervals. This is decided by the competent person (an inspecting engineer) and recorded in the written scheme of examination. It is common for the examination to be carried out at 26 or 24 month intervals, but the frequency of the intervals depends on factors such as the:

■ safety record and history of the system

■ length of time since the last examination

■ current condition of the system

■ operating conditions – for example, adverse environmental conditions

■ quality of the liquid or gas in the system

■ standard of supervision, operation and maintenance and inspection in the workplace

■ monitoring of the equipment.

Before the examination, the owner or user of the system should do all the necessary preparation work – for example, the system should be depressurised – so that the system can be examined safely by the competent person. The preparation work is included in the scheme of examination.

It is most important to emphasise that a pressure system should not be used after the date specified, such as the next date of examination, or until the examination certificate has been issued. This means that you should get the system examined *before* the expiry date of the current examination certificate. Generally, only small systems are exempt from this requirement.

Competent person

The competent person, whether an employee or contractor/consultant, must have sufficient practical and technical knowledge and direct experience of the type of system being examined. This enables the person to identify defects or weaknesses promptly and accurately, and to make a decision as to whether they might compromise the safety of the system.

Action in the case of imminent danger

If the competent person believes that the system is in a condition that creates imminent danger, the system must not be operated until the repairs, modifications or changes specified by the competent person in a written report have been made. The competent person has a *legal* duty to give a copy of the written report to the owner or user and to send another copy to the relevant enforcing authority within 14 days. The enforcing authority may check that the repair work has been done. If the owner or user has taken no action to remedy the danger, the enforcing authority may take enforcement action.

Operation and maintenance

Adequate instructions about the operation of the system and what to do in an emergency must be provided by the owner or user to the person operating the system. The person operating the system must follow the instructions. The system must be properly maintained in good repair to prevent danger.

Training

This autoclave in an AIDS research facility sterilises equipment using high-pressure steam. It must be regularly maintained and tested.

Employees who operate, install, maintain, repair, inspect or test a pressure system must be properly trained for the task they are carrying out and should be supervised. Regular refresher training is advisable, particularly if the system is complex.

Records

The written scheme of examination and the examination reports, together with information about the system's operation, repairs, modifications, design, construction and maintenance must be kept by the owner or user. This assists the competent person in carrying out the examination thoroughly.

The pressure vessel examination report should normally include:

- the name and address of the owner
- the address and location of the system and the name of the user
- an identification of the system or parts examined
- the condition of the system or parts examined
- the parts not examined
- the result of the examination
- any repairs needed and the time for completion

- any changes required to the safe operating limits and the date by which they should be made

- any changes to the written scheme of examination

- the date by which the next examination must be completed

- the date on which the examination took place

- the name and address of the competent person conducting the examination

- the signature of the competent person

- the date of the report.

Legal requirements

The main regulations covering pressure equipment and pressure systems are The Pressure Systems Safety Regulations 2000.

The Pressure Systems Safety Regulations 2000 impose safety requirements on pressure systems used, or intended to be used, at work. They include safety requirements for their design and construction; giving information and marking equipment; installation, operation, maintenance modification and repair; safe operating limits; written scheme of examination; the keeping of records; action in the case of imminent danger and action to prevent certain vessels from becoming pressurised.

Individual protection
Personal protective equipment

Personal protective equipment (PPE) is the last resort in controlling hazards and risks to the health and safety of employees. In many cases, the use of PPE is unavoidable because of the type of work being done – employees working in cold stores need warm clothes and construction workers need protective gloves, for example.

Key words and phrases

CE mark – the official safety marking required by the European Union for certain equipment that will be sold, or put into service for the first time, anywhere in the European Union.

hierarchy of control – a well tested system of graded health and safety controls.

personal protective equipment (PPE) – anything designed to be worn or held by someone at work to protect against one or more workplace hazards.

respiratory protection equipment (RPE) – personal protective equipment such as masks, respirators and breathing apparatus that protects against hazards such as dust, vapour, gas or oxygen-deficient atmospheres.

What is personal protective equipment?

Personal protective equipment (PPE) is anything designed to be worn or held by someone at work to protect against one or more workplace hazards.

Examples of this type of equipment are:

Head and eye
protection.

- gloves
- safety footwear
- safety helmets
- eye goggles
- hearing protectors
- respiratory protection equipment
- safety harnesses
- life jackets
- high-visibility jackets
- aprons and overalls
- clothing to protect against the cold.

Personal protective equipment does not include corporate uniforms (unless they are branded PPE items) or ordinary working clothes.

Where PPE is the only effective means of controlling the risks of injury or ill health, employers must ensure that it is available for use at work *free of charge*.

A form of control

Respiratory equipment
is needed in some
health-threatening
environments.

Personal protective equipment is the final control in the general **hierarchy of control** (see pages 39 to 40) used to reduce the risk of harm from work activities. The provision of items for personal protection should always be regarded as the last resort in protecting workers against a risk to their health and safety because:

- it is always better to eliminate a hazard from the work environment than to protect someone against harm (because it is far better to have control measures that protect *all* workers, rather than just individual workers)

- total protection is rarely achieved with PPE

- wearing PPE can be restrictive – for example, by affecting visibility or mobility or increasing body temperature.

Even so, there are many situations where there is no alternative but to provide personal protective equipment.

Leg amputated after cement 'burns'

A maintenance worker was helping to resurface a concrete yard. He was wearing ripped jeans and rubber boots and he knelt on the concrete to level it off. He developed a severe rash on his legs and suffered chemical burns that penetrated the full thickness of his skin. He failed to notice the damage immediately because the wet alkaline cement destroyed the nerve endings in his knees. His legs felt numb, but he did not realise this was because of chemical burns. As a consequence, his right leg had to be amputated below the knee. The company had provided no personal protective equipment (knee pads and/or protective trousers) and it failed to warn the worker about the dangers of wet cement.

Choosing PPE

This PPE helps to protect both the wearer and the patient.

Employers must provide suitable PPE for employees who may be exposed to a risk to their health and safety, except where other adequate controls have been made which are equally or more effective.

The employer must also assess the suitability of the PPE for the job to be undertaken and keep a record of the risk assessment of the work activities .

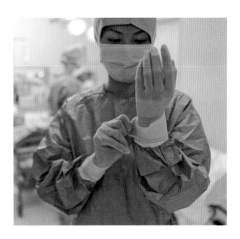

The protective equipment must be selected carefully to fit the wearer correctly after adjustment and to be effective in controlling the specific risk involved, without increasing the risk overall.

Comfort is also important, because employees tend not to use PPE if it is uncomfortable.

Most equipment will not cause problems to the average healthy adult. Where problems do occur (such as an allergy to latex), employers need to take medical advice as to whether the individual can tolerate wearing the equipment. (See also page 366.) Where hygiene is an issue – for instance, with respiratory equipment – the PPE must be provided for individual personal use.

All protective items must be maintained correctly to ensure that it is effective in protecting the wearer against the hazard.

Standards

European Union standards apply to the manufacture of PPE and every item should have 'CE' marked on it. The **CE mark** is the official safety marking required by the European Community for all equipment that will be sold, or put into service for the first time, anywhere in the European Community. It proves to the buyer and user that the product meets all the essential safety and environmental requirements defined in European Directives.

The manufacturer carries out the tests for the equipment to achieve the CE mark standard. In the UK, trading standards officers enforce the legislation covering equipment standards and they check that equipment comes up to the standard required.

Making the choice

A number of factors need to be taken into account when choosing suitable PPE, including:

- the nature of the job to be done
- the conditions where the exposure occurs
- the risks involved
- the demands placed on the worker – for example, the physical effort required to do the job
- how long the PPE has to be worn
- ergonomic requirements (people should be able to move as freely as possible)
- the need for communication and visibility while wearing PPE during work activities
- whether the PPE needs to be cleaned regularly, sometimes after every use
- the wearers' physical characteristics – for example, whether they have a beard or wear spectacles or are especially tall
- whether the PPE can be adjusted
- the state of health of the wearer
- the characteristics of the workstation of the employee
- the initial cost and maintenance costs.

If two or more pieces of PPE need to be worn for protection against one or more risks, then each piece of equipment must be compatible with the others. For example, some hearing protectors cannot be worn properly with safety helmets.

Using PPE

PPE needs to be maintained in efficient working order and in good repair. The type of maintenance depends on the type of PPE – for example, breathing apparatus needs specialist technical maintenance at regular intervals, but safety helmets require only periodic inspection, plus a daily check before use by the wearer.

Some PPE can be used by several people, so it needs to be cleaned and, in some cases, disinfected between use. Some other items are designed for single use and are disposable – for example, disposable overalls used for cleaning processes or disposable ear plugs. Appropriate storage must be provided for the PPE so it can be kept safely when it is not in use – for example, a carrying case for eye goggles.

Staff should be trained to understand the risks when using PPE, how to keep it in good condition and, if appropriate, how to wear it for full protection.

Training and instruction

Employees must be provided with information, instruction and training so that they:

■ are aware of the risks which the PPE will avoid or limit

■ understand the purpose it is to be used for

■ know how to keep the PPE in efficient working order and in good repair.

The training could also include how to:

■ select the appropriate PPE for the job in hand

■ correctly put on, fit and wear the PPE

■ maintain and store the PPE.

The appropriate level of instruction and training depends on the type of PPE. For example, wearing of gloves requires the minimal instruction, but the use of full breathing apparatus may require intensive theoretical and practical training. Whenever it is appropriate, employers must organise demonstrations for the correct way to wear and use PPE.

Supervision

Employers must take all reasonable steps to ensure that any PPE provided for employees is used properly. Managers need to establish disciplinary procedures to deal with staff who persistently fail to use the appropriate PPE. Supervisors are probably in the best position to control the use and effectiveness of PPE, but safety representatives may also be able to play a part in disseminating information about safe use and monitoring how PPE is used.

You may be involved in organising the storage, cleaning, distribution, issue and replacement of PPE. This should be recorded and audited and reviewed at appropriate intervals. Monitor the use of personal protective equipment, ensuring that staff use it for the relevant tasks, and clean and store it correctly. If the equipment is damaged or lost, staff should know to report it to their supervisor as soon as possible.

Make sure that information signage is kept in place, for example, signs about wearing hard hats on construction sites.

Risks

All protective equipment must be kept clean and in good repair.

The use of personal protective equipment can sometimes increase the risk. With some breathing apparatus, for instance, there is an increased risk that the user will trip or knock things over because vision is slightly impaired and the weight of the visor can make the wearer tire quickly. As the apparatus can also reduce the wearer's sense of smell, it is also possible that the user would be less alert to the smell of burning in the workplace.

Some protective clothing can make the wearer uncomfortably hot. Some full protective suits are loose fitting, so it is more likely that they could catch on something or become entangled in machinery. Some suits and breathing apparatus reduce movement, so they can restrict the wearer's reaction times to work or danger.

The use of ear defenders (or hearing protectors) can make communication between employees difficult, while some types of protective gloves (such as latex ones) can lead to dermatitis for some wearers.

If PPE is not cleaned properly after use, other users could be exposed to the hazard that the equipment is designed to guard against. Faulty maintenance of PPE can also lead to exposure to the hazard.

Poorly designed or poorly fitting PPE increases the likelihood that the wearer will be harmed, as the equipment may not be effective against a hazard. Workers must be trained in the proper use of the equipment.

Types of PPE

There is a wide variety of PPE available which is specific to the part of the body that needs to be protected. The PPE can also be designed with the hazard in mind.

Head protection

Head protection is used to protect against falls, falling objects, impact against fixed objects and entanglement. Crash helmets protect motor cycle couriers, riding helmets protect horse riders and safety helmets protect construction site and slaughterhouse workers.

Eye protection

Eye protection protects the wearer from flying debris, splashes from chemicals, molten metal, dust and laser light. Examples include safety spectacles, eye shields, goggles, face shields and hoods.

The different types of eye protection equipment are designed to protect the wearer against a particular hazard. They are used in work activities such as handling harsh chemicals in laboratories, schools and catering kitchens; carrying out metal grinding work or welding operations in engineering factories; working with molten metal in foundries; and using lasers in hospitals or in the entertainment industry.

Hearing protection

Hearing protection is used in any work activity where noise cannot be controlled by any other means.

Ears and eyes need to be protected during this work.

Hearing protectors (also known as ear defenders) and ear plugs are the most common ear protection. Hearing protectors cover the whole ear and ear plugs fit into the ear canal. Some ear plugs can be used indefinitely, some are disposable, while others are reusable. They come in graded sizes or as one-size-fits-all. Hearing protectors are more effective and reliable than ear plugs because they are adjustable and cover the whole ear.

Another type of hearing protection is a semi-insert. Pre-moulded ear caps are attached to a headband which presses the ear caps against the entrance to the ear canal.

Hearing protection can be designed to protect the ear against a specific type of noise such as a high-pitched sound. Some specialised protectors can detect a noise and generate a sound that partly cancels out the unpleasant noise.

Hand and arm protection

Different types of glove protect against cuts and abrasions, hot and cold temperatures, skin irritation and contact with toxic or corrosive liquids.

They can, for example, provide protection against bricks in the construction industry and rough, abrasive objects in warehouses and retail shops. Thermal gloves should be used when staff need to hold hot or cold objects – for example, in the retail and catering industries. Situations where protection against toxic substances are necessary include the maintenance of machinery and the preparation of pesticides on golf courses or in horticulture. Hairdressers should wear protective gloves when using chemical hair preparations. Chain-mail gloves are used by butchers to protect against knife cuts.

Foot protection

Safety footwear protects the wearer from things falling onto the foot or lower leg, or sharp objects penetrating the sole. Footwear can also be designed to reduce the amount of static electricity on the feet and improve slip-resistance in high-risk work environments. Examples of foot and leg protection include safety boots or shoes, clogs, foundry boots, wellington boots, anti-static footwear, gaiters and leggings.

Foot protection is used, for example, in the construction industry and in manual handling activities. People who work in cold conditions need thermal footwear. Foresters and tree surgeons need boots that protect against contact with a moving chainsaw. Foundry workers need protection against molten metal. Workers who have to enter flammable atmospheres need anti-static footwear to prevent ignition due to static electricity. Catering workers need footwear that is slip-resistant.

Respiratory protective equipment

A competent person should select the right sort of respiratory equipment for the working conditions.

Respiratory protective equipment (RPE) is designed to be worn in a contaminated atmosphere. There are two basic types of respiratory protective equipment.

Simple respirators give basic protection against harmful dusts, gases or micro-organisms. These are facemasks with filters or powered respirators which take contaminated air from the work environment and filter or clean it before it is inhaled.

Self-contained respirators or breathing apparatus, of the type used by the fire service, deliver uncontaminated air to the wearer from an independent source. They are for use in conditions, especially emergencies, in which the wearer would not survive without the breathing apparatus.

Body protection

Thermal jackets or body-warmers may need to be provided for retail assistants when they retrieve goods from storage.

Various types of garments are used to protect the body against different hazards. Overalls and aprons protect against hazardous substances in the chemical industry; thermal overalls and suits protect against hot and cold weather or working conditions in farming, forestry, horticulture, warehousing, retail and food production; life jackets help to prevent drowning in the fishing and leisure industries, while high-visibility jackets help to stop the wearer being hit by motor vehicles, trains or aircraft and in the construction, oil, shipping and aircraft industries. Bullet-proof and knife-proof vests are worn by the police and security personnel to protect them against violence.

Legal requirements

The Health and Safety at Work etc. Act 1974 prohibits employers from charging employees for personal protective equipment that is needed to carry out their work safely.

Employees must not damage or misuse equipment that is provided in the interests of health and safety at work.

The main requirements for PPE are covered in The Personal Protective Equipment at Work Regulations 1992. PPE must be properly assessed before use to establish its suitability for purpose. It must fit properly and be maintained and stored properly. Employees must be provided with adequate instructions on how to use it safely and wear it correctly.

Apart from the regulation about compatibility of PPE, The Personal Protective Equipment at Work Regulations 1992 do *not* apply where the following regulations apply: The Control of Substances Hazardous to Health Regulations 2002; The Control of Asbestos Regulations 2006; The Control of Lead at Work Regulations 2002; The Ionising Radiations Regulations 1999; The Noise at Work Regulations 1989 and The Construction (Head Protection) Regulations 1989.

Feature

Individual rights and PPE

The legal requirement to wear personal protective equipment can at times conflict with individual rights and individual requirements. Examples include the right to wear a turban, latex allergies and adaptations to the workplace.

Under The Construction (Head Protection) Regulations 1989, employers must provide suitable head protection, such as hard hats, for employees involved in construction work.

The Employment Act 1989 exempts Sikhs who normally wear turbans from wearing head protection, although Sikhs who do *not* normally wear turbans must wear the safety hats provided.

Where Sikh employees have the right to wear turbans on a construction site, employers need to ensure that they work only in areas where there is no risk, or an extremely low risk, of a head injury. This could imply that people wearing turbans cannot work in hard hat areas.

If a worker who is legitimately wearing a turban on a construction site suffers a head injury for which the employer is found to be liable, the employer might have to pay

damages. The compensation would be only for the injuries that the person was likely to have sustained in the same circumstances if he had been wearing a safety helmet.

Under the Disability Discrimination Act 1995, employers must make all reasonable changes to the workplace to enable people with a disability to continue to work there.

The Act defines disability as 'a physical or mental impairment which has a substantial and long-term adverse effect on a person's ability to carry out day-to-day activities'.

Some doctors, nurses, dentists, dental nurses and other health workers are allergic to the latex protein in the latex protective gloves they must wear.

Employers must make feasible relevant workplace changes if an employee with a latex allergy is considered to be disabled according to the Act. However, if the changes cannot reasonably be made, then the employer must offer the employee a suitable change of work within the organisation. Latex-free disposable gloves are widely available.

Responding to an accident – first aid

Health and safety measures include dealing with the injuries to employees resulting from accidents in the workplace. **First aid** is the immediate medical care given to keep someone alive, to prevent medical conditions deteriorating, or to minimise the consequences of injury and illness, or both. The care is given either until a doctor, paramedic or nurse can take over, or because the injuries are minor so that no additional treatment is required.

Key words and phrases

appointed person – someone appointed to take charge of a situation, in the absence of a first aider, where a serious injury or illness has occurred at work.

first aid – the immediate medical care given to keep someone alive, to prevent medical conditions deteriorating, or to minimise the consequences of injury and illness.

first aider – a person who has been trained in first aid and holds a current first aid certificate issued by an organisation approved by the Health and Safety Executive.

First aid facilities

The minimum provision for any workplace is:

- a suitably stocked first aid box, kit or travelling kit
- an appointed person to take charge of the first aid arrangements
- information for employees about the first aid arrangements.

Risk assessment

An assessment must be carried out to identify the hazards and the risks in the workplace to determine the extent of the facilities that should be provided. The assessment should be based on:

- any specific risks in the workplace such as dangerous machinery or hazardous substances
- any parts of the workplace where the level of risk is greater
- the type of accidents and ill health that have happened in the workplace
- the number of people that work in the workplace
- the number of employees with disabilities and special health problems
- the number of buildings on a site and whether they are spread out or close together
- whether there is shift work or out of normal hours operation
- whether employees spend most of their working day away from their base, such as travelling sales representatives, trainers, gardeners and tree surgeons
- how close the site is to emergency medical services such as a hospital
- whether employees work or travel alone as part of their job
- whether employees work at premises where there are other employers and self-employed people
- whether there are work experience trainees in the workplace
- whether members of the public visit the workplace.

As an example, an administration office with relatively few hazards and low levels of risk might have basic first aid provision such as a simple first aid box. In a coal mine or quarry, however, the number of hazards and the high level of risk means that far more extensive facilities are required – for example, a permanent first-aid room containing a basin with hot and cold water, a couch with waterproof protection and a store for first aid materials.

Checklists produced by HSE can help in the assessment of first aid needs.

First aid boxes and kits

First aid boxes and kits that meet the basic legal standard should be provided in every workplace or for every work team working away from base. They should contain a sufficient quantity of first aid materials based on the type of activity and the size of the workforce. The boxes and kits should contain only the first aid materials and nothing else. They should not, for example, contain any medicines. Remember that first aid is immediate action, so it does *not* include the treatment of illnesses. The exception to this is the giving of Asprin to a casualty with a suspected heart attack. You should ensure that employees do not attempt to hand out common medicines that are available for sale over-the-counter. If medicines are provided to employees or members of the public, employers and employees could become liable to insurance claims and civil court claims if the person receiving the medicine suffered an adverse reaction.

First aid boxes, kits and travelling kits usually contain items such as:

- a guidance card or leaflet on basic first aid

- individually wrapped, sterile dressings

- sterile eye pads

- individually wrapped triangular bandages

- safety pins

- individually wrapped, sterile, unmedicated wound dressings

- disposable gloves.

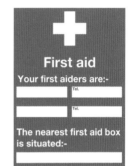

First aid rooms and equipment

Where the hazards present a high risk in a workplace – for example, in chemical works and large construction sites – employers must provide a suitably equipped and staffed first aid room. A designated person must be responsible for the room and its contents and should be available on call when employees are at work.

Facilities should be provided, such as a couch, chairs, wash basin, drinking water, hot water, soap, towels, working surfaces, stretchers and a first aid materials store. The first aid room should also be signposted. Records of all cases of first aid treatment should be kept near the first aid equipment.

First aiders

Employers must ensure that there are sufficient suitable persons available to give first aid to employees who are injured or become ill at work. The person must be a trained **first aider** and hold a valid certificate of competence in either First Aid at Work (FAW) issued by a training organisation approved by HSE or Emergency First Aid at Work (EFAW) issued by an HSE-approved training organisation or by an Ofqual or SQA accredited awarding body. FAW and EFAW certificates are valid for three years. Employers need to arrange retraining before certificates expire. The results of the first aid needs assessment will enable employers to ensure the type of training course chosen is appropriate for the circumstances of the workplace.

It is good practice for first aiders to do a refresher course annually – indeed, HSE recommends it. Records should be kept of the training and refresher retraining. There are some cases where first aiders should also do specialist training – for instance, where there is a serious risk of gas inhalation or exposure to toxic chemicals.

As a very rough guide there should be one first aider to every 50 employees, but detailed guidance is given in *First Aid at Work – The Health and Safety (First Aid) Regulations 1981 Approved Code of Practice and Guidance.*

Appointed persons

An appointed person is usually the one who calls the emergency services.

An **appointed person** usually stands in for first aiders when the first aider is away from the workplace. Such people are appointed by the employer to take charge of a situation where a serious injury or illness could occur in the absence of a first aider. Appointed persons are responsible for looking after equipment and facilities and calling an ambulance. If trained to do so, they can give first aid. It is good practice to train employees to be first aiders rather than rely on appointed persons.

Legal requirements

Under The Health and Safety (First Aid) Regulations 1981 employers must assess their first aid requirements and provide adequate first aid facilities and information for their employees. The regulations apply to all workplaces and to the self-employed.

There is *no* legal duty to provide first aid facilities for members of the public, but employers may wish to make them available in case of need. The Health and Safety Executive urges employers to consider members of the public when making an assessment of the first aid provision.

Sources of further help

Glossary

access equipment – ladders, steps, trestles, cradles, mobile elevated work platforms and any other type of work equipment that enables an employee to reach to, or stand at, a height above their own height.

accident – any unplanned event that results, or could have resulted, in personal injury or ill health; damage to, or loss of, property, plant or materials; damage to the environment; or loss of business opportunity. It is important to note that an accident includes events involving physical violence to a person at work.

active monitoring – regular proactive measurement of performance against safety management standards and targets.

acute – in the context of health, an immediate effect on health. There is a rapid onset of severe symptoms, usually after a single short-term exposure to a harmful substance.

aerosol – air-borne droplet.

alcohol – the chemicals ethyl alcohol and ethanol, or the common term for alcoholic beverages in general.

alcohol abuse – excessive consumption of alcohol.

appointed person – someone appointed to take charge of a situation, in the absence of a first aider, where a serious injury or illness has occurred at work.

approved code of practice – formal guidance, generally issued by the Health and Safety Executive (HSE) on behalf of the government, containing detailed information on how to comply with the law. This does not have the same legal force as a regulation, so a failure to comply is not in itself an offence. However, if an organisation follows a relevant approved code of practice, a court may considered this as evidence of good workplace practice.

arcing – a highly visible discharge of electricity through the air between two conductors.

asthmagen – a substance that causes sensitisation of the human airways, often leading to medical conditions such as asthma.

audit – a formal examination against a fixed standard by competent people who are independent of the area of work being audited.

bacteria – a very large group of microscopic single-celled organisms (independent life forms) which may be essential, beneficial or harmful to human health. A small number of types of bacteria can cause diseases such as food poisoning and tetanus.

benchmarking – a process used in management in which organisations compare their processes and performance against best practice or against similar organisations.

carcinogen – a substance that may cause cancer.

carcinogenic – a description of something that could cause cancer.

carpal tunnel syndrome – pain and tingling in fingers caused by pressure of a nerve as it passes through the carpal tunnel in the wrist.

carrier – in relation to lifting equipment, any device, such as a passenger lift car or the cage of a construction site hoist, used to support people being lowered or lifted. In rope-based systems, such as climbing, the harness is the carrier.

CE mark – the official safety marking required by the European Union for all equipment that will be sold, or put into service for the first time, anywhere in the European Union.

chronic – in the context of health and safety, a persisting and life-threatening illness that may take a considerable time to develop, usually after prolonged or repeated low-level exposure to a hazard.

circuit-breaker – an automatic device that breaks the flow of electricity through a circuit to protect it from damage caused by overload. A standard circuit breaker performs a similar function to a fuse by breaking the circuit if the current is excessive. It offers no protection from electric shock. See also residual current device.

classified person – an employee who is exposed to an effective dose of radiation that is over a legally set level in any one year.

cleaning schedule – a list that includes the work areas to be cleaned, the frequency of cleaning and the type of cleaning material to be used.

code of practice – practical guidance about how to achieve the standard required by the relevant legislation, usually developed through consultation within the relevant industry. A code of practice is not law, but it should be followed unless there is an alternative course of action that achieves the same or better standards.

competent – in relation to health and safety at work, a description of someone capable of carrying out work in a safe and healthy manner appropriate to the level of responsibility.

competent person – someone with the appropriate qualifications, knowledge and experience to identify the risks arising from a situation and the measures needed to control them. For example, a CORGI-registered gas engineer or technician is a person who is required by law to be approved by the Health and Safety

Executive before being permitted to carry out work on gas supplies and installations.

confined space – any enclosed area where there is a risk of serious injury or death due to the presence of hazardous substances or dangerous conditions.

control measures (or controls) – the arrangements made, or precautions taken, to reduce risk.

COSHH – the common abbreviation for the main piece of legislation that deals with hazardous substances: The Control of Substances Hazardous to Health Regulations 2002 and amendments.

COSHH sheet – see safety data sheet.

dangerous occurrence – a hazardous incident that arises out of, or in connection with, work and is specified in RIDDOR.

danger zone – in relation to work equipment, an area where employees are exposed to dangerous machine parts.

dead – in the context of electricity, a description of a system, equipment or wire that has been isolated from all sources of electricity.

decibel – the unit for levels of sound, often abbreviated to dB.

designated person – a person trained to be a first aider who holds an up-to-date first aid certificate issued by an organisation approved by the Health and Safety Executive.

(EU) Directive – European Union legislation that requires member states to achieve a particular result, but without dictating the means of achieving it.

display screen equipment – any alphanumeric (letters and numbers) or graphic display screen, usually as part of a computer system.

dose – in the context of hazardous substances, the amount of a harmful substance that is absorbed into the body.

dosimetry – the calculation of the dose that is absorbed into body tissue and other matter as a result of exposure to ionising radiation.

drug – a substance that has a physiological effect when in the body; a pharmaceutical product or ingredient prescribed as a medicinal treatment or used for illegal recreational purposes. Examples include narcotic, hallucinogenic or stimulant substances.

drug abuse – the illegal use of drugs and the misuse, whether deliberate or unintentional, of prescribed drugs or substances such as solvents.

DSEAR – the common abbreviation for The Dangerous Substances and Explosive Atmospheres Regulations 2002.

earth – in the context of electricity, a connection between an electrical system or equipment and the ground for safety purposes.

effective dose – a dose of radiation to the whole body.

electrical installation – the electrical cables and fittings in a building.

electric shock – a shock when a person touches live parts of an electrical circuit.

electrocution – death caused by electric shock.

emergency plan – the actions to be taken in a particular workplace in the event of a fire or other emergency.

environmental health officer (EHO) – an officer employed by local authorities to enforce health and safety law. Also known as environmental health practitioner (EHP) or regulatory officer.

environmental monitoring – tests to determine whether the work environment is safe and healthy for workers.

equivalent dose – a way of expressing a dose of radiation to one part of the body in relation to exposure of the whole body.

ergonomic design – the application of scientific data about human mental and physical capacities and performance to the design of work systems.

ergonomic principles – the degree to which a particular job is designed to fit the person, usually by a combination of the management of job design, workstation design, job rotation, training and so on.

ergonomics – the study of the interaction between people and their work.

European Commission – the executive branch of the European Union which proposes legislation and implements the decisions of the Union.

European Union – the economic and political partnership between 27 democratic European countries.

examinations – in a health and safety context, checks on equipment that are more thorough, but less frequent, than inspections. In the context of lifting equipment, an organised or formal evaluation involving measurements and tests.

exposure action value (EAV) – the daily amount of vibration exposure above which employers are required to take action to control exposure.

exposure limit level (ELL) – the maximum level of vibration an employee may be exposed to on a single day.

exposure limit value (ELV) – daily or weekly exposure of 87dB(A) or a peak sound pressure of 140dB(C).

fail to safety (or **fail-safe**) – a design that enables a machine to come to rest in a safe state if it stops working for any reason.

fall-arrest system – a personal fall-protection system to arrest and restrict a fall by preventing the user from hitting the ground. An energy-absorbing device limits the forces on the body.

first aid – the immediate medical care given to keep someone alive, to prevent medical conditions deteriorating, or to minimise the consequences of injury and illness.

first aider – a person who has been trained in first aid and holds a current first aid certificate issued by an organisation approved by the Health and Safety Executive.

flammable substance – any natural or artificial substance in the form of a solid, liquid, gas or vapour that is liable to catch fire.

fume – microscopic airborne particles produced when, for example, metals are heated during welding or as a result of certain chemical processes. A fume may smell foul and may be irritating or toxic.

fuse – in the context of electricity, a safety device that breaks the flow of electricity through a circuit to protect equipment from damage caused by overload. It offers no protection from electric shock. A fuse consists of a short piece of wire that melts ('blows') and stops electricity flowing to the appliance if the electric current reaches an unsafe level.

gas – an air-like substance that expands freely to fill any space available, irrespective of its quantity.

Gas Safe-registered – someone who is recognised as competent by Gas Safe, which is the examining and control organisation for gas fitters.

gas system – all gas installation pipework, fittings and appliances including ventilation and flues.

guidance – specific advice on how to achieve the standard required by the relevant legislation where there is no approved code of practice. Following guidance is not compulsory, but doing so

helps employers to comply with the law.

hand-arm vibration – mechanical vibration transmitted to hands and arms during work with hand-held powered equipment.

hand-arm vibration syndrome (HAVS) – a range of health problems in which there is damage to the blood flow, nerves, muscles, tendons and bones of the arm and hand as a result of using hand-held powered equipment at work.

hazard – a source of danger: any thing, condition or circumstance that could cause harm to people or damage to property. Anything with a potential to cause harm in the form of injury, ill health or damage.

hazard spotting – looking for and noting hazards in the workplace.

hazardous substance – a substance defined as being toxic, very toxic, harmful, corrosive, an irritant, a biological agent or a dust of any kind above a defined concentration in the air.

health – a state of complete physical, mental and social well-being, not merely the absence of disease or infirmity.

health and safety culture – the integration of health and safety awareness and controls into day-to-day organisational management practices. Also the attitudes, beliefs and behaviours towards health and safety within the organisation.

Health and Safety Executive (HSE) – the official British body responsible for enforcing health and safety law in many industries.

health and safety policy – a written statement of the organisation's arrangements for and implementation of its health and safety management system and activities.

health surveillance – the systematic monitoring of the health of an employee who may be exposed to harmful substances or harmful work activities. The purpose of the surveillance is to identify adverse health effects or inadequate health and safety controls.

hearing protection zone – any part of the workplace where an employee is likely to be exposed to high levels of noise and protection must be worn or exposure limited.

hierarchy of control – a well tested system of graded health and safety controls. The sequence helps organisations to determine their most effective health and safety controls.

hierarchy of protection – in relation to work equipment, levels of protection for safeguarding employees from dangerous parts of machinery. These levels of protection should be adopted in sequence.

ignition source – something that can light a flammable substance, causing a fire or explosion.

incident (near-miss or near-miss accident) – an unplanned event that does not result in personal injury, death or damage, but has the potential to do so.

information – verbal or written advice. in a form that is easily understood by the employees to whom it is being addressed.

in-running nip – nip points between a pair of moving parts, or moving and fixed parts, that can create traps into which clothing or parts of the body can be drawn.

inspection of equipment – visual checks by a competent person on items of equipment to verify that they can be operated, adjusted and maintained safely.

inspection of the health and safety system – the assessment of the health and safety performance of a workplace, which enables any necessary remedial measures to be taken.

installer – in the context of gas supply or installation, a person who carries out work on a gas system or a gas storage vessel.

instruction – guidance or direction regarding a specific procedure or action.

insulation – a low-resistance material surrounding anything electrical that keeps the electrical current safely contained.

intervention programme – a series of actions designed to improve workplace health and safety standards and to reduce the risks from health and safety hazards.

ion – an electrically charged atom or molecule resulting from the loss or gain of one or more electrons.

ionising radiation – electromagnetic waves, such as X-rays and gamma rays, or particles, such as alpha and beta particles, that break atoms and molecules into ions.

lifting equipment – work equipment for the lifting or lowering of loads, including the attachments for anchoring, fixing or supporting the equipment.

lifting operation – an activity involving the lifting or lowering of a load using lifting equipment.

live – in the context of electricity, a description of a system, equipment or wire that is connected to a source of electricity.

load – any movable object, including a person or animal.

local authorities – local councils delegated by the Secretary of State to enforce health and safety law in the commercial and retail sectors.

local exhaust ventilation – a ventilation system that captures and removes air contaminants at the point they are being produced before they escape into the workroom.

lower exposure action values – daily or weekly exposure of 80dB(A) or a peak sound pressure of 135dB(C).

management system – a framework of policies and procedures which allows an organisation to achieve its objectives.

manual handling or manual handling operation – any transporting or supporting of a load (including lifting, putting down, pushing, pulling, carrying or moving) by hand or by bodily force.

material safety data sheet – see safety data sheet.

medical health screening – medical test to determine the health status of individuals at work.

mesothelioma – cancer of the lining of the lung cavity or abdominal cavity due to exposure to asbestos.

mobile equipment – any work equipment that operates while it is travelling or is moved between work locations. Such equipment usually moves on wheels, tracks, rollers or skids. It may be manually operated, self-propelled, towed or remote controlled.

monitoring – regular, often daily, checks on what is going on in the workplace which help to deal with problems as they arise.

musculoskeletal disorders (MSDs) – conditions affecting the muscles, nerves, tendons, ligaments, joints, cartilage or spinal discs.

mutagen – a substance that may cause inherited genetic damage.

near-miss (incident or near-miss accident) – an unplanned event that does not result in personal injury, death or damage, but has the potential to do so.

noise – unwanted sound, or sound that could damage hearing.

non-ionising radiation – part of the electromagnetic spectrum (including ultraviolet, visible and infrared light and electricity power frequencies, microwaves and radio) that leaves atoms and molecules intact.

occupational deafness – deafness caused by exposure to high levels of noise in the workplace over long periods.

occupational health – a person's physical, mental and social well-being as a consequence of his or her work activities and environment.

over three-day injury – an injury that is not major, but results in the injured person being off work for more than three consecutive calendar days. The three consecutive days do not include the day of the accident, but non-working days should be counted in the three consecutive days.

owner – in the context of pressure systems, the employer or self-employed person who owns a mobile pressure system.

passive smoking – breathing in the smoke from other people's cigarettes, cigars or pipes.

performance indicators – measurements used to help an organisation to define and measure progress towards the organisation's health and safety goals.

permanent threshold shift – the prolonged exposure to loud sound that can permanently damage the ears' ability to detect soft sounds. This is also referred to as 'occupational deafness'.

permit to work – a formal document that specifies the work to be done and the precautions to be taken. The document forms part of a written system used to control certain types of work that are potentially hazardous.

personal protective equipment (PPE) – anything designed to be worn or held by someone at work to protect against one or more workplace hazards.

plant – machinery or equipment used in an industrial or manufacturing process.

platform – a horizontal surface raised above the level of the adjacent area, for a worker to stand on and work from.

portable equipment – in the context of electrical equipment, equipment with a lead and a plug that can be moved from one place to another.

pressure system – a system of one or more pressure vessels, associated pipework and protective devices.

pre-use check – checks on equipment by an operator before using the equipment.

primary legislation – main laws passed by the legislative bodies in the UK.

radiation – energy emitted or transmitted either as electromagnetic waves or as subatomic particles.

radiation employer – an employer who carries out work with ionising radiation.

REACH – an abbreviation for a European Community Regulation on chemicals and their safe use (Regulation (EC) No. 1907/2006), which deals with the Registration, Evaluation, Authorisation and Restriction of Chemical Substances.

reactive monitoring – the reporting and investigation of incidents and accidents relating to heath and safety.

reasonably practicable – what is practicable based on whether the time, trouble and expense of the precautions suggested are proportionate to the risks involved.

(EU) Regulation – European Union legislation that immediately becomes enforceable as law in all member states at the same time.

repetitive strain injury – a type of work-related disorder mainly affecting the upper limbs.

reportable accident – an accident that must, by law, be reported to the enforcing authorities. Such accidents are specified in RIDDOR and include those resulting in death, major injury, injuries that cause an employee to take more than three days off work and dangerous occurrences.

reportable disease – a disease that arises out of, or in connection with, work and is specified in RIDDOR.

representative of employee safety – an employee elected by non-union employees to represent them on health and safety matters.

responsible person – an employer, the duty manager, a self-employed person, the owner of premises or a vehicle, or the person in control of the premises at any time.

residual current device (RCD) or **residual current circuit-breaker (RCCB)** – a safety device fitted to an electrical circuit to offer a degree of protection against electric shock. It disconnects the supply if there is an abnormal current flowing to earth – for example, when someone touches a live conductor.

RIDDOR – The Reporting of Injuries, Diseases and Dangerous Occurrences Regulations 1995.

risk – a measure or scale of the likelihood that harm will occur from a particular hazard, and the severity of the consequences, including death, major injury, disease, minor injury, no injury and damage to property.

risk assessment – a systematic process for identifying workplace hazards and assessing the risks involved from those hazards.

safety – freedom from danger.

safety committee – a committee set up at the request of two safety representatives to deal with health and safety matters in the workplace.

safety data sheet – a document that must be provided by product manufacturers or suppliers to give vital information for using the product safely. Also sometimes referred to as 'COSHH sheets' or material safety data sheets (MSDS).

safety harness – personal protective equipment that is attached to a reliable anchor point.

safety lines – ropes that stop the user hitting the ground in the event of a fall.

safe operating limits – the operating limits (incorporating a suitable margin of safety) beyond which system failure is liable to occur.

safety nets – nets used to catch people or objects that fall from a height.

safety representative – an employee elected by a trade union members to represent them on health and safety issues.

safe system of work – a set of procedures for carrying out a task safely. The system is often in the form of formal written instructions, but is not necessarily so. The procedures are based on a risk assessment.

safe working load (SWL) – the maximum load that equipment may lift safely.

scheme of examination – written details of the formal examination and inspection of lifting equipment or a pressure system.

secondary legislation – the laws made under the authority of primary legislation.

sensitisation – a process by which the body becomes sensitive to a substance after it has entered or touched the body.

stress – an adverse reaction to external pressure.

substance hazardous to health – any substance that is defined as being very toxic, toxic, harmful, corrosive or irritant, or is a biological agent or a dust of any kind present in the air at above a defined concentration.

supervisory management (of health and safety) – the implementation and development of an organisation's health and safety policy.

temporary threshold shift – the exposure to high levels of noise for a short period that raises the ears' threshold of response so that the person cannot hear soft sounds for a while. Recovery takes a few hours to a couple of days.

tinnitus – a medical condition in which the sufferer experiences ringing in the ears.

toxicity – a measure of a substance's potential to cause harm.

traffic – vehicle or pedestrian movement in a workplace.

traffic route – a defined or non-defined route used by vehicles or pedestrians in a workplace.

training – preparing a person to achieve a desired level of skill, knowledge or competence through the means of information, instruction and practice.

training needs – the type and extent of training the workforce or an individual employee requires.

upper exposure action values – daily or weekly exposure of 85dB(A) or a peak sound pressure of 137dB(C).

use – in relation to work equipment, the term means starting, stopping, programming, setting, transporting, repairing, modifying, maintaining, servicing and cleaning.

user – in relation to pressure systems, an employer or self-employed person who has control of the operation of an installed pressure system.

vapour – a gaseous form of a substance that is normally a liquid at room temperature.

vehicle – includes cars, vans, heavy goods vehicles, fork-lift trucks and reach trucks.

vibration – rapid repeated movements back and forward or up and down that might also be described as shaking, jolting or oscillating. Vibration at work is normally caused by mechanically-operated and electrically-operated power tools or by driving vehicles, such as tractors.

violence at work – a physical assault on, or abusive or threatening behaviour toward, an employee at work or in connection with work.

virus – an exceptionally small microscopic particle that can infect the cells of a host organism, such as humans, and cause diseases, such as 'flu or winter vomiting disease.

welfare – in the context of health and safety, the promotion of employee well-being and comfort by the provision of facilities such as those for personal hygiene, eating and resting.

whole body vibration (WBV) – shaking or jolting of the body through a supporting surface. Vibration transmitted through the seat of equipment or through the feet.

work – activities that people carry out specifically in the course of their occupation.

work environment – the surroundings in which work is carried out, including buildings, rooms, sites, the air, temperature and lighting.

work equipment – apparatus used at work including machines, appliances, tools, installations, ladders, hoists and lift equipment.

workplace – any place, or places, where employees, or the self-employed, are likely to work or where they have to go in the course of their employment or incidentally to it.

workplace exposure limit (WEL) – the maximum concentration of an airborne substance, averaged over a specified time, to which employees may be exposed by inhalation under any circumstances.

workplace transport – any vehicle or piece of mobile equipment used by employees, self-employed people or visitors to a workplace. It does not include vehicles travelling on a public road.

work premises – any building or space, including outdoors, where work takes place.

work-positioning system – a personal fall-protection system to support the user in tension or suspension so that a fall is prevented or restricted.

work-related upper limb disorders (WRULDs) – conditions resulting from prolonged and frequent activity that damages the muscle, tendon or joint involved so that it becomes painful and has a reduced function.

workstation – an assembly comprising a work surface, such as a desk, all the necessary equipment needed to carry out the assigned tasks and the immediate surrounding area affected by the work activity at the workstation.

Websites

General

General health and safety
Essentials of health and safety at work

www.hse.gov.uk/pubns/books/essentials.htm

Health and safety starter pack for small businesses
www.hse.gov.uk/smallbusinesses/pack.htm

HSE's Myth of the Month hse.gov.uk/myth

Workplace health advice services available to small businesses

www.hse.gov.uk/workplacehealth/

www.sahw.co.uk/

Benefits of health and safety
www.hse.gov.uk/business/business-benefits.htm

www.hse.gov.uk/businessbenefits/casestudy.htm

www.betterbusiness.hse.gov.uk

By topic

Accidents and ill health – costs
Health and Safety Executive's 'Ready Reckoner'

www.hse.gov.uk/costs/

Asbestos
www.hse.gov.uk/asbestos

www.hse.gov.uk/asbestos/repsguide.pdf

British Lung Foundation

http://www.lunguk.org/

Confined spaces
www.hse.gov.uk/confinedspace/

COSHH
COSHH Essentials is step-by-step guidance, aimed specifically at small firms, to help them to control health risks from chemicals. Users enter readily available information about the chemicals they use and the way that they use them. The system then automatically identifies the correct control solutions and produces easy-to-follow instructions on how to put the guidance into practice and carry out other duties required by COSHH.

www.coshh-essentials.org.uk/

www.hse.gov.uk/coshh/index.htm

Catering Information Sheet No 22 Safe use of cleaning chemicals in the hospitality industry
www.hse.gov.uk/pubns/cais22.pdf

Solvents Construction Information Sheet No 27 (revision 2)

www.hse.gov.uk/pubns/cis27.pdf

Occupational skin disease
www.hse.gov.uk/skin/index.htm

COSHH Essentials guidance
www.hse.gov.uk/pubns/guidance/index.htm

COSHH guidance on service and retail
www.hse.gov.uk/pubns/guidance/srseries.htm

List of approved workplace exposure limits
updated www.hse.gov.uk/coshh/table1.pdf

Avoiding ill health at open farms

www.hse.gov.uk/campaigns/farmsafe/ecoli.htm

REACH
http://ec.europa.eu/environment/chemicals/reach/reach_intro.htm

Drugs and alcohol
www.hse.gov.uk/alcoholdrugs/

Electricity
www.hse.gov.uk/electricity/index.htm

Ergonomics
Factors affecting health and safety
www.hse.gov.uk/humanfactors/index.htm

European health and safety
European Agency for Safety and Health
http://agency.osha.eu.int

Fire and explosion
www.hse.gov.uk/fireandexplosion/index.htm

Fire gateway www.fire.gov.uk/Workplace+safety/

INDG216 – Dispensing petrol as fuel – Health and Safety guidance for employees
www.hse.gov.uk/pubns/indg216.htm

www.hse.gov.uk/explosives/index.htm

Dust explosion in the food industry
www.hse.gov.uk/food/dustexplosion.htm

First aid
First aid at work
www.hse.gov.uk/firstaid/index.htm

INDG347 (rev)1 – Basic advice on first aid at work
www.hse.gov.uk/pubns/indg347.pdf

How to become a first aid training provider
www.hse.gov.uk/firstaid/training.htm
www.hse.gov.uk/firstaid/assessmenttool.htm

Gas safety
www.gassaferegister.co.uk

www.hse.gov.uk/pubns/indg238.pdf

www.hse.gov.uk/pubns/indg285.pdf

Health surveillance
Disease Reduction Programme website

www.hse.gov.uk/drp/index.htm

Legionnaires' disease
www.hse.gov.uk/biosafety/diseases/legionnaires.htm

Legislation
Health and safety legislation website

www.hse.gov.uk/legislation/index.htm

UK legislation

www.opsi.gov.uk

http://osha.europa.eu/

www.workplacelaw.net

Manual handling
Manual handling assessment charts

www.hse.gov.uk/msd/mac/

www.hse.gov.uk/msd/index.htm

Storage and warehousing industry health and safety

www.hse.gov.uk/warehousing/index.htm

Fork-lift truck dangers warning after worker paralysed
www.hse.gov.uk/press/2007/gnnne22307.htm

Management
The well managed organisation

Guidelines for Boards of Directors, HR directors and Senior Managers

www.hse.gov.uk/services/wellmanaged.htm

Health and safety management and business economic performance

www.hse.gov.uk/research/rrhtm/rr510.htm

Institute of Directors and Health and Safety Commission – Leading health and safety at work

www.iod.com/hsguide

Musculoskeletal disorders
www.hse.gov.uk/msd

Noise
www.hse.gov.uk/noise

www.noiseatwork.info/

PPE
A short guide to the Personal Protective Equipment at Work Regulations 1992

www.hse.gov.uk/pubns/indg174.pdf

Revised guidance on the correct selection and safe use of RPE

www.hse.gov.uk/pubns/guidance/rpe3.pdf

www.hse.gov.uk/pubns/guidance/rpe5.pdf

www.hse.gov.uk/pubns/guidance/p50.pdf

Pressure systems
www.hse.gov.uk/pubns/indg178.pdf

Reporting accidents, incidents and ill health
Public reporting of occupational health and safety

www.hse.gov.uk/research/rrhtm/rr515.htm

Reporting of incidents in the workplace – RIDDOR

www.hse.gov.uk/riddor/index.htm

Risk assessment
http://hse.gov.uk/risk/

Five steps to risk assessment

www.hse.gov.uk/pubns/indg163.pdf

Example risk assessments

http://hse.gov.uk/risk/casestudies/index.htm

Safety representatives
www.hse.gov.uk/workers/safetyreps/index.htm

Health and safety for safety representatives

www.dennismac.co.uk/

Sickness absence
www.hse.gov.uk/sicknessabsence/index.htm

www.hse.gov.uk/sicknessabsence/toolkit.htm

Slips and trips
Watch your step website

www.hse.gov.uk/watchyourstep/index.htm

www.hse.gov.uk/slips/index.htm

www.hsenews.com/2006/11/08/slips-and-trips-case-studies/

Slips assessment tool

www.hsesat.info/

Slips and trips mapping tool

www.hse.gov.uk/slips/mappingtool.pdf

Preventing slips and trips at work

www.hse.gov.uk/pubns/indg225.pdf

Smoking
Advice on smoking at work

www.hse.gov.uk/contact/faqs/smoking.htm

www.smokefreeengland.co.uk/

Statistics
www.hse.gov.uk/statistics/index.htm

Occupational health statistics
www.hse.gov.uk/statistics/overall/ohsb0506.htm

Stress
www.hse.gov.uk/stress/index.htm

Research Report: A business case for the management standards for stress
www.hse.gov.uk/research/rrhtm/rr431.htm

LAC 81/4 – Work related stress
www.hse.gov.uk/lau/lacs/81-4.htm

Local authority sector stress case studies
www.hsenews.com/2006/11/29/local-authority-sector-stress-case-studies/

Training
Bring a smile to safety training
www.hse.gov.uk/pubns/books/napo/index.htm

Vibration
www.hse.gov.uk/vibration

Control the risks from hand-arm vibration
www.hse.gov.uk/pubns/indg175.pdf

Control back-pain risks from whole-body vibration
www.hse.gov.uk/pubns/indg242.pdf

Violence
www.hse.gov.uk/violence/

The Suzy Lamplugh Trust
www.suzylamplugh.org/

Ban bullying at work
www.banbullyingatwork.com/

Work equipment
www.hse.gov.uk/equipment/index.htm
www.hse.gov.uk/pubns/indg229.pdf

Worker involvement
www.hse.gov.uk/involvement/index.htm

Workers
www.hse.gov.uk/workers/index.htm

Work at height
www.hse.gov.uk/falls/

Regulations
www.opsi.gov.uk/si/si2005/20050735.htm

www.opsi.gov.uk/si/si2007/20070114.htm

The Work at Height Regulations 2005 (as amended) A brief guide
www.hse.gov.uk/pubns/indg401.pdf

Safe Use of Ladders: An employer's guide
www.hse.gov.uk/pubns/indg402.pdf

A toolbox talk on leaning ladder and stepladder safety
www.hse.gov.uk/pubns/indg403.pdf

Top tips for ladder and stepladder safety
www.hse.gov.uk/pubns/indg405pdf

Avoiding Falls from Vehicles (INDG395)
www.hse.gov.uk/pubns/indg395.pdf

Mobile elevating work platforms
www.hse.gov.uk/falls/mewps.htm

Tower scaffolds CIS10
www.hse.gov.uk/pubns/cis10.pdf

WAIT toolkit – Work at height access equipment information toolkit
www.hse.gov.uk/falls/wait/index.htm

Workplace
Thermal comfort
www.hse.gov.uk/temperature/thermal/index.htm

Local exhaust ventilation
www.hse.gov.uk/pubns/wis23.htm

Workplace transport
www.hse.gov.uk/workplacetransport

Workplace Transport Safety: An Overview
www.hse.gov.uk/pubns/indg199.pdf

Working Platforms on Fork Lift Trucks
www.hse.gov.uk/workplacetransport/pm28.pdf

Work-related upper limb disorders
www.hse.gov.uk/msd/index.htm

Musculoskeletal disorders case studies
www.hse.gov.uk/msd/experience.htm

Working with VDUs
www.hse.gov.uk/pubns/indg36.pdf

Preventing back pain and other aches and pains to kitchen and food service staff
www.hse.gov.uk/pubns/cais24.pdf

Young people at work
www.hse.gov.uk/youngpeople/index.htm

Organisations

Professional and examining bodies

British Institute of Occupational Hygienists

The professional body for occupational hygiene in Great Britain

www.bioh.org

British Safety Council

An occupational health, safety and environmental organisation which works with companies to develop safe systems of work.

www.britishsafetycouncil.co.uk

Chartered Institute of Environmental Health (CIEH)

A professional, educational and awarding body for health and safety at work and other environmental health matters.

Chadwick Court, 15 Hatfields
London SE1 8DJ
T: 020 7827 5800
F: 020 7827 5865
E: sales@cieh.org
U: www.cieh.org

National Examination Board in Occupational Safety and Health (NEBOSH)

An independent awarding body for health and safety.

Dominus Way, Meridian Business Park,
Leicester LE19 1QW
T: 0116 263 4700
F: 0116 282 4000
E: info@nebosh.org.uk
U: www.nebosh.org.uk

Royal Society for Public Health

A professional, educational and awarding body for health and safety at work and other public health matters.

3rd Floor, Market Towers
1Nine Elms Lane
London SW8 5NQ
T: 0203 177 1600
F: 0203 177 1601
E: info@rsph.org.uk
U: www.rsph.org.uk

The Institution of Occupational Safety and Health (IOSH)

A non-profitmaking organisation for occupational safety and health.

The Grange, Highfield Drive, Wigston,
Leics LE18 1NN
T: 0116 257 3100
F: 0116 257 3101
U: www.iosh.co.uk

The Royal Environmental Health Institute of Scotland (REHIS)

A professional, educational and awarding body for health and safety at work and other environmental health matters.

3 Manor Place, Edinburgh EH3 7DH
T: 0131 225 6999
F: 0131 225 3993
U: www.rehis.org

The Royal Institute of Public Health (RIPH)

Due to merge with the RSH in late 2008 to become the **Royal Society for Public Health**.

The Royal Society for the Prevention of Accidents (RoSPA)

A registered charity providing information, advice, resources and training in all areas of life.

Edgbaston Park, 353 Bristol Road, Edgbaston,
Birmingham B5 7ST
T: 0121 248 2000
F: 0121 248 2001
U: www.rospa.co.uk

The Royal Society for the Promotion of Health (RSH)
Due to merge with the RIPH in late 2008 to become the **Royal Society for Public Health**.

Government

Department of Health (DoH)
The UK government health department.

www.doh.gov.uk

Hansard
The official record of the British Parliament.

www.parliament.the-stationery-office.co.uk/pa/cm/cmhansrd.htm

Health and Safety Executive (HSE)
www.hse.gov.uk – main website

www.hsedirect.com – health and safety legislation, guidance etc.

www.hsebooks.co.uk – bookfinder

www.hsl.gov.uk – laboratory website

www.hseni.gov.uk – the Northern Ireland website

RIDDOR
The incident contact centre for reporting accidents, diseases and dangerous occurrences.

www.riddor.gov.uk

Her Majesty's Stationery Office
Source of copies of UK legislation and government departmental reports.

www.hmso.gov.uk

Local government

Local Authorities Co-Ordination of Regulatory Service
An organisation co-ordinating and giving advice on regulatory services.

www.lacors.com

www.info4localgov.com
A reference source for local authority professionals, with links to health and safety websites.

International

Centre for Occupational Health and Safety
Health and safety information from Canada.

www.ilocis.org

European Law
A site summarising European law.

www.europa.eu.int/eur-lex

European Agency for Safety and Health at Work
An information network.

http://europe.osha.eu.int

European Union
europa.eu.int

Occupational Health and Safety Administration (OHSA)
An American government department working to prevent work-related injuries, illnesses and deaths.

www.osha.gov

References

Regulations

Fire (Scotland) Act 2005, as amended

Health and Safety at Work etc. Act 1974

The Confined Spaces Regulations 1997

The Control of Asbestos Regulations 2006

The Control of Lead at Work Regulations 2002

The Control of Noise at Work Regulations 2005

The Control of Substances Hazardous to Health Regulations 2002, as amended

The Control of Vibration at Work Regulations 2005

The Dangerous Substances & Explosive Atmospheres Regulations 2002

The Electricity at Work Regulations 1989

The Equipment and Protective Systems for Use in Potentially Explosive Atmospheres Regulations 1996

The Fire Precautions (Workplace) Regulations 1997 (as amended)

The Fire Safety (Scotland) Regulations 2006

The Gas Safety (Installation and Use) Regulations 1998

The Health and Safety (Consultation with Employees) Regulations 1996

The Health and Safety (Display Screen Equipment) Regulations 1992

The Health and Safety (First-Aid) Regulations 1981

The Health and Safety (Offences) Act 2008

The Ionising Radiations Regulations 1999

The Lifting Operations and Lifting Equipment Regulations 1998

The Management of Health and Safety at Work Regulations 1999

The Manual Handling Operations Regulations 1992

The Personal Protective Equipment at Work Regulations 1992

The Pressure Systems Safety Regulations 2000

The Provision and Use of Work Equipment Regulations 1998

The Regulatory Reform (Fire Safety) Order 2005

The Reporting of Injuries, Diseases and Dangerous Occurrences Regulations 1995

The Safety Representatives and Safety Committees Regulations 1977

The Work at Height Regulations 2005 (as amended)

The Workplace (Health, Safety and Welfare) Regulations 1992

Guidance and codes

Accidents
HSG 96 The costs to Britain of workplace accidents and work-related ill health in 1995/96 1999

HSG 245 Investigating accidents and incidents 2004

INDG 355 Reduce risks – Cut costs 2002

INDG 90 Understanding ergonomics at work – Reduce accidents and ill health and increase production by fitting the task to the worker 2003

Injuries and ill health caused by handling in the food and drink industries – HSE information sheet Food Information Sheet No 23 2000

Accident investigations
HSG 245 Investigating accidents and incidents – A workbook for employers, unions, safety representatives and safety professionals 2004

MISC 491 Work-related deaths – A protocol for liaison HSE

Asbestos
HSG 210 Asbestos essentials task manual 2007

HSG 213 Introduction to asbestos essentials 2001

HSG 227 A comprehensive guide to managing asbestos in premises 2002

HSG 264 Asbestos: The survey guide 2010

HSG247 Asbestos: the Licensed Contractors Guide

L127 The management of asbestos in non-domestic premises. Approved Code of Practice and Guidance 2006

L143 Approved Code of Practice Work with Materials containing Asbestos

INDG 223 A short guide to managing asbestos in premises 2009

INDG 418 Asbestos kills: a quick guide to protecting yourself 2007

MDHS100 Surveying, sampling and assessment of asbestos-containing material 2001

The Control of Asbestos Regulations 2006: A guide for safety representatives HSE/TUC

Competence
HSE Human Factors Briefing Note No. 2 – Competence

Managing competence for safety-related systems – HSE Guidance

www.hse.gov.uk/consult/condocs/competence.htm

Display screen equipment
HSG 90 VDUs: An easy guide to the regulations (2003)

L26 Work with display screen equipment: Health and Safety (Display Screen Equipment) Regulations 1992 as amended by the Health and Safety (Miscellaneous Amendments) Regulations 2002

INDG 36 (rev3) Working with VDUs (2006)

Drugs, alcohol and passive smoking
INDG 91 Drugs misuse at work – a guide for employers 2004

INDG 240 Don't mix it! A guide for employers on alcohol at work 1996

Electricity and electrical equipment
HSG 38 Electrical test equipment for use by electricians 1995

HSG 85 Electricity at work – Safe working practices 2003

HSG 107 Maintaining portable and transportable electrical equipment 2004

INDG 209 Controlling health risks from the use of UV tanning equipment 2005

INDG 229 Using work equipment safely 2002

INDG 231 Electrical safety and you 2005

INDG 236 Maintaining portable electrical equipment in offices and other low-risk environments 1996

INDG 237 Maintaining portable electrical equipment in hotels and tourist accommodation 2004

INDG 354 Safety in electrical testing at work 2002

IEE/IET Code of Practice for In-Service Inspection and Testing of Electrical Equipment

IEE/IET Health & Safety Briefing – Portable Appliance testing

Emergencies
HSG 191 Emergency planning for major accidents 1999

INDG 246 Prepared for emergency 1997

Fire safety
Fire Safety An employer's guide – www.archive.official-documents.co.uk/document/fire/index.htm

INDG 370 Fire and explosion – How safe is your workplace? A short guide to the Dangerous Substances and Explosive Atmospheres Regulations (2004)

INDG 407 Storing and selling fireworks safely – Advice for anyone selling fireworks

First aid
L74 First aid at work – The Health and Safety (First-Aid) Regulations 1981 – Approved Code of Practice and Guidance 2009

INDG 214 First aid at work 2006

INDG 347REV1 Basic advice on first aid at work 2006

Flammable substances
HSG51 The storage of flammable liquids in containers 1998

HSG103 Safe handling of combustible dusts: precautions against explosions 2003

HSG140 The safe use and handling of flammable liquids 1996

HSG176 The storage of flammable liquids in tanks 1998

HSG178 The spraying of flammable liquids 1998

L133 Unloading Petrol From Road Tankers – Approved Code of Practice and Guidance 2003

L136 Dangerous Substances and Explosive Atmospheres Regulations 2002: Approved Code of Practice and Guidance 2003

INDG227 Safe working with flammable substances 2005

INDG216 Dispensing petrol as fuel – Health and Safety guidance for employees

BS EN 50073 The selection and use of flammable gas detectors 2004 HSE

Gas supply and equipment
L56 Safety in the installation and use of gas systems and appliances Gas Safety (Installation and Use) Regulations 1998 Approved Code of Practice and Guidance 1998

INDG238 Gas Appliances: Get Them Checked, Keep Them Safe 2004

INDG285 Landlords – A Guide to landlords' duties: Gas Safety (Installation and Use) Regulations 1998 (2004)

Hazardous substances
HSG 97 Step by step guide to COSHH assessment 2004

HSG 110 Seven steps to successful substitution of hazardous substances 1996

HSG 173 Monitoring strategies for toxic substances 1997

HSG 193 COSHH essentials – Easy steps to control chemicals 2003

HSG 262 Managing risks of skin exposure at work 2009

L5 Control of Substances Hazardous to Health Regulations 2002 – Approved Codes of Practice and Guidance (5th edn) 2005

L55 Preventing asthma at work – How to control respiratory sensitisers 1994

L132 Control of Lead at Work – Control of Lead at Work Regulations 2002 Approved Code of Practice and Guidance 2002

INDG 136 COSHH: A brief guide to the regulations 2005

INDG 233REV1 Preventing contact dermatitis at work 2007

INDG 350 The Idiot's guide to CHIP (Chemicals (Hazard Information and Packaging for Supply) Regulations 2002

EH40 Occupational Exposure Limits 2002 (includes maximum exposure levels) 2003

EH64 Summary criteria for occupational exposure limits

Agriculture Information Sheet (AIS 23) Avoiding ill health at open farms – Advice to farmers (with teachers' supplement) and AIS23 (supplement) Avoiding ill health at open farms – Advice to teachers

Catering Information Sheet No 22 Safe use of cleaning chemicals in the hospitality industry

Construction Information Sheet No 27 (revision 2) Solvents

IAC 27(rev2) Legionnaires' disease – a guide for employers HSE

INDG 376 Essential information for providers of residential accommodation

Health and safety policies
HSG 250 Guidance on permit-to-work systems 2005

HSE Human Factors Briefing Note No. 8 – Safety – Critical Communications

Health and safety reports
Director Action on Safety and Health – Measuring and Reporting on Corporate Health and Safety Performance – Towards Best Practice, Royal Society for the Prevention of Accidents 2001

Health surveillance
HSG 61 Health surveillance at work 1999

INDG 245 Biological monitoring in the workplace 1997

INDG 304 Understanding health surveillance at work – an introduction for employers 2004

INDG 399 Managing sickness absence and return to work in small businesses

Health surveillance for occupational asthma G402 HSE

Ionising radiation
HSG95 The radiation safety of lasers used for display purposes 1996

L121 Work with ionising radiation – Ionising Radiations Regulations 1999 Approved code of practice and guidance 2000

INDG 209 (rev1) Reducing health risks from the use of UV tanning equipment

INDG 147 Keep your top on – health risks from working in the sun 2005

INDG 224 Controlling the radiation safety of display laser installations 1996

INDG 334 Working safely with ionising radiation Guidelines for expectant or breastfeeding mothers 2001

INDG 337 Sun Protection – advice for employers of outdoor workers 2001

Cancer Research UK 'Strategies for the Workplace' and 'Skin Cancer'

Lifting equipment and operations
HS(G) 6 Safety in working with lift trucks 2000

HSG246 Safety in the Storage and Handling of Steel and Other Metal Stock 2005

L113 Safe use of lifting equipment

Lifting Operations and Lifting Equipment Regulations 1998: Approved Code of Practice and Guidance 1998

L117 Rider-operator lift trucks: Operator training – Approved Code of Practice and Guidance 1999

INDG 290 Simple guide to the Lifting Operations and Lifting Equipment Regulations 1998 (1999)

Management and management systems
HSG 48 Reducing error and influencing behaviour 1999

HSG 65 Successful health & safety management 1997

HSG 137 Health risk management: A practical guide for managers in small and medium-sized enterprises 1995

HSG 151 Protecting the public – Your next move 1997

L21 Management of health and safety at work – Approved Codes of Practice & Guidance Management of health and safety at work Regulations 1999 2000

INDG 275 Managing Health and Safety – Five steps to success

Institute of Directors and Health and Safety Commission – leading health and safety at work www.iod.com/hsguide

INDG 399 Managing health and safety 2004

INDG 417 Leading health and safety at work: Leadership actions for directors and board members 2007

Manual handling
HSG 76 Warehousing and storage: A guide to health and safety 2007

HSG 115 Manual Handling – Solutions you can handle 1994

HSG 119 Manual handling in drinks delivery

HSG 149 Backs for the future 2000

L23 Manual Handling – Manual Handling Operations Regulations 1992 Guidance on regulations 2004

INDG 143(rev2) – Getting to grips with manual handling – a short guide for employers 2004

INDG 348 Mark a parcel, save a back 2002

INDG 383 Manual Handling assessment charts

INDG 398 Are you making the best use of lifting and handling aids? (2004)

INDG 412 Warehousing and storage – Keep it safe 2007

HSL/2002/31 Benchmarking of the Manual Handling assessment Charts (MAC)

Musculoskeletal disorders
HSG 57 Seating at work 1998

HSG 60 Upper limb disorders in the workplace 2002

HSG 121 A pain in your workplace – Ergonomic problems and solutions

INDG 171REV1 Aching arms (or RSI) in small businesses – Is ill health due to upper limb disorders a problem in your workplace? 2003

LAC 58/1 Supermarket checkouts and musculoskeletal disorders

Better display screen equipment work-related ill health data

www.hse.gov.uk/research/rrhtm/rr561.htm

A staged approach to reducing musculoskeletal disorders (MSDs) in the workplace – Whysall, Haslam and Haslam, 2005
www.hse.gov.uk/research/rrhtm/rr545.htm

Noise at work
HSG 138 Sound solutions – Techniques to reduce noise at work

HSG 232 Sound solutions for the food and drink industries 2002

L108 The Control of Noise at Work Regulations 2005. Guidance on Regulations 2005

INDG 362 Noise at work: Guidance for employers on the Control of Noise at Work Regulations 2005

INDG 363 Protect your hearing or lose it! 2007

Personal protective equipment
L25 Personal protective equipment at work (Second edition): Guidance on regulations Personal Protective Equipment at Work Regulations 1992 2005

HSG 53 Respiratory protective equipment at work 2005

INDG174REV1 – A short guide to the Personal Protective Equipment at Work Regulations 1992 2005

INDG330 Selecting protective gloves for work with chemicals: Guidance for employers and health and safety specialists 2000

INDG288(rev1) Selection of suitable respiratory protective equipment for work with asbestos 2003

Pressure systems
L122 Safety of pressure systems – Pressure Systems Safety Regulations 2000 – Approved Code of Practice 2000

INDG 171 Written schemes of examination – Pressure Systems Safety Regulations 2000 (2006)

Reporting accidents
L73 A guide to the Reporting of Injuries, Diseases and Dangerous Occurrences Regulations 1995 – Guidance on Regulations 1999

Risk assessment
HSG 183 Five steps to risk assessment – Case studies

INDG 163(rev2) Five steps to risk assessment 2006

INDG 420 Getting specialist help with health and safety 2007

Safety signs
L64 Safety signs and signals: The Health and Safety (Safety Signs and Signals) Regulations 1996 – Guidance on Regulations 1996

IND(G) 184 Signpost to the Health and Safety (Safety Signs and Signals) Regulations (1996)

Slips and trips
HSG 155 Slips and trips – Guidance for employers on identifying hazards and controlling risks 1996

HS(G) 156 Slips and trips – Guidance for the food processing industry 1996

INDG 225 REV1 Preventing slips and trips at work 2005

Slips and trips: Summary guidance for the catering industry HSE Catering information Sheet No 6

Assess slips risk on smooth floors using HSE's free Slips Assessment Tool software (SAT). www.hsesat.info/

Health and Safety Executive Slips and trips mapping tool
www.hse.gov.uk/slips/mappingtool.pdf

Stress
HSG 218 Managing the causes of work-related stress: A step-by-step approach using the Management Standards 2007

INDG 406 Tackling stress: The Management Standards Approach 2005

MICS 714 Making the Stress Management Standards work

Training, instruction and information
HSG 165 Young people at work – A guide for employers 2000

HSG 199 Managing health and safety on work experience – A guide for organisers 2000

HSG 222 Effective health and safety training 2001

INDG 345 Health and safety training 2001

INDG 364 The right start – Work experience for young people: Health and safety basics for employers 2002

Vibration
HSG 170 Vibration solutions (1997)

L140 Hand Arm vibration – The Control of Vibration at Work Regulations 2005 Guidance on Regulations (2005)

L141 Whole-body vibration – The Control of Vibration at Work Regulations 2005 Guidance on Regulations (2005)

INDG 175 REV2 Control the risks from hand-arm vibration – advice for employers (2005)

INDG 242 REV1 Control back-pain risks from whole-body vibration – advice for employers (2005)

INDG 296 Hand-arm vibration (2005)

Violence at work
HSG 100 Prevention of violence to staff in banks and building societies

HSG 133 Preventing violence to retail staff 1995

HSG 229 Work-related violence case studies 2002

INDG 69 Violence at work 2000

INDG 73 Working alone in safety – Controlling the risks of solitary work 1998

Violence and aggression to staff in health services – Guidance on assessment and management (Health Services Advisory Committee, HSE)

Welfare
L24 Workplace health, safety and welfare – Approved Code of Practice Workplace (Health, Safety and Welfare) Regulations 1992 1996

INDG293 – Welfare at Work – Guidance for employers on welfare provisions

CIS18(rev1) Provision of welfare facilities at fixed construction sites 1998

CIS46 Provision of welfare facilities at transient construction sites 1997

Work environment
HSG 37 An introduction into local exhaust ventilation 1993

HSG 38 Lighting at work 1998

HSG 54 Maintenance, examination and testing of local exhaust ventilation 1998

HSG 55 Health and safety in kitchen and food preparation areas

HSG 132 How to deal with sick building syndrome – Guidance for employers, building owners and building managers 1995

HSG 194 Thermal comfort in the workplace – Guidance for employers 1999

HSG 202 General ventilation in the workplace – guidance for employers 2000

HSG 252 A recipe for safety 2005

L8 Legionnaires' disease – The control of legionella bacteria in water systems: Approved Code of Practice & Guidance 2000

L24 Workplace health, safety and welfare – Approved Code of Practice Workplace (Health, Safety and Welfare) Regulations 1992 1996

L101 Safe work in confined spaces Confined

Spaces Regulations 1997 Approved Code of Practice Regulations and Guidance 1997

INDG 173 Officewise 2006

INDG 244REV2 Workplace health, safety and welfare 2007

INDG 258 Safe work in confined spaces 2006

INDG 293 Welfare at work – Guidance for employers on welfare provisions 2007

INDG 337 Sun protection 2001

INDG 382 Driving at work 2003

Work equipment
HSG 107 Maintaining portable and transportable electrical equipment 2004

L22 Safe use of work equipment – Provision and Use of Work Equipment Regulations 1998 – Approved Code of Practice and Guidance 1998

INDG 229 Using Work Equipment Safely 2004

INDG 291 Simple guide to the Provision and Use of Work Equipment Regulations 1998 (1999)

WAIT toolkit – Work at height access equipment information toolkit www.hse.gov.uk/falls/wait/index.htm

Work at height
HSG 33 Health and safety in roof work

HSG 150 Health and safety in construction 2006

INDG 401 REV1 The Work at Height Regulations 2005 (amended) 2007

INDG 402 Safe use of ladders and stepladders 2005

INDG 405 Top tips for ladder and stepladder safety 2005

Working together
HSG 217 Involving employees in health and safety 2001

L87 Safety representatives and safety committees – Approved Code of Practice and Guidance 1996

L95 A guide to the Health and Safety (Consultation with Employees) Regulations 1996 Guidance on Regulations 1996

INDG 232 Consulting employees on health and safety 1999

Workplace transport
HSG 136 Workplace transport safety – Guidance for employers 2005

INDG 199 rev1 Managing vehicle safety at the workplace 2005

INDG 382 Driving at Work 2003

Index and acknowledgements

Index

A

access equipment 168, 169, 175, 372 – see also **work equipment**

access to vehicles 214

accident 18-30, 231, 367-370

– definition of 17, 18, 372

– investigations 36, 82, 86, 147-151

– manual handling injuries 130, 194, 201, 205

– recording 103, 133

– reportable 81, 83, 378

– reporting 140-146, 382

– statistics 29

– triangle 19

acoustic barrier 252

aerosol 9, 11, 372

alcohol 15, 266-270, 372, 381, 387

alcohol abuse 266, 268, 372

apparatus 331 – see also **work equipment**

appeal (legal) 58

appliance 331 – see also **work equipment**

appointed person 367, 370, 372

approved code of practice 45, 49, 55, 372

arcing 297, 298, 372

asbestos 235-236, 381, 386

asthma, occupational 237-238

asthmagen 222, 226, 372

audit/auditing 32, 38-39, 74, 127-133, 372

authorised officer 50

B

back injury 10, 15, 200

barrier 122, 165, 170, 171, 172, 210, 338, 345

biological hazards 14

board of directors 37, 52, 64, 68

body protection 364

C

carcinogen/carcinogenic 9, 13, 226, 232, 372

carrier (lifting equipment) 342, 343-347, 372

CE mark 328, 336, 360, 372

checklist vi, 130, 166-168 – see also **relevant topic chapters for specific checklists**

chemicals 224-234, 326-327, 381, 387, 388 – see also **substances hazardous to health**

Chemicals (Hazard Information and Packaging for Supply) Regulations, The – see **CHIP**

cherry picker – see **mobile elevating work platform**

CHIP/CHIP3 222, 234, 387

circuit breaker 297, 299, 300, 373, 378

cleaning/cleanliness 165, 280-281, 283, 287, 334

cleaning schedule 163, 278, 326, 373

code of practice 45, 55, 373

collapsing structure 176

collective protective measure 35, 122

communication 68, 71, 77, 88-89, 254-255

competent 42-43, 72, 74, 222, 228, 373

competent person 32, 42-43, 68, 75, 83, 112, 118, 122, 130, 198, 212, 300, 301, 308, 317, 318, 334, 340, 345, 349, 354, 373

confined spaces 55, 126, 236, 286, 291-292, 327, 331, 373, 381, 386, 390

conflict, handling 74, 77-78, 91-92

consultation 55, 68, 75, 77, 78, 82, 83-84, 88, 89-90, 91, 97, 119, 133, 210, 212, 221, 232, 262, 386, 390 – see also **communication**

contractors 6, 38, 70-94, 103, 107, 114, 124, 213, 216, 236, 301, 302, 303, 386

controls/control measures 2, 28, 35, 72, 110, 115, 373 – see also **relevant topic chapters for specific controls**

Control of Asbestos Regulations, The 55, 70, 139, 365, 381, 386

Control of Lead at Work Regulations, The 55, 70, 139, 365, 386, 387

Control of Noise at Work Regulations, The 44, 55, 120, 139, 250, 255, 386, 389

Control of Substances Hazardous to Health Regulations, The (COSHH) 44, 55, 70, 120, 139, 158, 226, 234, 365, 386, 387

– assessment 131

– definition 222, 373

Control of Vibration at Work Regulations, The 55, 120, 139, 158, 256, 259, 265, 386, 389, 390

Construction (Design and Management) Regulations, The 70, 93

Construction (Head Protection) Regulations, The 365, 366

corporate homicide 62

corporate manslaughter 62

D

dangerous occurrence 140, 142, 143, 373

Dangerous Substances and Explosive Atmospheres Regulations 2002, The 222, 232, 234, 327, 374, 387

Acknowledgements

Many individuals and organisations have helped directly and indirectly towards the preparation of this book. We would particularly like to thank Robert Barrett, Tessa Blewchamp, Roger Clarke and Anne Hughes for their comments on the draft. Illustrations from HSE publications and other Crown Copyright materials are reproduced by permission.

The main sources of information for the chapters are as follows. Abbreviations used are:

DTLR – Department for Transport, Local Government and the Regions

HSE – Health and Safety Executive

HSG – Health and Safety Guidance

Part 1 What is health and safety at work?
Reduce Risks – Cut Costs The real costs of accidents and ill health at work INDG355

Water company BDDE 20 Revitalising Health and safety in Construction – South West Water

Basil Butler quoted on page 25 from HSG 96 The costs of accidents at work HSE

Part 2 – How do we eliminate hazards and reduce risk?
Health and Safety at Work etc. Act 1974

The Management of Health and Safety at Work Regulations 1999

The Personal Protective Equipment Regulations 1992 (often referred to as

'the PPE regs')

The Provision and Use of Work Equipment Regulations 1998 (often

abbreviated to PUWER)

The Manual Handling Operations Regulations 1992

The Workplace (Health, Safety and Welfare) Regulations 1992

The Health and Safety (Display Screen Equipment) Regulations 1992 (often

referred to as 'the DSE regs')

The Lifting Operations and Lifting Equipment Regulations 1998 (often

abbreviated to LOLER) ;

The Control of Substances Hazardous to Health Regulations 2002 (often

abbreviated to COSHH)

The Control of Noise at Work Regulations 2005

The Health and Safety (First Aid) Regulations 1981

The Reporting of Injuries, Diseases and Dangerous Occurrences Regulations 1995 (often abbreviated to RIDDOR).

The Work at Height Regulations 2005

The Control of Asbestos at Work Regulations 2006

The Control of Lead at Work Regulations 2002

The Confined Spaces Regulations 1997

The Health and Safety (Display Screen Equipment) Regulations 1992

The Ionising Radiations Regulations 1999

The Pressure Systems Safety Regulations 2000

The Safety Representatives and Safety Committees Regulations 1977

The Control of Vibration at Work Regulations 2005

The Electricity at Work Regulations 1989

The Gas Safety (Installation and Use) Regulations 1998

Example on page 52 of tree and local council quoted in Health and Safety at Work August 2002

Example on page 53 of member of the public killed by reversing lorry quoted in Croner Health and Safety case law 9 June 2001

Part 3 – Who should be involved in health and safety at work?
Institute of Directors and Health and Safety Commission – leading health and safety at work

Example on page 86 of a partnership agreement based on Scottish Power plc quoted in 'Take action – Putting Health and Safety in your strategic agenda' DTLR and HSE seminar 29 May 2002

Example on page 88 of partnership between management and trade unions based on Kodak Ltd, Harrow 'Take action – Putting Health and Safety in your strategic agenda' DTLR and HSE seminar 29 May 2002

Part 4 – Why should we create a positive health and safety culture?
Health and Safety Statistics 2006/2007 HSE

Source of hierarchy of control: HSG 65 Successful health & safety management

Part 5 – How can we implement good health and safety standards?
Example on page 36 of major food company, H J Heinz Co Ltd, Wigan, in Take action – Putting Health and Safety in your strategic agenda DTLR and HSE seminar 29 May 2002

L21 Management of health and safety at work

Approved Code of Practice and Guidance Management of Health and Safety at Work Regulations 1999

INDG 163(rev1) Five steps to risk assessment

Example on page 112 of unloading a ship quoted in Health and Safety at Work January 2002

Example on pages 113 of carbon monoxide poisoning quoted in Health and Safety at Work February 2002

The risk-rating chart on page 115 first appeared in *Risk Assessment Principles and Practice*, CHGL 2002.

L73 – A guide to the Reporting of Injuries, Diseases and Dangerous Occurrences Regulations 1995

HSG 61 Health surveillance at work

Monash University

Cardiff and Vale NHS Trust: Lord Hunt's Speech for the 4th International Symposium on Confidential Reporting Systems, 30 November 2006 – HSE website

Example of an improvised work system on page 125 quoted by the Health and Safety Executive

Example of new beds saving back injuries on page 130 quoted by the NHS

Part 6 – How can we control specific risks?
HSG 155 Slips and trips Guidance for employers on identifying hazards and controlling risks HSE

HSG 156 Slips and trips Guidance for the food processing industry HSE

HSG 33 Health and safety in roof work HSE

HSG 150 Health and safety in construction HSE

HS(G) 60 Upper limb disorders in the work place. A guide to prevention

L26 Display screen equipment work – Guidance on the regulations

HSG 76 Health and safety in retail and wholesale warehouses

INDG 199 Managing vehicle safety at the workplace

HSG 136 Workplace transport safety

Example on page 215 of a bakery and reversing accidents based on Warburtons Bakery quoted in 'Take action – Putting Health and Safety in your strategic agenda' DTLR and HSE seminar 29 May 2002

HSG 218 Managing the causes of work-related stress: A step-by-step approach using the Management Standards 2007

L23 Manual Handling Manual Handling Operations Regulations 1992 Guidance on regulations HSE

General Risk Assessment Guidelines INDG 143(rev1) Getting to grips with manual handling – a short guide for employers HSE

Example on page 203 of back injury from lifting mattresses quoted in Health and Safety at Work

June 2002

Example on page 205 of back injury among medical and residential staff based on Wigan and Leigh NHS Trust quoted in 'Take action – Putting Health and Safety in your strategic agenda' DTLR and HSE seminar 29 May 2002

Illustrations on page 207 from L23 Manual Handling Operations Regulations 1992: Guidance on Regulations, HSE

Hazard warnings and signs on page 223 courtesy of Signs and Labels Ltd

L5 Control of substances hazardous to health (4th edn)

Control of Substances Hazardous to Health Regulations 2002 Approved Codes of Practice and Guidance HSE

Example on page 230 of a painter and hydrofluoric acid based on The Lancet, Vol. 358, November 2001 and Health and Safety at Work January 2002

The control of legionella bacteria in water systems Approved Code of Practice L8 HSE

Illustration on page 250 from L108 Reducing noise at work Guidance on the The Control of Noise at Work Regulations 2005 HSE

IND(G) 240L Don't mix it! A guide for employers on alcohol at work

TUC guide on alcohol and drugs at work

HS(G) 100 Prevention of violence to staff in banks and building societies

Example on page 273 of efforts to reduce violence in a hospital emergency department based on Queens Medical Centre and Nottinghamshire Police 'Take action – Putting Health and Safety in your strategic agenda' DTLR and HSE seminar 29 May 2002

L24 Workplace health, safety and welfare Approved Code of Practice

Workplace (Health, Safety and Welfare) Regulations 1992 HSE

HSG 202 General ventilation in the workplace Guidance for employers

Example on page 291 of painters overcome by fumes quoted in Health and Safety at Work June 2002

HS(G) 85 Electricity at work Safe working practices

HSG 107 Maintaining portable and transportable electrical equipment HSE

L56 Safety in the installation and use of gas systems and appliances Gas Safety (Installation and Use) Regulations 1998 Approved Code of Practice and Guidance HSE

http://news.bbc.co.uk

Fire Safety – an employer's guide, HSE books

INDG 227 Safe working with flammable substances

HSG 140 The safe use and handling of flammable liquids

http://www.buncefieldinvestigation.gov.uk/index.htm

INDG 308 The safe use of gas cylinders HSE

L22 Safe use of work equipment Provision and Use of Work Equipment Regulations 1998 Approved Code of Practice and Guidance HSE

Examples of guards and protection at source on pages 337-338 from HSG 55 Health and Safety in kitchens and food preparation areas HSE

L113 Safe use of lifting equipment Lifting Operations and Lifting Equipment Regulations 1998 Approved Code of Practice and Guidance HSE

L122 Safety of pressure systems Pressure Systems Safety Regulations 2000 Approved Code of Practice HSE

L25 Personal protective equipment at work Guidance on regulations

Personal Protective Equipment at work Regulations 1992

L74 First aid at work The Health and Safety (First-Aid) Regulations 1981 Approved Code of Practice and Guidance

Picture credits